PROPHESYING
PEACE

PROPHESYING PEACE

DIARIES 1944 – 1945

———

James Lees-Milne

MICHAEL RUSSELL

© Michael Bloch 1977

This edition published 2003
by Michael Russell (Publishing) Ltd
Wilby Hall, Wilby, Norwich NR16 2JP

Printed and bound in Great Britain
by Biddles Ltd, Guildford and King's Lynn

ISBN 0 85955 283 7

CONTENTS

PREFACE

An autobiography may be a lyric, even a work of fantasy. A biography may be an elegy, even a work of art. A diary cannot be any of these things. It is necessarily spasmodic and prosaic. But it must be spontaneous. It must not be doctored. Naturally the editor has a duty to determine how much of it should be withheld, and how much published. In this respect I am helped once again by Mr. Ian Parsons, who has been unsparing with his advice and his blue pencil. I am greatly indebted to him.

Since, then, a diary is merely a day-to-day chronicle of events, non-events and opinions, it will be full of inconsistencies and contradictions. It reflects the author's shifting moods, tastes, prejudices and even beliefs, to few of which he may remain constant for long. Thus on Sunday he may be wildly in love with life; and on Monday he may be suicidal. On Tuesday he may go to three cocktail parties, and on Wednesday prepare to enter a Trappist monastery. On Thursday he may adore someone whom on Friday he may abhor. On Saturday morning he may rob a church box, and the same evening give the proceeds to his favourite charity. Unlike the calculating autobiographer and biographer, the candid diarist does not know himself. Nor is he to be known by his diaries, for he is an irrational being, a weathercock, a piece of chaff drifting on every wind of circumstance. And if anyone needs proof of this assertion, he has only to look beneath the mask into his own soul.

I thank most gratefully my old school friend, Sir Rupert Hart-Davis, for laboriously reading through the proofs and correcting many mistakes of spelling and punctuation. His vigilance has been invaluable to me.

J. L.-M.

19 Lansdown Crescent,
Bath.

1944

I had tea in Jamesey Pope-Hennessy's flat. He was discussing with Miss
Eve Kirk a posthumous portrait he wants her to do for him of Father
Burdett. Dame Una who joined us after tea said Miss Kirk was a
convert of Father Burdett, and had at one time supposedly been in
love with her own brother. The Dame asked me if I kept my diary
for posterity. 'Perhaps,' I answered, 'but it won't be read until fifty
years after my death.' 'Since *we* can't possibly die,' Jamesey said,
'that means never. Just as well.' The Dame looked wise and said
nothing.

Bridget Parsons lunched with me, or rather, since we went shares, we
lunched together. The arrangement, however necessary, seems all
wrong. We agreed that the Ritz is no more expensive than anywhere
else these days, and far more agreeable.

Sir Edwin Lutyens has died. He was the best architect of our time.
Robert Byron always maintained this. Lutyens had the manner of a
genius. I only once met him while staying at Batsford with the
Dulvertons. He came over with some friends, and after tea took me
aside in order to regale me with puns and obscene witticisms. Very
funny too. I remember Victoria Dulverton saying afterwards how
nervous she was lest he might say things that would embarrass her.
He was leonine, breezy, untidy, flamboyant and inspired.

At dinner Wyndham Goodden told me that his wife had left him
with two babies on his hands. I have never seen a man so unhappy.
I tried to cheer him by pointing out to him his blessings – doubtless a
fatuous thing to do at such a time. But what else could I do? Besides
he does have blessings. As I left his door the siren went, and I walked
home during a raid over the Thames estuary. It was a beautiful, clear
moonlit night under a violet starry sky. I saw the shells bursting in the
east like innumerable stars twinkling, but heard not a sound. Orange
flares were reflected in the Serpentine as I crossed the Park. On my
return at 12.45 the telephone rang, and my heart leapt. It was Oliver
Messel inviting me to a party in the Norwich Assembly Rooms next
Wednesday. Very sweet of him, but quite impossible.

At 6 went to a meeting to wind up the Federal Union Club at the Squires' flat. Only the Squires, Keith Miller-Jones, Sainsbury and Miss Ward present, a sad little gathering. I thought of poor Robert Byron, our President, and Derek Rawnsley, the fair, fanatical young man who also was killed. Keith and I walked to Brooks's and dined there. He recommended my reading Festing Jones's life of Samuel Butler. When young, Keith knew Festing Jones, who told him many anecdotes of Butler. The third unpublished sonnet of Butler to Miss Savage began, 'Had I the desires of a common sailor after three weeks' abstinence,' or words to that effect. Butler had a woman upon whom he vented his appetite, often, according to Festing Jones, without troubling to unbutton his trousers.

John Betjeman lunched with me at Brooks's, the first time since the war. He seemed to enjoy himself, jumping up and down in his chair and snapping his fingers, in laughter. He is sweeter and funnier than anyone on earth. He never changes, is totally unselfconscious, eccentric, untidy and green-faced. He works at the Ministry of Information and simply hates it, returning every Saturday till Monday to Uffington. In his *Daily Herald* articles he surreptitiously damns the war and progress, and the left wing. Talked about the slave state in which we are already living. Said he loved Ireland but not the Irish middle class. Only liked the country eccentrics like Penelope's distant relations, the Chetwode-Ailkens. When they claimed to be cousins Penelope retorted, 'No, you can't be. Your branch was extinct fifty years ago.' When the Betjemans left Ireland de Valera sent for them. Penelope said to him, 'My husband knows nothing of politics; or of journalism. He knows nothing at all.' She offered to plan an equestrian tour for de Valera, and her last words to him were, 'I hope you won't let the Irish roads deteriorate. I mean I hope you won't have them metalled and tarmacked.'

After luncheon we talked of architecture and the Greek Revival. John said that there had been no book on this style yet; and that K. Clark's *Gothic Revival* ignored Morris and the serious purpose of mid-nineteenth-century Gothic. He said there was an architect, by name May, still living in Sussex, who had been articled to Decimus Burton. May told John how in 1879 he took his prospective wife to see Burton, whose single comment was, 'Approved.' We walked down

Jermyn Street and he pointed out two buildings by Morphew that had singular merit. Any surviving Georgian building provoked him to say, 'They ought to have that down. That's too good.' I showed him the Athenian Stuart façade in St. James's Square, which to my surprise he did not know. He is a committed High Churchman, and wishes to edit a church magazine after the war. Suffers much from guilt complexes over his youth, which must surely have been more innocent than most people's — 'but the flesh hasn't been so provoking during the past fortnight'.

As we passed the site of Pennethorne's old Geological Museum he reminded me of our visits years ago during luncheon breaks. There was never a soul, either an attendant or visitor. We used to insert into the dusty glass cases old chestnuts and pebbles which we labelled with long names in Latin, invented by us amidst peals of laughter. They remained where we put them until the building was pulled down.

Wednesday, 5th January

George Scherhof ('Sarcophagus' Betjeman calls him) gave me luncheon at Brown's Hotel. He has returned from Algiers with a broken arm and shoulder blade, badly mended, and is in great discomfort. He is a captain in the army. He told me his father and mother were both Prussians, 'the worst sort,' he said. But he loves his mother. He was born in England. What a hideous accident birth is. It is a toss-up whether one is fighting with or against one's nearest and dearest, and indicates the folly of the whole damn thing.

Friday, 7th January

I had meant to dine at home but Eardley Knollys induced me to have a drink in order to show me the Samuel Palmer etchings he has just bought. The land of faery they lead one to. Heavenly things, but what does one do with them? Framed and hung on a wall they are lost. And in a portfolio they are equally lost.

Saturday, 8th January

I lunched at Rick Stewart-Jones's Café and sat next to Ethel Walker who talked about twentieth-century painting. She railed against Emerald Cunard for being taken in by Marie Laurencin. She heartily dislikes Emerald, as I would expect her to. Throughout the meal she fed her dirty old white dog on its chain. It was difficult to understand what she was saying because of mouth trouble. I guessed by the unyielding shape of her jaw that her teeth were false, quite apart from their unnatural whiteness. And so they proved to be, false to their poor owner – for she had hardly spoken with a little too much throwing back of the head and wide opening of the lips, as though to flaunt these glorious new appendages when they fell, or rather spurted out in one piece. Dexterously she caught them in her right hand. I behaved with absolute correctness, merely turning my eyes with deep solicitude upon the revolting dog. She went on to explain, quite undeterred by the incident, that she paints as well today as she has ever done. I marvelled, when I looked at those filmy blue eyes, that this could be so. She said she learnt at the Slade with John, who was a god, handsome, gifted and desired by all, till seduced by drink. Wilson Steer was the worst teacher in the world. He never instructed his pupils, but in a melancholy voice would say slowly and sleepily, 'If I were you I would make the nose longer, the arms fatter; give more light to the hair,' and so on. She hated George Moore, whom she called a cad and a lecher. He told her that the first time he met Emerald Cunard was at an exhibition; and that Emerald went up to him and asked him to kiss her on the lips. I don't believe this story.

Sunday, 9th January

I went to tea with Dame Ethel. She lives at 127 Cheyne Walk, further west than my house. Her Victorian apartment is undecorated, drab and grubby. I should have gone at 4 and was too late to see her pictures properly, for it was a dark day. The room was stacked with pictures. We sat on two broken-down armchairs by a coal fire. At last the kettle boiled on the hob. I was given a mouse-nibbled Digestive biscuit to eat. When I left at 5.30 she said, 'Perhaps one day you will let me paint you?' 'I should love to sit to you,' I said. She asked 'When?' I said, 'Next Saturday morning.' She fixed the time and said, 'Don't let's think of money.'

At 6.30 I went to Viva King's house in Thurloe Square. She is pretty, fair-skinned, silver-haired, plump, well-dressed and very intelligent without being blue-stocking. Norman Douglas was present. I was surprised to find an old man, nearly 80 I should say, sitting on a low sofa, rather hunched up, unrecognizing, with a regular-featured but red face, and beautifully brushed white hair parted in the middle, drinking whisky. He had just come in before me and was not yet lit up, for he has to drink a great deal, lives in rooms near by, is lonely and, I am told, disreputable. We talked about *Home Life with Herbert*

Spencer by two old ladies, with whom Spencer lived out his remaining years. He was eccentric and selfish to a degree unparalleled. Norman Douglas laughed a lot in an unregistering way, and spoke very little. Viva rather cross with him.

Monday, 10th January

Meeting day. Matheson is leaving on 1st March for six months. I wrote him a note, which he showed Esher and Zetland, that I did not want to become secretary if it entailed abandoning my historic buildings work, and that I could not anyway cope with the secretarial routine. I feel very unwell nearly all the time.

Went to Lady Crewe's party. It was hell. Not much to drink, hardly anyone I knew, and the atmosphere far from relaxed. Lady Crewe is awkward and shy. I talked a bit with Hamish Erskine about Rosslyn Chapel, which he wants the Scottish National Trust to take over. He says he is so blind in the dark that this evening he found himself cocking a leg over the bonnet of a bus, supposing it to be the way in. I watched Mrs. Keppel hobbling round the room and smoking from a long holder. She is rather shapeless, with hunched shoulders, a long white powdered face. She was gazing with mournful eyes as though in search of something. Colonel Keppel, with big moustache, is very much a Brigade of Guards officer of the old school.

Wednesday, 12th January

Went to Pierre Lansel again for injections. I have not the courage to tell him that I simply cannot continue with them, and would prefer to be bayoneted any day.

Dined at Sibyl Colefax's Ordinary and sat next Baroness Budberg and Olga Lynn, who asked to have me as neighbour. Both of them hugely fat, plain and delightful. The Baroness talked to me about Catholicism and the Greek Church, to which she belongs. She said she much disliked the Roman faith and could not swallow the Pope or Infallibility. Oggy Lynn discussed the war, saying she predicted in 1939 that it would end in the spring of 1945, and that the soundest man about the war was General Aspinall-Oglander. After dinner I talked to Mrs. Oglander about Nunwell, their home in the Isle of Wight, and then to the General, who is compiling a history of the place and the Oglanders. The earliest family letters date from the fourteenth century. I enjoyed this evening, and returned at 10.30.

Motored to Loose Wool House, Kent, that detestable little half-timbered atrocity. There I went over the furniture that is ours. The tenants offer to buy it for over £100, and good riddance to bad rubbish. Very friendly, very *quelconque* people who have evidently made money. They kindly gave me luncheon which they called dinner, and we drank tea afterwards. On leaving I was presented with four eggs, of which two were ducks'. At Stoneacre the old woman took me round. The house is still in good trim, the tenant not returned from Canada yet. Then to Bradbourne, and had a brief survey of this wonderful house which the horticultural people maintain jolly well on the whole. The director has good taste, and is a splendid man with all the right ideas. A crisp, sunny day which deluded me into thinking that life still held forth promise and fulfilment. Continued to Sole Street where the contours of God's orchards are homely. Met Daphne Baker on the road. She gave me tea at the Tudor Yeoman's House. Three unimportant little National Trust properties I have seen today, and one superb house, which is not ours and only protected by covenants.

I went to the office early. Then shopped. No books, no shoes, in fact nothing bought – and a thick fog. Went to the Leicester Galleries to see the Michael Sadler collection now on show, before dispersal. Probably the best collection of modern paintings we shall see for a long time, certainly have seen since the war. Horrible Picasso self-portrait, all in angles, but Mark Gertler's mother and Henry Lamb's death of a peasant among the best. Oh, the Renoir lady in blue too, but I coveted a hundred others. I understand that several have already been bought by K. Clark, Raymond Mortimer and Harold Nicolson.

Lunched at the café, and General Kennedy, D.M.O., beckoned me to him. Catherine is in waiting. He has two days off and is bored stiff. I asked him how he whiled the time away. He said by painting king-fishers over and over again, poor man. He is courteous, gentle and appealing. All afternoon I worked like a demon, then prepared tea for Ethel Walker who did not come. At 5.30 she rang the bell, having failed the first time to push open the iron gate. She and the dog ate two cakes. She closely studied the Peter Scott drawing of me and asked to see a photograph of me. None could be found. She said the least beautiful part of the female anatomy for drawing was the breast. I refrained from saying I could think of a less beautiful part.

At 6 in the fog I reached Hyde Park Gardens for Sir Ian Hamilton's 92nd birthday party. He was standing in the hall, dressed in a white waistcoat and a red carnation, being flashlight-photographed, with some Highland pipers. A crowded party, lots of Americans and Highlanders in kilts.

At 7.15 to Emerald's. She was speaking on the telephone on business as I came in, so I read the evening paper. She said Jamesey was dining with her and pressed me to stay. Then the siren went, and I consented. There was a great to-do about ordering a third cover, and Emerald lost her temper on the telephone, and stormed. She said the chef was a liar, she would speak to the Minister of Food, she would come downstairs and make a 'scandal' in the hall by screaming at the telephonist, that the waiters were all Nazis or Bolsheviks, she did not know which, the Dorchester was like a commercial traveller's doss house, the place Bedlam, a charity institution in a Dickens novel, like Dotheboys Hall, and so forth. Luckily James arrived in the middle of all this and I was not left alone to feel uncomfortable. Afterwards dinner upstairs passed happily enough. We lamented that the younger generation, never having been to the continent, only thought of European cities, which their fathers had revered as seats of culture, as targets to be bombed. We were allowing the continental seats of learning to be wiped out, and making little boys from the suburbs into heroes for committing these acts of barbarism. J. and E. talked Balzac. Emerald said we must live after the war in Paris, where the trees are all 'fluorescent' because there is no smoke in the atmosphere, and the women are beautiful and dress in silks and satins to match the horse carriages in which they drive, because there are no motors.

Sunday, 16th January

Today I really was intending to go to Cumberland Lodge, for Stuart Preston had pledged himself to accompany me. Magdalen FitzAlan-Howard rings me up at least once a week and I make a succession of excuses. But this morning she telephoned to say the fog was very thick. Indeed it was so bad here that I had to postpone. Stuart and I lunched instead very happily at the Travellers. The fog got thicker and thicker, and gorgeously yellow. When we stepped into Pall Mall it was like a blanket. How I love it. We somehow managed to reach Cheyne Walk by bus. S. spent the rest of the day sprawling over his books on the floor, sprawling over the armchair, sprawling over everything.

We had a Country Houses Committee this afternoon, which passed all right. Eardley's scheme for making Montacute into a furnished house was accepted.

I walked away from the Georgian Group meeting with Gerry Wellington, who talked about the future of Apsley House. In the afternoon Mortimer Wheeler addressed the S.P.A.B. committee on the work done, or rather not done, so far by the British authorities in North Africa and Italy. He gave a depressing and infuriating picture. The apathetic, ignorant and casual attitude shocked even me, who never cease to deplore British philistinism. It appears that up to date only three British experts have been sent to Italy to join twelve American experts, already there. They have no authority to act, and so their presence is merely an encumbrance to the Americans. Nothing is done to protect historic monuments when British troops withdraw from operations, except to billet more troops in them, and so render them more ruinous than they were during the fighting.

This evening I dined at Claridges with Alfred and Clementine Beit. Arrived at 8 and waited in the hall. Espied Gerry likewise sitting waiting. He said, 'Shall we have a drink?' I said, 'A good idea.' 'We will not have cocktails. They are too expensive,' he said in that well-known way. Actually I sympathize with him. So we each paid for a small glass of sherry at 4/–, which was preposterous. He told me that his gross income today was £40,000. After income and super tax there was £4,000 left over. Out of this he has to pay schedule A on Stratfield Saye and Apsley House, which leaves him barely enough for wages and food. I asked whether he had any servants at Apsley House. He said, 'Oh yes, I have the chamberlain's wife and the house carpenter.' He said he did not pay death duties on either of these two houses, or the lands attached, because they don't belong to him, but to Parliament. He is applying to Parliament to take back Apsley House – with the gift of the valuable contents which are his – on condition that they will make it into a museum under his guidance, and allow him to live in a corner of it. It is, he says, a perfect museum, not having been altered in any particular since the Great Duke's death in 1852.

Joan Moore joined us. At 8.30 it occurred to us that the Beits might have taken a private dining-room, which is what they had done. Joan and I talked of passionate, desperate, hopeless love. General conversation after dinner. Most enjoyable it was too. I walked in the rain to Hyde Park Corner with Gerry, who feigned to be nervous, cautious and old-mannish, as though it became his new ducal status. He kept saying it was a terribly long way to go. I think a person's age can be measured by his reaction to the blackout. Gerry was, however, charming, as he always is to me. He says that being a duke and inheriting two houses is like having a glittering present every day.

Thursday, 20th January

Johnnie Dashwood and Clifford Smith lunched with me at Brooks's to discuss West Wycombe affairs. I sensed they disliked each other.

Hamish dined alone with me at Brooks's. A boozy evening. I had three whiskies and soda before dinner. We had a bottle of burgundy at dinner, and two glasses of port each after dinner. Hamish told me all about his bravery, for which he got the M.C., treating it all as a great joke. His gun was shot to atoms and he received wounds all down the left side. His sergeant dragged him to safety. He denied that he was courageous. There was no alternative to what he had to do. A few times only he had a sense of personal fear when at close quarters to the enemy. The German soldiers were kind to prisoners. The Italian were only interested in their money. They have no respect for us and deadly fear of the Germans, who say, 'If you do so and so, we shoot,' and do shoot. Whereas we say the same, and don't shoot. He recounted his escape and hiding in a ditch, while hearing Germans shout, '*Fritz, wo ist er?*' I said, 'I suppose if they had found you, they would have bayoneted you on the spot?' He looked surprised and said, 'Not at all. They would have clapped me on the shoulder and said, "Bad luck! Now we must lock you up again." ' But he was anxious then. 'I had my rosary and was racing round it faster than you could have gone round the inner circle.' I said, 'When the Germans left and you realized you were safe, what did you say to Our Lady?' 'Whoopee, Virge!' We went back to his mews and drank beer till 2.30. He prepared a bed for me and said before he went to the bathroom, 'I hope you will be comfortable, but if you can't sleep you will have to come to mine,' which was a great double bed. When he came back I said, 'You were quite right in saying the sheets on my bed would only reach to my navel.' So Hamish said, 'Well, you'd better come to my bed, though I have wasted a clean pair on yours for nothing.'

Sunday, 23rd January

At 10.30 Stuart met me at Paddington Station. While waiting for him I watched a woman passenger have a row with an officious woman ticket collector at the barrier. The first threw the other's ticket puncher to the ground. The second threw the first's handbag to the ground, took off her own coat, and flew at her opponent. They punched and scratched and finally became interlocked, each grasping the other's hair which came away in handfuls. I felt quite sick and intervened. Then they both hit me. I roared for help, and two policemen dragged the combatants apart. The other passengers, mostly soldiers, merely looked on.

From Windsor station we made for the Park and down the Long Walk, the far end of which is felled, the elm trunks being quite rotten. Fine day with a biting wind. I had my filthy old mackintosh on which always puts me in the wrong frame of mind. It's curious how the clothes one is wearing dictate one's mood. Stuart kept saying, 'I do hope there is a good luncheon, and lots to eat.' I had misgivings.

There were only us and the family. Lord FitzAlan is past conversation now, having become very old and deaf. Magdalen has no conversation anyway, but is not deaf. Alethea looked sad and cold, no wonder. Stuart tried to be bright. I felt ill at ease, and suddenly realized I would have been able to make more effort if alone, without S. As we went into the dining-room Magdalen said, 'I hope there will be enough for you to eat. There is only soup.' It was too true. S. took some Scotch broth, and Alethea said, 'I should put some potato into it if I were you.' I overheard S. exclaim, 'What! potato in the soup? No thanks.' He soon did, however, on discovering that this really was the only dish. We got up rattling. S. was very forgiving on the way back. In Windsor we had a filthy tea at the Nell Gwynne café, to make up for the non-luncheon.

Tuesday, 25th January

Kathleen Kennet went to the National Gallery early and took a seat for me, good soul, and bought sandwiches. Myra Hess fed our two starved souls with delicious Mozart.

I behaved badly tonight by cutting Sibyl Colefax's Ordinary, which annoyed her, and cutting the boring Dr. Dietmar's dinner too. Harold Nicolson asked me to go to a play with him. It was *There Shall Be No Night*, a propaganda play, but excellent, with Lynn Fontanne and Alfred Lunt. She is a woman I could love and marry, I told Harold. At King's Bench Walk afterwards Harold discussed his political perplexities. He has been offered by Eden a seat in the Lords, which Harold toys with, because of the independence it promises. On the other hand if there is a chance of his getting back into the Commons at the next

12

election, he will refuse. He thinks there is little chance. He cannot stand as National Labour again, and will not stand as Tory or straight Labour. Would like to stand as Liberal but the Liberals have opposed him in his constituency. I said, 'Damn the lot, and be a lord.' Harold looked shocked, and maintained that the problem was of the greatest consequence.

Thursday, 27th January

Curious how much I dislike going away, and three days' absence from London seems like exile. I had a very comfortable first-class sleeper to Plymouth, yet the knowledge that I would be called at 5.30 a.m. kept me from sleeping. Actually the train was two hours late and I was not called till 6. Why couldn't it have been at 7.30? Arrived Falmouth very late. Had breakfast at 9.30 with the town librarian who is very worried about the fate of Arwenack Manor. To him, poor old man, the salvation of this house is his life's purpose. We went there, and it is *not* of architectural importance. In Elizabethan times it was a large mansion, and there are remains of a banqueting hall, one outer wall to be exact. The place was held by the Killigrews and burnt out in the Civil Wars. What is left of the house is now tenements. Today the R.A.F. occupy part of it. The young officer in command who took us round made intelligent suggestions. But blotted his copybook in the librarian's eyes by suggesting that a guest house was the most fitting use, come peace-time. I agreed, but the librarian was greatly pained. I had to tell him that it was not the N.T.'s concern, but I would recommend that Falmouth corporation should save it from demolition, and the surrounding land from development.

I left Falmouth by a 12.40 train, having been given an enormous Cornish pasty by the dear old librarian. It was his own luncheon. I did not get to Sherborne till 8.30. A honeymoon couple in my carriage were douched with confetti as the train drew out, and I was covered. The stuff even got down my neck. What can be the origin of this barbaric custom?

Friday, 28th January

Today was devoted to Sherborne Castle. At 10 the solicitor, who was also staying at the Digby Arms, took me to Rawlence, the agent's office, and the three of us motored to the Castle grounds bordering the town. We walked through the large walled gardens and the large stable yard. Then motored past the house towards the Palladian bridge, uphill to see the deer, but not as far as the unsightly American hospital buildings. Walked round the park and returned to the entrance. At first glance the outside of the house is disappointing. The cement rendering makes it gloomy. The plate-glass windows gives it a blind, eyeless look. Yet the house reminds me of Westwood Park in that it too has a central late-Elizabethan block (built as a hunting lodge by Sir Walter Raleigh) to which four arms were added in Restoration times. The dressings are of Ham stone. Fine entrance gates at the south and north sides, forming two open courts. Like Westwood the house is terribly confusing inside, for it is very tall, with many floor levels. There is little inside to take the breath away, but much that is good, notably the great marble chimneypieces of Jacobean date and, above all, the two interior porches in the downstairs dining-room. The great saloon is oddly shaped with two broken arms at the ends because of Raleigh's hexagonal towers, into which on all floors one constantly seems to be walking. At present the furniture is stored away, for American troops have requisitioned the castle. There are cavernous basements.

So far the lordly owner has not appeared, and we three of low degree lunch at the hotel. Twice Rawlence is called away to be advised by the Colonel's butler at what time we are to appear for coffee, port and cigars. The Wingfield Digbys are in Raleigh's lodge for the 'duration'. The Colonel is a stooping M.F.H., with the manner of one. Very autocratic, very conscious of his not inconsiderable dignity. He addresses Rawlence as Major Rawlence, in spite of the latter's father and grandfather also having been agents to the family, and Rawlence being every inch a gent. Rawlence addresses him as Colonel, and often as Sir. An awkward interview takes place. I explain as best I can what the transaction would involve. But they are not the sort of people to welcome public access.

After the interview we sallied forth to the pleasance. The Colonel and Mrs. W. D. took us over the old ruined castle and through the very beautiful wooded walks round the lake. Here we came upon Raleigh's Seat, where the servant is said to have thrown the water over his master while he was smoking; and Pope's Seat, where the poet wrote letters to Martha Blount. The Colonel showed little interest in these fascinating associations. When, on the second Seat being pointed out, I responded excitedly, the Colonel snorted, 'Pope indeed. I've no idea which pope it could have been.'

The Wingfield Digbys, finding that I was to dine alone, very kindly bade me dine with them. They showed me some rare miniatures—of Arabella Stuart, Kenelm Digby and Venetia Digby; also a jewel given to Ambassador Digby by the court of Spain. I liked the W. D.s although Anne Rosse had previously warned that they might not like me. And there was one awkward moment when, à propos of nothing, the Colonel exclaimed, 'I can't stick Roman Catholics. One can smell 'em a mile off,' or words to that effect. Mrs. Wingfield Digby, who, although her sentiments were clearly the same as her husband's, wished to appear open-minded, then said, 'But, Freddy, they do have a right to their own point of view,' adding after a pregnant pause, 'Of course one can't trust them one yard.' I thought it best to remain mum.

Anne had also told me a hair-raising story of the Colonel's behaviour during a severe frost. The lake at Sherborne froze, and people from near and far assembled to skate, as they do on these occasions, without by your leave. So 'Cousin Freddy' climbed up one of the Castle towers, and with a rifle peppered the ice to make it crack.

Saturday, 29th January

Up early and while it was not properly light went to the Abbey. A fine fan-vaulted ceiling to the nave. The chief ornament is a monster marble monument to a Digby Earl of Bristol signed by John Nost about 1698. Pope in a letter written from Sherborne commented favourably upon it. I looked at the old Hospital chapel next door, walked through the Close and the School to Sherborne House, now a girls' school, to see the Thornhill staircase walls and ceiling. This house belongs to the Digby estate. The Thornhill paintings are flaking through having been varnished over with coach varnish by a Digby predecessor. The stair rail turns into a gnarled, knuckled fist over the bottom newel.

Caught an 11 o'clock train to Semley station where I parked my bag and, with the aid of my map, walked to Pythouse, up a hill with the finest imaginable view across the Nadder valley towards Wardour. Sang (wildly out of tune, of course) all the way at the top of my voice. Pythouse is the prototype of nearby Dinton and the owner Colonel Stanford-Benett had asked me to pay him a visit. House built about 1800 with great Ionic portico. The side elevations are attached to wings by rounded angles, not very pretty. But what a setting, backed by trees! The old man is stone deaf. The house full of paying guests. Nothing remarkable about the interior, but a curiously narrow, long staircase. The first Benett was secretary to Prince Rupert, and they have a number of Charles I's letters and his death mask. The Stanford-Benetts are so old that by the time luncheon was over they were worn out. At 2.30 I rose to go. Wandered round the place by myself before setting off for Semley station. Got to Waterloo at 7 and gave Bridget Parsons dinner. She at her most beautiful. I firewatched in the office, rushing there at top speed when I heard the siren at 10.30. There was much gunfire. Lovel, the office caretaker, told me shrapnel fell on his steel helmet, and a large jagged bit just missed his shoulder.

Sunday, 30th January

That wretched old Ethel Walker and her dirty old dog came to tea. She talked of religion and the spheres of heaven having recently been cleansed. How it benefits the world at this nadir of spatial circum-navigations I fail to appreciate.

Thursday, 3rd February

I gave a luncheon party at the Ritz—Sibyl Colefax, Honey Harris and Cyril Connolly. The Ritz was crowded and there was much noise. I did not hear one word Sibyl uttered, and not for one instant did she draw breath. I asked Cyril whether he had heard anything, and he said nothing at all. The party was not therefore a rollicking success as far as the host was concerned.

At 6 I met Alvilde Chaplin at Mrs. Gordon Woodhouse's flat. Mrs. Woodhouse is old and little, but agile and rapid. Full of conversation. She was seated at a clavichord when I entered. After Alvilde joined us she turned to another clavichord made by Tom Goff. She played a Bach prelude, and I thought how lovely. After some more I decided that the instrument was too thin. I needed more volume to be satisfied. When I remarked that I could not claim to be really musical, she stopped. She talked about her house, Nether Lypiatt, and called in Lord Barrington who showed me his sepia drawings of the house. He is a sweet, friendly, simple creature, and I would suppose not up to her exacting intellectual level. Went on to dine with Bridget in Mount Street. B. had bad toothache, and was wearing a turban and dressing-gown with no buttons down the front. It was a diaphanous garment. 'Did she expose that blue varicose vein?' Anne asked me later. B. rattled off a host of questions, which is her present conversational technique, as though eagerly seeking information. Poor B., she is infinitely pathetic, for all her beauty and fastidiousness, which does not extend to her dress.

Friday, 4th February

Started off at 10.30 this morning for Norfolk, taking Geoffrey Houghton-Brown with me. Now he *is* a relaxed companion.

16

After the mugginess of the past few days the sudden cold and fierce north wind has come as a shock. But from inside the fairly warm car the wide landscape of East Anglia, which the storm clouds and fitful sunbeams were chasing, was very dramatic. Having gone out of the way to look at Wimpole from the end of the great elm avenue, we first stopped in Cambridge, bought books and drank coffee. On to Ely, stopping outside the town to eat sandwiches and feast on the distant cathedral. Admired the satisfactory marriage of the mid-Victorian barrel roof, painted by, I believe, a Le Strange of Hunstanton, with the Norman nave. Drove on to Norfolk and looked at the outside of Ryston Hall, built in the 1650s by Sir Roger Pratt. Ryston is still owned by a Roger Pratt. The Inigo Jones-like central portion can be detected under the Soane alterations. Stopped at Stoke Ferry Hall. It was empty. We pushed open a window at the back and walked into the deserted house. The soldiery have just vacated, so the condition is deplorable. Not by any means a remarkable house. High, plain, red-brick façade to the street, dated 1788 – the category of doctor's or solicitor's house. Spacious and well proportioned within. Spacious, many-walled garden. Everything I like, yet this pleasant old house is not worthy of the Trust, I fear. The conditions attached to the offer are not attractive; and besides, who would wish to live here? We continued past romantic Oxburgh Hall which we looked at from the road, and peered at the fine Bedingfeld terracotta monuments through the church windows. On to Swanton Morley. Tried in vain to find the vicar or anyone who might know where exactly was the site of Abraham Lincoln's forebears' cottage. No one of the four inhabitants we asked could tell. No one seemed to care. Nor did Geoffrey or I for that matter.

Just as it was growing dark the car konked out at the end of the lime walk at Blickling. In a downpour we pushed it to Miss O'Sullivan's door. Geoffrey stayed at the inn, I in Miss O'Sullivan's flat.

Saturday, 5th February

In the morning we went round the house looking at the furniture salvaged by me from the R.A.F.'s quarters. After a stroll in the garden, we drove on to Cromer, a mechanic from Aylsham having mended the car. The points needed adjusting. Found an hotel for G. in Cromer. It was the only one open in the whole town, a dingy, dirty building on the sea front. I arrived at Felbrigg in time for luncheon with Wyndham Ketton-Cremer in his great hall, barely warmed by one small stove. Otherwise no heating and no electric light. Only oil lamps at night.

In the afternoon he and I motored to Beeston Hall, the property of his late brother, whose presumed death in action was announced in the press this week to Wyndham's infinite distress. A bomb has lately fallen in front of the house. In any case the house, altered Georgian, has not much merit. We proceeded to Beeston Priory and Farm, both owned by Mrs. Reynolds, a rich farmer's widow. The Priory ruins, scheduled by the Ministry of Works, are extensive. Ivy-clad nave walls and some Early English pointed window heads. Mrs. Reynolds is of that splendid, sturdy yeoman stock, like the Miss Smyths of Earlswood Moat House. She is integrity personified, quick-witted, direct and talkative to boot. With the Priory she enjoys some curious rights of pasturage over the surrounding lands, not her own. These she jealously cherishes, and accordingly prevents building development over much of the coast here. At tea she gave us such a spread as I have not enjoyed for years. Farm bread and butter with apple jelly, and a rich rum cake, the best I have ever eaten. She made me take some away with me.

I was very tired after Wyndham's excellent dinner, and slept in front of the stove in spite of the cold. We talked about his book, *Norfolk Portraits*. He is a delightful, cultivated man; a most conscientious landowner. Perhaps a little too good to be true, a little too old for his age.

Sunday, 6th February

Left Wyndham at 10. A glorious still, sunny morning, the pattering of raindrops on crisp, curled leaves and the sucking up of puddles in the rutted drive clearly audible. Picked up Geoffrey in Cromer. At Gunton we got out, and walked to the edge of the lake, looking across at the house which some years ago was gutted by fire. In Norwich G. wanted to attend Mass in an ugly but well-built Catholic church. I was struck by the drabness of the packed congregation compared to what it would have been in 1939. In the cathedral three old women and one American formed the congregation. Looked at Sweet Vi, the late Bishop's girl friend in marble, kneeling in the ambulatory, very smug and Edwardian. In Wymondham Abbey we admired Comper's gilt reredos.

Tuesday, 8th February

A large deputation of the Liverpool City Council came to see me this morning about the Speke Hall lease and the heirlooms, all of which, ghastly fakes for the most part, they want. Horne, playing the part of
18

the tough lawyer, supported me, taking the part of the generous fool. The combination worked well.

A young member of the Trust called for me at the office and at 11.30 we set off in the car for Hitchin. He is a nice, earnest black-coated worker, called Teagle, madly keen on archaeological remains, birds and nature. He hikes every weekend in the summer in the Home Counties with his wife, and stays in youth hostels. I took him to a British restaurant in Hitchin where we had a tolerable meal of thick soup, roast mutton and baked potatoes. This was quickly over and we went to an area of land which he has found and wants us to save. We got out and walked for an hour. A small river valley bounded by a straight stretch of the Icknield Way. In this sunswept, windswept landscape our noses ran. He wiped his nose with the back of his hand. I had one handkerchief and debated with myself whether to share it. Decided against. I motored him as far as Ayot St. Lawrence where we looked at the old ruined church and the new. At the gate of Bernard Shaw's house I parted with him.

Shaw's Corner is a very ugly, dark red-brick villa, built in 1902. I rang the bell and a small maid in uniform led me across the hall to a drawing-room, with open views on to the garden and the country beyond, for the house is at the end of the village. There was a fire burning in the pinched little grate. Walls distempered, the distemper flaking badly in patches. The quality of the contents of the room was on a par with that of the villa. Indifferent water colours of the Roman Campagna, trout pools, etc. in cheap gilt frames. One rather good veneered Queen Anne bureau (for which G.B.S. said he had given £80) and one fake lacquer bureau. In the window a statuette of himself by Paul Troubetskoy. On the mantelpiece a late Staffordshire figure of Shakespeare (for which he paid 10/–), a china house, the lid of which forms a box. Only a few conventionally bound classics, plus Osbert Sitwell's latest publication prominently displayed on a table. Two stiff armchairs before the fire and brass fender. A shoddy three-ply screen attached to the fireplace to shelter from draughts anyone sitting between the fire and doorway.

I waited five minutes and looked around, at a chronometer and the serried row of Shakespeare plays in soft leather bindings. Presently the door opened and in came the great man. I was instantly struck by the snow-white head and beard, the blue eyes and the blue nose, with a small ripe spot over the left nostril. He was not so tall as I imagined, for he stoops slightly. He was dressed in a pepper-and-salt knickerbocker suit. A loose, yellow tie from a pink collar over a thick woollen vest rather than shirt. Several waistcoats. Mittens over blue hands. He evidently feels the cold for there were electric fires in every room and the passage. He shook hands and I forget what he first said. Nothing special anyway. Asked me to sit down, and put questions to me straight off, such as, could he make over the property now and retain a right of user. His friend, Lord Astor (Arstor), had done so. I had not expected the strong Irish brogue. This peasant origin makes him all the more impressive. It put me in mind of Thomas Carlyle, of whom, curiously enough, he spoke. I said I preferred Mrs. to Mr. Carlyle. He said Carlyle was out of fashion because of the prevailing anti-German prejudice; that there had been worse husbands than he. G.B.S. said he wished to impose no conditions on the hand-over, but he did not wish the house to become a dead museum. Hoped it would be a living shrine. He wanted to settle matters now, for since his wife's death he was bound to re-make his will, and in three years' time he might be quite dotty, if he was alive at all. He is 88, and very agile. He showed me his statuette, which he likes, and bust (copy) by Rodin which he does not care for. Took me into his study where he works at an untidy writing table. In this room is another Queen Anne bureau. The wall facing it is covered with reference books, and all the bound proofs of his own books, corrected by him. These, I said, ought to remain here. There are no pictures or photographs of his wife to be seen. The dining-room is far from beautiful. It contains some fumed oak furniture and a portrait of him done in 1913. He ran upstairs, pointing admiringly to the enlarged bird etchings on the stair wall. He showed me his wife's room and his bedroom, and the one spare room. He has lived in this house since 1908.

When he smiles his face softens and becomes engaging. He is not at all deaf, but comes close up to one to talk, breathing into one's face. His breath is remarkably sweet for an old man's. Having looked upstairs we descended. He tripped going down, and I was afraid he was going to fall headlong. He then said, 'We will go out and have a look at the curtilage' – rolling the 'r' of this unusual word. It was fearfully cold by now, and raining heavily. He put on a long, snow-white mackintosh and chose a stick. From the hall hat-rack, hung with a variety of curious headgear, he took an archaic rough felt hat, of a buff colour, high in crown and wide of brim. In this garb he resembled Carlyle, and was the very picture of the sage, striding forth, a little wobbly and bent perhaps, pointing out the extent of the 'curtilage' and the line of the hedge which he had de-rooted with his own hands so as to lengthen the garden. The boundary trees of spruce were planted by him. 'Trees grow like mushrooms in these parts,' he said. We came to a little asbestos-roofed summer house that revolves on its own axis. Here he also writes and works. There is a little table covered with writing material, and a couch. The summer house was padlocked. I said, 'Do you sit out here in the winter then?' 'I have an electric stove,' and he pointed to a thick cable attached to the summer house from an iron pylon behind it. 'This will be an attraction to the *birthplace*, if it survives,' he said. We passed piles of logs, which he told me he had chopped himself. He showed me his and his wife's initials carved on the coach-house door and engraved on a glass pane of the greenhouse. Took me into the coach-house where there are three cars under dust sheets, one a Rolls-Royce. 'When I want to use this,' he said, 'I become very decrepit, and the authorities allow me coupons.' We continued down the road.

A collie puppy dog met us in the road and jumped up at the old man who paid it much attention. He led me to Revett's curious church. He explained at length that the reigning squire began demolishing the old church because he considered it 'an aesthetic disgrace' and 'barbarous Gothic'. The Bishop stopped it entirely disappearing, but not the erection of Revett's church in the 'fashionable Palladian'. G.B.S. walked up the steps and with reverence took off his hat. We walked inside. The interior is certainly cold and unspiritual. 'But it has good proportions,' Shaw allowed. The worst mistake is the ugly coloured glass in the windows. Classical churches are always spoilt by coloured glass. The organ case is contemporary. When we left he tapped with his stick a scrolled tombstone and made me read the inscription. It was to some woman who had died in the 1890s, aged 76, and below were inscribed the words, 'Cut off ere her prime,' or words to such effect. 'That,' G.B.S. said, 'is what persuaded me to come and live in the parish thirty-six years ago, for I assumed I stood some chance of at least reaching my ninetieth year.' We continued past the house and across the field, to the old church. He explained that although he never worshipped in the church he had spent £100 on its preservation. He remarked that the font had been overturned at some time. Took me outside to see the grave of Queen Victoria's tallest army officer, and admire the tracery moulding on a doorway, now blocked, at the west end. He wishes to buy the little corner cottage in order to destroy it, because it hides a view of the church from his own house. By the time we got back to the house I was wet through.

Tea was brought on a tray to the drawing-room. A glass of milk only for him; but tea and cakes for me. I was given a mug to drink out of. We talked of Esher's letter to *The Times*, of which he heartily approved. Decried the madness of the times, and the war. He said wars cease to be wars when chivalry is altogether excluded, as now, and become mass murder. That we had yet to witness the day when conscientious objection would be organized on such a universal scale that wars just could not happen. Up to now conscientious objection had failed, but one day it would succeed. It would be interesting to see how it would work if ever this country declared war on Soviet Russia. The present war was due, not to man's wickedness, but to his ignorance. In the last war he wrote a letter to *The Times* urging that air-raid shelters be provided for children. *The Times* refused to publish it because the editor was shocked by the implied suggestion that the enemy could, or would bomb schoolchildren. The *News Chronicle* refused likewise. I asked, 'What would you do if you were given Winston Churchill's powers and position today?' He said wisely enough, 'All action depends upon actual circumstance, but I would endeavour to bring fighting to an instant conclusion.' I said, 'I doubt whether the Germans would follow suit.' He condemned the folly of insisting upon unconditional surrender. There can be no such thing. The Government ought to tell the Germans what conditions we would accept and what terms we should impose. He mocked at the press's pretence that Winston Churchill and Stalin were in agreement. Their aims were becoming more and more widely divergent. He was nauseated by the lies disseminated by the press. At the same time he laughed at the Left Wing for supposing that today they could achieve their aims by general strikes, for 'You do not do well to starve on the enemy's doorstep.'

We talked about Hardy's Max Gate. 'Pull it down,' he said. He advised the National Trust to hold his house alienably, so that, supposing in twenty years' time we found that his name was forgotten, we could reap the benefit of selling it. He liked the idea of our holding T. E. Lawrence's Cloud's Hill, for 'it is good for nothing else'. Talked a lot about Lawrence. Said people would not grasp that T.E.L. was physically under-developed and never grew up, scarcely shaved, and also was mentally adolescent. He used to tell Lawrence that he knew no one who kept his anonymity so much in the limelight. He and his wife corrected the proofs of *The Seven Pillars*. The published version was scarcely recognizable. The Shaws cut out so much that was sheer guilt complex. Lawrence was tormented by the recollection of the lives he had personally 'terminated'. Lawrence's great discovery had been that the surest way of directing affairs of any department was by enlisting at the bottom and remaining there. His was the lowest rank of aircraftsman and he had to pretend to be illiterate in order to avoid promotion. Shaw tried to persuade Baldwin, 'that pure humbug', to give T.E.L. a pension. Lawrence refused to consider one although he confessed to Shaw that sometimes to get a square meal he would hang around the Duke of York's steps until a friend took him off to luncheon.

At 5.15 G.B.S. jumped up, saying it was getting dark and he had kept me a quarter of an hour too long. Thanked me for coming. I said I had enjoyed the afternoon immensely. He said he had too. Before I left however he talked about his will again; said he would not leave any money to his relations for he did not wish them to grow up in idleness and luxury. He wanted to leave his money for the sole purpose of inaugurating a new alphabet of something like 140 letters instead of the 26. He had calculated that the saving of expense in print and paper within one generation would be enough to finance three more world wars. And if that didn't appeal to this government, what would? He came on to the road without hat or coat and stood until I drove off. In the mirror I watched him still standing on the road.

Thursday, 10th February

Dined at Sibyl Colefax's Ordinary in the Dorchester and sat between Emerald and Christabel Aberconway. The latter blinks her eyelids at one and acts the clown, whereas she is shrewd, shrewd. She threw a knife and fork at Professor Joad while dining at Emerald's, which is good marks for her. After dinner talked with Cyril and Rosemary Hinchingbrooke about religions. Cyril is all for them as purveyors of a moral standard so long as they are not heaven inspired. I said the trouble about religions was that they purveyed not one, but several conflicting moral standards.

Saturday, 12th February

Oh, such a ridiculous ceremony! At noon to the American Embassy. In an ugly back room like a schoolroom a contingent of black, or rather dark yellow American troops, Angus Malcolm, the Bonham-Carters, myself and the press waited. Soon Thurtle of the M.O.I., Lord Zetland, Colonel Jack Leslie and the American Ambassador entered and sat under two flags of the U.K. and U.S.A. Speeches ensued and Colonel Leslie handed the deeds of the site of Abraham Lincoln's ancestors' cottage at Swanton Morley to Lord Zetland. Zetland spoke well, succinctly, and not dully. The Ambassador, who is a handsome,

23

dark man, with low brow and jet eyes, read a well composed speech on Lincoln's democratic ideals, but so haltingly and shyly that I felt embarrassed for him. It is strange that he should be so painfully shy.

Talked to Professor Richardson at Brooks's. He is determined the Georgian Group shall extend its functions so as to become the arbiter of taste in modern architecture, a dangerous step for a preservation society in my opinion. Accompanied him to the Courtauld Institute for the Georgian Group reception. Left as soon as decently possible with Dame Una and James. Over tea the Dame very censorious of the new Archbishop for encouraging Catholics to agitate over the Education Bill. She strongly deprecates Catholics concerning themselves with political issues, as they do in Ireland. I don't think I agree any more than I agreed with the Professor this afternoon. The truth is I can't come to snap decisions, but like to have time to think matters over. My mind works slowly and creakily.

Sunday, 13th February

Lunched at Kathleen Kennet's house. He ill in bed. K. and I walked across the Park to the Albert Hall to a Beethoven concert. On the way she told me she had written a letter to *The Times* (which they have not published) to the effect that she would gladly sacrifice Rome for the life of her two sons. (So likely that she will be given the choice!) This silly argument angered me. She was cross and threatened not to see me again and to have me reported to the police for holding subversive views. I replied that I was quite indifferent to these threats. A coolness ensued.

To tea with Emerald. How funny she was. I recall Gerald Berners's definition of Sibyl Colefax's and Emerald's parties. The first was a party of lunatics presided over by an efficient, trained hospital nurse; the second a party of lunatics presided over by a lunatic. It is impossible to recollect or record accurately Emerald's particular funninesses. She told us how Count So-and-So shocked her correct husband, Sir Bache, by bringing to Nevill Holt where they lived his Austrian mistress for a week's hunting. 'My dear, she was an Abbess' — by which she meant a chanoinesse, a hereditary dignity.

Monday, 14th February

Matheson made Martineau take the Finance Committee today and me the Executive. Martineau was so nervous that he called every committee member 'Sir' between each word, and even members of the staff. My heart bled for him. Esher said to me, 'I have never seen a

24

fellow in such a stew. You seemed to do all right,' which, strictly speaking, was not the case, for I knew nothing of half the items on the agenda, Matheson having dealt with them exclusively. I am too charitable to suspect that he was gloating over our discomfiture.

Wednesday, 16th February

News has come of the bombing of Monte Cassino monastery. This is comparable with the German shelling of Rheims cathedral in the last war. No war-mindedness can possibly justify it.

Thursday, 17th February

James Mann of the Wallace Collection lunched with me. He agreed that we had far better lose the war than destroy Rome. He came to discuss the future of Sir Edward Barry's house, Ockwells. Sir E. has made him an executor. He has advised Sir E. to sell the property now, but at a reasonable figure, and not to stick out for a fancy price. I wrote again to Captain John Hill suggesting Mr. Cook as a purchaser.

Friday, 18th February

I dined at Emerald's and sat next to Joan Moore and Lady Russell, wife of Sir Claud, retired ambassador to Portugal. She is half-Greek. Aubrey Moody, a new friend of Emerald's, present. He sends her flowers all the week, according to Joan. Emerald persistent in calling upon me to talk about my visit to Bernard Shaw, which I was loth to do, because I could see that the Ambassador did not want to listen. Emerald likes every guest to play a part. She is like a prompter in the theatre, or a conductor at the opera. Having failed over G.B.S.— fortunately—she made me read aloud a letter which Daisy Fellowes had just received, beginning, 'Divine Creature, I have been chaste since 1st January, which I find uncomfortable . . . I am faithful to you and White's Club only. I adore you.' We agreed that it was not a serious love letter.

On my return at 12.30 Joan telephoned, and we talked for half an hour. The instant she put down the receiver the sirens went, and the worst raid for years occurred. The noise of guns was deafening. Miss Paterson and I went downstairs and ate buns in the kitchen, trembling with fear. When the all-clear sounded, there were fires to be seen in all directions. The result is, we brought down five raiders only, and four of them over France.

By the evening I was very tired for I slept badly last night. On returning home was obliged to shelter in South Kensington tube during another severe and noisy raid. A lot more fires and a bomb dropped on the Treasury buildings. The Carmelite church in Kensington destroyed.

Dining with the Moores in Ladbroke Grove, Garrett said, 'Look at Jim's nose!', and indeed I felt it burning red from the sudden heat after the intense cold outside. Emerald said that a certain duke – she would not disclose which – remarked about his wife, whom E. had been praising, 'Yes, but you don't have to sleep with her.' 'Now, dear,' E. remarked, 'isn't that what you call caddish?' There was only one answer. Joan said that recently a visiting Polish general sat next to a handsome English general who spoke in a deep voice about strategy. Suddenly the English general took out a powder puff, then a lipstick. It was the Duchess of Marlborough.

Alfred Beit talked to me about the parliamentary amenities group and the bombing of monuments versus lives argument. Said the Bishop of Chichester was responsible for raising this unnecessary and irrelevant matter in the Lords by suggesting that all German cultural centres should be spared. Alfred said the only hope of doing our cause good was by keeping calm, not writing emotional letters to the press, but sending to the ministers concerned a deputation of the most respected M.P.s from the Amenity Group. The Beits motored me to Chelsea across the Park. The gates were closed, so I got out and opened them.

Alec Penrose and Eddy Sackville-West lunched today, for Alec said he wished to meet him again. Alec began by being inscrutable and delusively diffident. That is what I like about his plain, dour face and manner. After a bit he blossoms into the sensitive, poetical man he is. His poem he sent me for Christmas is proof enough. Eddy in a *voix blanche* mood. The windows of the west front of Knole have been blown out by a bomb in the park. The heraldic beasts on the gable finials turned round on their plinths and presented their backs to the outrage committed. What proud and noble behaviour!

At midnight a very bad raid. Miss P. and I sat on the stairs in our fur coats, cowering. It was the noisiest raid I have ever heard. It lasted an hour. For a stretch of five minutes the gunfire was so continuous that it was like prolonged thunder rolls. The little house shook. Did not hear whistling of bombs, but frequent concussions. There were no fires visible from our windows.

Wednesday, 23rd February

Ate at the delicious Churchill Club canteen for 2/6. At 7.30 Kenneth Clark lectured on 'How to Look at Pictures', and showed slides. I was deeply impressed by the felicity of his choice of words, the rhythm of his sentences, the total lack of apparent contrivance. It was a scholarly talk, yet not above the audience's heads. And they a society lot.

I returned to my office at 9.15. Christopher Gibbs on fire-watching duty with me. We talked until 10.30 when the sirens went. We donned our steel helmets and joined the other firewatchers from our block. We were both astonished by the unashamed way in which most of them, including the men, admitted that they were not going to take risks in putting out incendiary bombs, or rescuing people. I said in surprise, 'But I thought that was what we were here for!' Several close crumps shook the building so that one and all ducked to the ground. One—I speak for myself—feels foolish on rising again. Christopher and I went out several times between the bursts of gunfire to look around. A clear, starry night. It was beautiful but shameful to enjoy the glow of fires, the red bursts of distant shells and the criss-cross of searchlights. I suppose that Nero derived a similar thrill from watching the Christians used as human torches, and did not feel ashamed. Then we saw the slow descent of what looked like a lump of cotton wool. Our leader lost his head, shouting, 'It's a German parachute! We must run. It's coming down here,' etc. In fact it was far away. I rather wickedly said, 'On the contrary I think it may be a land mine,' which sent him off in terror. Christopher Gibbs, who has been a colonel in the war, was furious with the man. I could not help ragging him in very bad taste, for it seemed so funny. I am far better in raids when I have something to do, especially when others lose their heads. Fear then seems driven away by farce.

Thursday, 24th February

There is no doubt our nerves are beginning to be frayed. Frank telephoned this morning. I could tell by his voice he was upset. He said he was going to leave the Paddington area and thought Chelsea or

Belgravia would be safer. I said I doubted whether the Germans discriminated to that extent. This evening I went to see a crater in the road, now railed off, in front of St. James's Palace, at the junction of Pall Mall with St. James's Street. The Palace front sadly knocked about, the clock awry, the windows gaping, and shrapnel marks on the walls. A twisted car in the middle of the road. Geoffrey's Pall Mall flat devastated, and the Lelys from Castle Howard he has just bought presumed lost. The staircase to the flat quite gone. A colonel who lived above him has entirely disappeared, only two buttons of his tunic and a part of his cap have been retrieved. In King Street Willis's Rooms finally destroyed, one half having gone in the raid of 1941 when I was sheltering in the Piccadilly Hotel. Poor Frank Partridge's shop devastated, and presumably Leonard Knight's. Drowns, the picture restorers, where I took the two Greville primitives, gone altogether. This is an ill-fated area. The London Library received a hit. Whereas fewer bombs are dropped than formerly, they must be of larger calibre, for the damage they do is greater. A huge bomb fell last night at the World's End killing many people. Miss P., alone in Cheyne Walk, was buffeted by blast. Poor little Mrs. Beckwith's house in Battersea bombed, and she didn't come to work today, but sent her daughter to tell us before we left for the office. During the luncheon hour Miss P. and I cleared up some of the grit and dust that had collected in the house. So far no windows broken here.

This evening at 9.45 another raid of an hour. The weather is cold, the air clear, the moonless sky starry. Lovely weather for bombing. There was one ugly moment when a big bomb dropped near. It provoked a deafening cannonade of guns in retaliation.

Friday, 25th February

After work I went to Hamish's for a drink. How could one exist without a drink these days? Or two drinks? Jennifer Heber-Percy there. She said she once laughed so uncontrollably in the High Street, St. Albans, that she did herself a mischief, as my Aunt Dorothy expresses it. People noticed, yet she could not help herself. It happened outside an inn. When she looked up she saw the name of the inn was The Waterspout. She was so convulsed that she started all over again.

Saturday, 26th February

Jamesey lunched at Brooks's. His mother has been ill with double pneumonia and consequently J. has been in a great state. He said we must meet more often. We went to the London Library for five minutes and met John [Pope-Hennessy] in the art room, which has caved in. All the books are scattered but unharmed. Most of them have already been removed from this exposed room to safety. All the glass, and skylights smashed. I promised to go tomorrow and help salvage. The rest of the afternoon spent at home drafting the Annual Report and finishing Virginia Woolf's *A Haunted House*.

Sunday, 27th February

Made my breakfast, washed up, did the minimum of dusting, and, packing a small suitcase with a tidy suit, went off to Mass in the Sardinian chapel. Found there was no Mass, and was furious, cursing outwardly which put me in a worse state of grace than ever. So, read the papers in Brooks's and walked to the London Library in my corduroy trousers and an old golfing jacket. Joined the volunteers for two exhausting hours in salvaging damaged books from the new wing which sustained a direct hit on Wednesday night. They think about 20,000 books are lost. It is a tragic sight. Theology (which *one* can best do without) practically wiped out, and biography (which *one* can't) partially. The books lying torn and coverless, scattered under debris and in a pitiable state, enough to make one weep. The dust overwhelming. I looked like a snowman by the end. One had to select from the mess books that seemed usable again, rejecting others, chucking the good from hand to hand in a chain, in order to get them under cover. For one hour I was perched precariously on a projecting girder over an abyss, trying not to look downwards but to catch what my neighbour threw to me. If it rains thousands more will be destroyed, for they are exposed to the sky. It is interesting how the modern girder-constructed buildings withstand the bombs, for those parts not directly hit, but adjacent to hit parts, twist but resist the concussion to a surprising extent. For instance, the stairs and floors of metal are perfectly firm even when projecting into space. You can walk to the very edge of the abyss.

To lunch with Stuart at the Travellers where I washed and changed, although my hair remained glutinous with dirt. Hamish joined us. When the two went off to play bridge with Nancy, I returned to the London Library for another hour and a half. Again was a link in a human chain passing bucket-loads of shattered books from hand to hand. It was very exhilarating and very exhausting.

Miss P. went at luncheon time to see our bombed charwoman in Battersea. She was shocked by the condition of her house. No ceilings, or rather no plaster left to them, no glass, no light, and dirt and dust indescribable. No doors fitting, and woodwork torn off. Mrs. Beckwith dares not leave the house for fear of looters. Miss P. said she did not understand how humans could live in such conditions. And the Borough says it can do nothing for Mrs. B. because she is lucky enough to have a roof over her head. We must do something.

I dined with Harold Nicolson at Boulestin's, to meet Robin Maugham who failed to turn up. There was a young man called Myles Hildyard. Fair-haired, tough, nice. Oddly enough he is the person whose diary of an escape from the Germans in Crete I was lent by Woodbine Parish, and which I so much admired.

Harold told us several stories about literary celebrities. In 1919 he dined with Proust, who made H. tell him all he had done that day. He did not let him omit one detail, and made him describe events from the beginning. Who called him in the morning? Was the bath water run for him? What razor did he shave with? Did he use lotion? And what was it called? Why this? How that? Virginia Woolf had a similar appetite for little things. Her curiosity was insatiable. She wanted to know what pen nibs office clerks used, and how often they changed their blotting paper. Harold feels sure that posterity will always read her for her observation of detail if for no other reason. Sociologically she is important, as well as literarily. Harold is clearly fascinated by Virginia Woolf. She had no memory. I told him that Logan Pearsall Smith said *The Mark on the Wall* in her last book, *A Haunted House*, was a direct crib from Thackeray. Harold maintained that all great artists plagiarized, and he told the story I have heard before of her being threatened with a libel action for taking a live lady novelist's name for a tombstone inscription in *The Voyage Out*.

H. said that Henry James hated George Moore. Mrs. Hunter, determined to bring them together, invited them both to stay for the same weekend, or, more correctly, Saturday to Monday, as she would have termed it. On Sunday morning she sent them off for a walk together. They returned. George Moore without a word went upstairs. James sat down on a sofa. 'Well,' said Mrs. Hunter, 'and how did you get on?' Henry James replied, 'Of all the literary figures I have met in a long life, I have never met one more absolutely, more persistently, more irredeemably — *dull*, dear lady.'

Roger Senhouse told me at the Travellers that Kenneth Clark's library in Hampstead has been burnt out, not in an air raid, but the moment after an electrician left the house. Roger showed me a book of Flaxman's drawings in original boards for which only two guineas is asked.

Friday, 3rd March

Said good-bye to Rick Stewart-Jones, who has at last got a commission, but in the Pioneer Corps. This army unit is always referred to with contempt, but I daresay fulfils just as necessary and honourable work as the crack regiments.

I lunched with Nancy and Bridget at Gunter's. Speaking of Alice Harding whose husband has returned to her and is all solicitous affection, Bridget said 'But I thought they were ruptured?' 'No, they are un-ruptured now,' said Nancy. 'In fact they are trussed.'

Saturday, 4th March

Finished reading *Mansfield Park*, which more than ever convinces me that Jane Austen is trivial, facetious and commonplace.

Sunday, 5th March

Hamish, Stuart and I dined together in Sloane Square. Hamish spoke of the vulgarity of the Edwardians, in particular his three aunts, Sutherland, Warwick and Westmorland, and how contemptible their behaviour was, but with little true conviction. S. and I told him that he was essentially an Edwardian sibling. S. said, 'You are like a highly bred, high stepping little pony.' 'Yes,' I added, 'with highly polished brass coronets on your blinkers, as you paw the air in front of your mistress's front door, highly curbed, highly glossy and highly arrogant.' H. was delighted. 'Go on,' he said. Then he said he intended to get Lady Angela Forbes, another aunt, to dictate to him some inside Edwardian gossip, such as her experience of hiding under the low bedstead in which her half-sister Lady Warwick was lying with King Edward VII, and of getting covered with bruises from head to foot in consequence. With all his absurdities Hamish has a keep-your-distance attitude, which Stuart says he respects.

Went to Partridge's Bruton Street shop to look at the Blickling pictures which have suffered severely from two foot of water rushing into the strong-room in King Street during the raid. Partridge's lost a third of their own things. The Holbein of Henry VIII, Zucchero of Queen Elizabeth and Samuel Scott of the Thames, all from Blickling; very bad indeed. All the varnish off and what to my eye seemed much of the paint too, the bare canvas showing. But the restorer wiped the surfaces with a rag and some methylated spirit and the pictures miraculously reappeared for an instant, then faded away. If treated at once they can be saved, he maintains.

Dined at Alvilde's in the Princess de Polignac's old flat. Exquisite dinner, a rich curry with plenty of onion, and a pudding of bananas and much beside. Eddy, his friend Mrs. Richards, and the Strathallans there. A jolly evening discussing food ad nauseam, regurgitation and wind—favourite subjects of Eddy's.

Tuesday, 7th March

The National Trust has held an open competition for a group of cottages and a village hall at West Wycombe. Two hundred and forty competitors. All today the three judges, Edward Maufe, Darcy Braddell and William Weir, were unpacking and rejecting designs. By 6 o'clock they had only got halfway through, leaving some twenty for reconsideration. I was amazed at the dullness of most of the designs. Very few were positively modernistic, and very few neo-Georgian. The vast majority were commonplace and rubbishy.

Went to a National Gallery concert to hear Irene Scharrer. She is an unintellectual, or do I mean an un-architectural pianist. It took me an hour to get home from dining with Tony Beaumont and Brinsley Ford (Captain in Army Intelligence). I read in the bus Vita's book on Knole into which she has poured her heart, and soul.

Wednesday, 8th March

I am extremely busy at the N.T. now that Matheson is away. There seem to be endless committees to prepare agendas, minutes, and reports for, and have them all circulated. The post of acting secretary has its drawbacks.

This evening I went to the Dorchester for one of Sibyl's Ordinaries in a hideous, linenfold-panelled room upstairs. Sibyl ill with a cold and could not come. I sat next to Harold and Nancy. Emerald Cunard joined the dinner late as usual. I was rather sorry she came at all for her personality is so strong that she monopolizes. We were seated round a large round table, and from the moment she entered the room Emerald took over the conversation. She made repeated bad shots, but by dint of inexhaustible efforts like a hurdy-gurdy player she occasionally hit upon a good tune, and was quite funny. She told a story of Lord Curzon sending her two notes, one an invitation to dinner and another, obviously intended for somebody else and put into a wrong envelope. It began: 'My beautiful white swan, I long to press you to my heart.' Harold gave an instance of Curzon's blatant rudeness. He once summoned Sir George Clerk to see him in his room in the Foreign Office. He kept him standing, while he wrote out invitation cards in his own hand. He turned to Clerk and said, 'I suppose you too occasionally entertain in your small way.' Harold reminded Lord Curzon of this story. Curzon indignantly rebutted it, saying, 'It căn't be true. It căn't be.' Then, 'I believe I did. I believe I did,' and his shoulders shook with laughter. Harold told Curzon that his staff were frightened of him. Curzon was distressed by this information. He was sensitive about people's opinion of him, just as Lloyd George is. Underneath the imperious façade was a kind-hearted man, more human than his contemporaries Asquith, Balfour and Bonar Law. Emerald emphasized the important part women played in politics behind the scenes in those days. For instance, Lady Curzon sent Lord Crewe to Paris and she, Emerald, sent Lord D'Abernon to Berlin. Emerald said Lady Randolph Churchill had the loveliest mouth of any woman, and admirers stole photographs of her from other admirers. Her grandmother, said Emerald, was a Red Indian, called Sitting Bull; and her sister, Mrs. Moreton Frewen, was the mistress of King Milan of Serbia. I walked away with Nancy who said that at times Emerald seemed practically gugga. 'Gug', said Nancy, who always abbreviates. I rather took against Emerald tonight.

Friday, 10th March

A strange luncheon at Claridges with the Secretary of the Royal Medical Society who wants to rent a N.T. country house for his society. A very affected old gentleman. He revealed that he was married to the Lord Chancellor's daughter and had a son who was a Papist convert.

Dined with Geoffrey Houghton-Brown to meet John Fowler, Sibyl Colefax's working partner. A very sympathetic man. He has a large upper lip which makes him look like the duchess in *Alice in Wonderland*. Also a very handsome young man with steel-blue eyes, called Ian McCallum. He works on the Architectural Press.

Saturday, 11th March

Angus Acworth lunched to discuss the future of the Georgian Group. He wants to get the Duke of Wellington to resume chairmanship. He fears that if the Group relaxes into being just another preservation body it had better die altogether. I agreed that we must bear in mind Robert Byron's objective, which was that it should be a ginger group. To achieve this purpose it was to resort to any and every weapon, mockery, vituperation, scurrility, pillorying if needs be prime ministers and archbishops, with gloves off. Our methods were what distinguished us from the S.P.A.B. and the old societies, established before the flood. Acworth thinks the Georgians should now co-ordinate with the other societies to the extent of setting up under one roof. The idea occurred to me that when the N.T. deputation to Morrison takes place we might ask for the Government's financial assistance to forward this end.

I dined with Grandy Jersey at the Hyde Park Hotel. I have not seen him since 1939 when he was beautiful, wan and pale like some rare hot-house lily. He is still pale but has grown a sandy moustache. He is just as suspicious and cautious as ever. Virginia unfortunately was not present. After dinner, back in his flat in Chesham House, he launched upon the purpose of our meeting. First he produced a plan of the Osterley estate. Then he disclosed that he wanted the Trust to take it over. For six years this is what I have been hoping might happen. At 11 I went to the office to firewatch. Lovell told me they had made a mistake in the rota and I was down for tomorrow. Since it was so late I stayed the night on the spare office camp bed.

Sunday, 12th March

Caught a Waterloo train this morning for Weybridge, there joining Geoffrey Houghton-Brown, John Fowler, young Ian McCallum and Hardy Amies. From the station we walked to Oatlands Park and lunched in the hotel. Spent the afternoon in the sun looking at the grounds and then the grotto. The present house is a huge, ugly shapeless pile, chiefly of 1860 though incorporating earlier work. There is a square Osborne-like tower at one corner. The grounds laid out by Kent between 1740 and 1755 have a long, steep terrace down to a

34

serpentine lake. There are many Palladian urns along the terrace and two stone gate-piers at the drive entrance, not very fine in design and somewhat top heavy. The grotto however is fascinating. It must have been constructed about 1795 by a Duke of Newcastle. It is extremely elaborate. Unfortunately it is fast deteriorating, being at the mercy of children who pick the shells off the walls. The outside is made of decayed lava stone, encrusted with large fossils and sea urchins. It contains an upstairs room in bad condition, the walls inlaid with fluorspar and vauxhall looking-glass plates, the ceiling hung with great stalactites of felspar. Below are wonderful passages and a subterranean hall dripping with stalactites. The walls are decorated in rude chevrons of glittering red and blue stones, and lit by specially constructed windows once filled with stained glass, judging from the few bits that remain. There is a tiled bathroom, its walls and ceilings decorated with whorls of mussel shells, and great conches. Of its kind this is far the best grotto I have ever seen, a superb plaything of variety and imagination. John Fowler was greatly impressed. He thinks it must have taken at least five years to make, and was probably done, not by amateur members of the family but by trained Italian grottoists. From the lead pipes everywhere in evidence it is apparent that the walls were made to drip and cascade with water, when the rare stones glistened. There are niches for flambeaux. Chandeliers may have hung from some of the stalactites. In front of the grotto is a deep depression which was at one time a pool for swans and ducks. The hermitage nearby was pulled down just before the war. I took three photographs of the outside of the grotto, but the light was bad and my lens too narrow to take the interior, unfortunately.

Tuesday, 14th March

I lunched with G. M. Trevelyan at the Goring Hotel before the Estates Committee meeting, at which I felt uncomfortable. Try as I did I could not master the intricacies of the Government's white paper on sheep farming.

Wednesday, 15th March

These are days of feverish activity in the office. Besides, I am desperately preparing my lecture for tomorrow at the Raynes Park County School. Yesterday too there was another hideous air raid. Two high explosives in Anderson Street and Cliveden Place, Chelsea, one near Heinz Dietmar's lodgings so that all his windows were blown out. In our office, as a consequence of this raid, there were no gas fires and no telephone. We all sat in overcoats shivering with cold today.

Took the 9.10 to Shrewsbury, arriving after 1 o'clock. Walked to the Lion and lunched there. Looked at the ballroom built on to the back of the hotel. It is a sort of Assembly Room of Adam date and style, well proportioned, with plaster walls and marble chimneypieces with lions' heads carved on them. A gallery, and doors with classical dancing figures painted à la Angelica Kauffmann. Delightful and provincial.

Hired a car for £1 to take me to Pitchford Hall. A most glorious day, though keen and sharp. The black-and-white of this house is a bit too much of a good thing. The house is supposed to be late fifteenth or early sixteenth century, but I suspect it to be much later. The clock-tower porch is obviously Jacobean. The north wing extension of 1880 was well done, but over-contributes to the black-and-white. However today the place looked highly romantic amid the buds of spring, flowering crocuses and primroses. Met Forsyth, the architect, in the drive who told me Sir Charles Grant was waiting for me. Was conducted upstairs to a small, shapeless end room in the west wing, where he sprawled, listening to the European news in that way country people do most of the livelong day. He is well over 60, still handsome, and rather mischievous. Indeed a sweet man who must once have been very attractive. He is an old friend of that fellow General, Lord Sackville. Eddy told me that he remembers him staying at Knole years ago. The two men were discussing something rather excitedly. Lord Sackville said, 'What you can't understand, Charlie darl—', and stopped dead. Too late, Eddy's mother, who was present, rose from her chair and stalked out of the room, head in air.

Now Sir Charles vegetates, and talks volubly and a little irrelevantly about his ancestors, his friends and acquaintances. He galloped me through the house, pointing out the contents which he thought he would give with it. But so rapid was our progress that I could not take in individual things. I don't think there is much that is very good. The rooms have an oddly incongruous early Victorian air, which is sad and romantic. All the rooms are low and dark in spite of the sun shining outside, the birds singing and the water falling over the stones. He dearly loves the place. His proposals are vague however, and he does not intend to transfer any land over and above what the house stands on, even omitting the orangery and walled garden. While he was talking to me on the lawn Lady Sybil approached. Out of the corner of one eye I saw a fat, dumpy figure waddling and supporting herself with a tall stick. She wore a long, blue coat down to her calves. One foot had on a stocking, the other was bare. On her head was an orange bonnet, draped with an orange scarf which floated down to her ankles. She had orange hair kept in place by a wide-meshed blue net. She took great care to shield her extraordinary face, extraordinary because, although the skin is beautiful, the shape is absolutely round and the lips are the vividest orange I have ever beheld. She looks like a clairvoyante preserved in ectoplasm. As a special favour she took me to the orangery where she lives all the time, for she hates the house. She says it is haunted. She cannot sleep on the east side for the noise of the water, or on the north because of the graveyard. She and Sir Charles send messages to each other throughout the day and night, and meet for coffee on the lawn when the weather permits. She would not allow Forsyth to come near the orangery, which is her sanctum, converted by her into one large living-room with a wood fire, and one bedroom. She talked incessantly for an hour, complaining how the aeroplanes swooped so low that she lost her voice and was obliged to move into a caravan in a ploughed field to escape from them. Said that her French maid 'never revealed that she was mad', when she came to her, and stole all her, Lady S.'s clothes. The only way she recovered them was by sending the maid to confession. The abbess made her give them all back. Her gruff laugh and her low, sepulchral voice and disjointed phrases reminded me of Lady Crewe, her sister. She had sprained her ankle—hence the one bare leg—and made me pour a solution of Ponds Extract over it out of a heavy lead Marie Antoinette watering can.

Forsyth motored me to Attingham where I stayed the night. I walked into the deer park looking for Lord Berwick. Found him exercising his little dog, Muffet. He talks to me far more confidently than he used to. I think he is one of the most endearing men I have ever met in my life—feckless, helpless and courteous. We had a good dinner of four courses, including chicken and burgundy. Lady Sybil Grant said of him, 'Poor Tom, he should not have lived in this age. He cannot drive a car, ride a bicycle, fish or shoot. He would have stepped in and out of a sedan chair so beautifully.'

Saturday, 18th March

Forsyth came soon after breakfast which I had in my bedroom. Lord Berwick met him and showed him round the house. Forsyth was greatly impressed. Indeed I am more and more impressed by the beauty of the house, the rich-toned Pompeian walls and the crimson damask and the gilt furniture. We drove to Pitchford. Sir Charles was out fishing and Lady Sybil either enshrined in her orangery or seated in the delicious tree house, which is of half-timber with a rococo plaster ceiling and walls. I visited the church to look at the fine thirteenth-century Crusader effigy carved in oak, the effigy and Gothic table all of a piece. I walked round the policies and arrived at the tree house. Climbed up to it and, not finding Lady Sybil, went inside. Forsyth took me into the roof of the house to show me how poor its condition was. When the nineteenth-century extensions were built the main part was re-roofed. Terrible amputations of the main beams had been perpetrated, and flimsy struts of deal substituted for stout oak purlins and rafters.

We drove back to St. Albans. Stopped on the way at Wall to look at our Roman remains and the dreary little museum full of broken pottery displayed in cardboard boxes. The stone foundations are split by successive frosts and need covering with sheds, though how anyone who has seen Roman temples above ground can be bothered with these miserable subterranean fragments is beyond my comprehension. The property is poor, down-at-heel and neglected. At Towcester we stopped for a hurried tea in a tiny cheap café. Coming out after paying the bill I ran into Georgia Sitwell in her policewoman's uniform. Forsyth said to me afterwards in his Uriah Heep-like manner, 'What beautiful ladies you do know, Mr. Lees-Milne.' 'Yes, don't I,' I answered.

On my return to London telephoned Bridget who dined with me at the Ritz. Across the dining-room we spied Nancy dining with Peter Rodd who had walked into her shop this morning, having come straight from an Italian beachhead after three years' absence. They sent a note across to us and joined us for beer after their dinner. Peter, looking bronzed, tough and well, was slightly drunk, and grinned and laughed a good deal. Even so, Bridget and I expected he might lash out at poor Nancy at a moment's notice, and on the slightest provocation. She at once turned into a different Nancy, apprehensive, solicitous, and adoring. We plied Peter with questions, but he never answered any. Instead he talked incessantly in his boring manner without appearing to listen to one word we said. We gathered from the exaggerated things he did say in disparagement of the Americans, much to Nancy's relish, that they were disliked by the English troops. There is much resentment over their being in command of our armies. Peter said that quite 60 per cent of the American troops had venereal diseases and so were incapacitated from fighting; that they pitched our crack troops into impossible positions and the Brigade of Guards was cut to pieces in consequence. Also that Simon Combe, my company commander, when captured and led off by Germans, seized a tommygun, slew five of them, and escaped. He will get a decoration for this. Peter had been in charge of Italian refugees in the Anzio area, and said he had great difficulty in preventing American troops from jumping on to the relief ships taking the refugees to Naples. The Italians have no liking for the English, but think favourably of the Americans because of the money they can extract from them. The sad truth is that one should believe only a quarter of what Peter says.

I accompanied B. to her flat and stayed the night at Brooks's.

Monday, 20th March

A. W. Lawrence lunched with me at the Grosvenor Hotel. He is a brother of Lawrence of Arabia. I had expected an older man. Instead he looks barely 40. He resembles Raymond Mortimer in build and has the same thick, dark, unruly hair, which, unlike R.'s, is unbrushed. He has a slightly contemptuous, slightly mocking smile. He answers abruptly, deliberately, as though to assert his disrespect for people and authority. Not good-looking; a lean face, clear skin, but dark and swarthy. Not like his brother in appearance. He stares at you with penetration while he speaks. I had invited him in order to ask if he would contribute to the appeal the N.T. is issuing for money for Seathwaite farm in Borrowdale, out of the Seven Pillars of Wisdom Fund, of which he is a trustee. He seems prepared to help.

Tuesday, 21st March

Went to see Dame Una after work. She is up and better, but looks thin and white. Complains that now restrictions are imposed upon the sea coast, there is nowhere she can go to recuperate. Talked about her monumental *Life of Dickens*, which is finished. Dickens, she said, had the power of hypnotizing his audiences. His sex life was very odd, and she deals with this at length. She said Jamesey had been asked by Batsford to write a book about the House of Commons, all material found, but J. may decline because he so much hates politics. John is writing a book on Domenichino. He came down to talk likewise. Dame Una lent me her book on Russia in which there are two chapters about Tsarkoe Selo and Pavlovsk, the palaces built by the Scottish architect, Charles Cameron. She says the raids we have now are more terrifying than the old ones, but James is courageous, consolatory and efficient during them.

Tonight at 1 a.m. there was another raid. The sirens woke me from a sound sleep. I hoped there might be no guns, but they soon started. I got out of bed and Miss P. handed me my fur-lined coat. Together we crouched on the stairs in our chosen corner. The windows rattled with the thunder of guns. We quailed and did not speak. When the gunfire subsided I put on my gumboots and walked to Battersea Bridge. Actually the raiders tonight had kept to the south-east. I saw distant fires across the water making the sky red, but none near at hand.

Thursday, 23rd March

The three assessors finally awarded first prize to the winner of the West Wycombe Cottage Competition this morning. It is not to my mind a very beautiful elevation, and has two pointed gables which I think feeble and reactionary. However they find the planning so much better than the second winner's, whose elevation to my eye was preferable. Maufe had to leave early, but Darcy Braddell and William Weir lunched with me at Overton's off crab. The wonderful William Weir is a little deaf and on the verge of senility. Braddell was rather short with him and inclined to leave him out of the talk. Braddell is a sweet man, but what sort of architect I cannot tell. He said he was Ernest George's last pupil. George would draw every detail of his designs for a room or building for his faithful carver to reproduce. He would lie full length on the floor, rapidly and accurately sketching. When commissioned to design a building, he would ask what style was required — Gothic? Queen Anne? Jacobean? Not a thing done today fortunately. Braddell said that the more cultivated and academically educated an architect the worse he was, and the less creative. *Vide* George, Blomfield, Baker. Both he and Weir agreed that Lutyens was the greatest architect since the late Georgians of the early nineteenth century. And of these Decimus Burton was the most brilliant.

Ian McCallum dined with me at Brooks's. He is an enthusiast. He regards as deplorable reactionaries Richardson, Rendel and Braddell. Rendel he hates; and says that when he was President of the Architectural Association the students turned him out. Ian is a pacifist and conscientious objector who has twice been to prison, once with hard labour, for his convictions. He says prison atrophies the sensibilities so that life becomes grey and the prospect of ultimate release cannot evoke a spark of happy anticipation. There was a raid at midnight, but nothing serious.

Stuart told me what he considers the worst thing ever said of anyone: John Betjeman's description of Charles Fry as 'a phallus with a business sense'.

After dinner the sirens went. The guns sounded very distant, so borrowing Stuart's American steel helmet I decided to walk home from Tyburnia. While in Hyde Park and before I reached the Serpentine, the guns beside me opened up cruelly. I put on the steel helmet and cowered under a tree, with the trunk between me and the tarmac road. As there was no building to shelter in I decided it was safer to stay under the tree branches, which might break the fall of the shrapnel raining down like hailstones. I heard it crackling through the leaves and thudding on the grass. On the road it struck sparks as it fell. The noise of the Hyde Park guns was deafening, and the rocket shells were specially frightening. One gun close to me blew out the tails of my overcoat with blast at every shot. I was lonely and felt as though I were in no man's land. The gunfire seemed horizontal with the ground. There was a continuous thunder for three-quarters of an hour. They say this was the noisiest London raid of the war. Occasionally I heard German planes diving. But there were no fires, and I heard no bombs.

Sunday, 26th March

Breakfasted at Brooks's and rang up Clementine Beit who said, 'Yes, do bring the Sergeant,' thinking I meant any old sergeant, a driver perhaps, and asked, 'Does he eat at our end of the house, or the other?' I told Stuart this, and he was not amused. Today has been wonderful. Bright, warm sun; the earth dry and brown for there has been no rain. This augurs ill for the summer, perhaps well for this horrifying impending invasion. I drove Stuart to Hughenden. Mrs. Langley-Taylor received us in the new wing built forty years ago by Coningsby Disraeli, Dizzy's nephew and heir. I recall being brought here in about 1930 from Oxford, and being received by Coningsby Disraeli in the library. He was wearing a dusty velvet skull cap and, if I remember right, a blue velvet jacket and string bow tie. The main part of the house is at present used by the R.A.F. for target-spotting, and cannot be entered. Mrs. Langley-Taylor told me that after the war nearly every room will be furnished for show, and that Major Abbey, when he bought the property also bought the Disraeli contents. Hughenden will make a splendid and interesting National Trust property for three reasons—its historic association, its mid-Victorian architecture and furnishing, and its amenity land on the outskirts of horrid High Wycombe. The park is beautiful and well maintained. Some fine trees, and the garden laid out in Victorian parterres with plenty of terracotta urns and insipid statuary of cherubs and angels, now put away, which Queen Mary called 'sugar babies' when she visited the place. I was delighted with Hughenden. It is deliciously hideous. Disraeli stripped it of its white stucco, revealed the red brick, and added the ugly window surrounds and crenellations. Mrs. Langley-Taylor showed us Disraeli's bedroom, which is now her own. She said Lady Desborough remembers being patted on the head by Disraeli here, and being repelled by his greasy black curls.

After luncheon we all lay in the sun in a field and talked. The Sergeant was a great success with the Beits.

Tuesday, 28th March

Anthony Wagner lunched with me and was optimistic about future planning legislation. He now works at the Ministry of Planning under Lord Woolton. In normal times he is a herald. Nice, quiet, dark, reserved, taciturn man. This evening I dined at Rules with Acworth, Keeling, M.P., Oliver Messel and John Summerson to discuss our policy at the forthcoming meeting of the Georgian Group next Saturday. We decided to press for the appointment of a small subcommittee to consider particular questions of policy, a new secretary, the enlisting of local authorities' support, and a post-war getting together of all the amenity societies.

Wednesday, 29th March

After a morning at Cliveden, making notes for my guidebook, and Stoke Poges, where Hubert Smith, the Trust's new agent, agreed with me that we should not allow part of our field to be taken for additional burial space for what are no longer 'rude forefathers of the hamlet', but the genteel residents of suburbia—to Osterley.

What a decline since 1939! Now total disorder and disarray. Bombs have fallen in the park, blowing out many windows; the Adam orangery has been burnt out, and the garden beds are totally overgrown. We did not go round the house which is taken over by Glyn Mills bank, but round the confines of the estate. There are still 600 acres as yet unsold. Smith and I both deprecated the breezy way in which the Osterley agent advocated further slices to the south-east of the house being sold for building development, in order to raise an endowment. It is going to be a difficult problem how to estimate figures where so much is so problematical, viz. the outgoings associated with the museum, the number of visitors and the potential building value of the land itself.

I am quite sure that of the inside of Cliveden the public need only see the hall, drawing-room, and the 'Louis Quinze' dining-room. Apart from a few Reynoldses and the Blenheim tapestries there is nothing much in the furniture line.

Thursday, 30th March

Started off in the N.T. car at 10 o'clock for Gloucestershire and drove without a break to Nether Lypiatt Manor, near Stroud, to lunch at this wonderful little house with Mrs. Gordon Woodhouse. There were Mr. Woodhouse, a little, dull old man with a flabby hand, genial Lord Barrington with hairs growing out of his cheeks and ears, and homespun Miss Walker, daughter of Sir Emery, the friend of William Morris. The house is perched high on a hill, overlooking a built-up village. It is compact and tall, with two flanking wings, one new so as to balance the other old one. It is unspoilt late seventeenth century, and perfect in every way. In fact an ideal, if not *the* ideal small country house. It retains all its wainscotting, doors with high brass handles and locks, one lovely chimneypiece in the hall, of white stone against a ground of blue slate. The rich staircase has three twisted balusters to each tread. There is much good furniture, including several Barrington family portraits. The forecourt enclosure with stone piers and balls, the contemporary wrought-iron gates, and the Cotswold stable block complete the dependencies.

Mrs. Woodhouse was wearing a kind of black satin bonnet, not becoming, and a black knitted dress. Luncheon consisted of one egg in a jacketed potato. The boiler having just burst the household was in a state of perturbation. There is one servant. It is a curious colony. Mrs. Woodhouse talked a lot about houses and Ted Lister, whose irascibility amuses her. After luncheon she and Lord Barrington took me round the house, and he took me round the garden, which is enchanting, with modern yew walks and a flourishing young lime avenue, the trees planted closely together. There is an obelisk to the horse of the builder of the house who 'served his master good and true, and died at the age of forty-two'.

I went on to Woodchester Priory, arriving at tea time. But no tea because my host, bluff ex-naval commander Bruce Metcalfe, was conducting a unit of American soldiers, lecturing them good humouredly but bombastically, and boasting of English customs in a manner which I found condescending and embarrassing; but not they, it seemed. I did not take to him at first—and did later, as usual. I wondered how I was going to stick this visit until the following morning. The Commander and his wife live in this by no means small house with absolutely no servants at all. It is an H-shaped Tudor building with pointed gables, and was spoilt in the last century by the insertion of plate glass, and the addition of a French-style tower. The Commander showed me the site of the Roman Villa which is uncovered every ten years. Thank God it is covered now. We had dinner in the kitchen. Mrs. M. benignant, jolly, and friendly.

I find that I take an hour or two to adjust myself to different sorts of people. Going as I do from the sophisticated to the simple, the rich to the poor, the clever to the stupid. I get bewildered. But in the end I usually manage to adapt myself. Which means of course that I am a chameleon, with little or no personality of my own. I assume the qualities of others. I am a mirror of other people's moods, opinions and prejudices. But I am pernickety, and would not doss down in anybody's bed just for a crust or a new pair of shoes.

Sunday, 2nd April

Bridget and I lunched together in the Ritz Grill. As she sat down she said querulously that Emerald and Sir Robert Abdy were joining us. This they did at 2 o'clock. Bridget rather surly with Emerald for coming but I was glad to see her for she is usually bright and gay. Sir R. was totally different from the picture of him I had formed in my mind. That was of a little black old dormouse, somewhat like Gerald Berners. But not at all. Abdy is youthful, tall, fair, with light horn-rimmed spectacles; and very charming and unaffected. I was obliged to build up an entirely different personality behind the exterior I had so grievously misrepresented to myself. Emerald began in true form by grumbling to the waiters about the food. She ought to know that in the fifth year of the war choice of food for luncheon after 2 o'clock on a Sunday is limited. After saying that she would eat nothing, she ate everything. She said Kenneth Clark made the mistake of depreciating his own scholarship. This surprised me. 'Yes,' she repeated, 'I have advised him not to be so diffident, or people will cease to respect him.' She said, 'Supreme self-confidence is the essential quality if one is to achieve anything; and one must be an expert on at least one subject, or another.' I said, 'You may be right there; but surely K. has already achieved *everything*. I would have thought he was not the least bit self-depreciatory.'

44

Walking past Buckingham Palace I looked at it critically for the first time. What a heavy, uninspired, lumpish elevation! The Corinthian pilasters are too small for the heavy entablature; the columns in the centrepiece ought to be disengaged. As for the circular basin of the Victoria Memorial, it is not too bad, and the bas-reliefs are good. But the black Michelangelesque figures are far too large and out of scale with the monument.

Good Friday, 7th April

At 8.45 a car ordered by Michael Rosse came to take me and Bridget, whom I picked up in Mount Street, to King's Cross. We were in such good time that we were on the platform by 9.20 and discovered in front of us an earlier train to Doncaster than the 10.30 which we had meant to catch. There then ensued one of those scatter-brained hesitations, indecisions and muddles. I said we must stick to the later train, for we would merely have to wait at Doncaster, if we arrived earlier than expected. B. said we might just as well wait at Doncaster as at King's Cross. I said King's Cross was preferable—besides, secretly I wanted to telephone someone. For nearly ten minutes we argued about which station was preferable, B. obdurately sticking out for Doncaster. Anyway she settled the matter by hurling her luggage into a carriage just as the 9.30 was leaving. I had to shove her from behind and then throw my luggage and haul myself through the door, followed by execrations from the guard. On arrival at Doncaster we were obliged to wait in the cold. B. complained that it was a loathsome station. While waiting for the car we munched a slice of stale cake which I managed to buy in the station hotel.

We reached Womersley at 2.30. Michael was there for the day only and had to depart before midnight, because all leave had been cancelled. We did not see him again. But with Anne Rosse I am always happy. She giggles, makes the most wicked innuendoes, and giggles again. The noise she makes is like an extremely lyrical burn rushing over pebbles, and her witticisms have to be caught on the wing. Her merriment is infectious, and it is laced with just a dash of arsenic.

Monday, 10th April

As usual I have eaten too much, drunk too much, and I feel lethargic. I should never stay away longer than two nights. The truth is that like a cart horse I must be working, regularly, with only the shortest of breaks in between. I have however read *Edwin Drood*, and finished the hateful *Cousin Pons*.

Thursday, 13th April

At midnight Emerald rang up. She talked of Tintern Abbey, of Bertie Abdy who is unwell, of the Invasion (she says all the Americans are leaving London — which signifies something is afoot), of Dickens and of Balzac. After half an hour's discussion of *Cousin Pons* she rang off abruptly, without warning.

Saturday, 15th April

I caught the 1.15 to Reading where Gerry Wellington met me at the station in his small car, for he gets twenty gallons a month for being a duke. Drove me straight to the Reading museum where he showed me the Roman relics from Silchester, on loan from his family. I was most interested in the small, homely objects like door keys and hinges. It is so strange that Roman things differ so little from our own. Arriving at the entrance to Stratfield Saye park we stopped at the first duke's great polished granite pillar, with his image by Marochetti standing on the top. It is carefully executed, and the huge blocks of granite are finely cut. Stopped again to look at the house from the east clairvoyée, down a straight vista across the park. The house is not particularly striking from this distance; an indistinguishable huddle of buildings. Stopped again at the 1750 church, of Greek cruciform. A spectacular monument inside to the Pitt builder of the house signed by Christmas and dated 1640. It is rare for so early a monument to be signed. A Wellington monument by Flaxman, and another by Boehm. The great galleried family pew in which the Iron Duke worshipped was swept away by an ignorant vicar just before Gerry succeeded, greatly to his annoyance, chagrin and disappointment, for while abroad he had been looking forward to worshipping in it. In its place a hideous substitute, with a monster linenfold door of fumed oak, has recently been erected. Close to it is a mural tablet of Donne period to an incumbent who 'for forty years was a most painful preacher'.

The western view of Stratfield Saye house clearly shows it to date from Charles I's reign. The original red brick was covered with a dull compo rendering in the eighteenth century, which is a pity. The house reminds Gerry of West Horsley, the Crewes' house in Surrey, with its Kew Palace-like pedimented gables. Odd pilasters resting on nothing appear upon the first storey in typical Charles I non-style. The stable and coach-house blocks, axial with the house, are of the same date. The house is low-lying, unpretentious, having been built, as an early guide book describes it, 'for convenience rather than for parade', by the Rivers family. They made alterations in the 1740s and added a wing in the 1790s. Benjamin Wyatt carried out work for the first duke, and added the porch and conservatory. The east front is not so regular as the west, and the terraces are deformed by messy Edwardian flower beds. Gerry, who hates flowers, will soon have them away. The pleasure grounds contain fine specimens of every tree, hard wood and soft. There is a rustic garden-house made of wood, *circa* 1840, with *trompe-l'oeil* inlaid walls, like the sides of a Nonesuch box. Under a tree is Copenhagen's gravestone. The heavy gilded state coach in the coach-house is in splendid condition.

Having eaten little luncheon I was famished, but tea consisted of only a few of the thinnest slices of bread and butter imaginable. After tea we did a tour of the inside of the house, beginning with the hall. When my stomach started to rumble with hunger Gerry looked at it with a reproachful air, and said nothing. It went on making the most awful noise like a horse's. The hall has a gallery along the wall opposite the entrance. The open balusters were boxed in so as to prevent the servants being seen from below by the visitors. Gerry's mother used to say that nothing of them was visible save their behinds, as they crouched and bobbed across the gallery. There are some pictures so huge that they can only hang sloping. In the flagged floor are inset two large mosaic pavements from Silchester. The whole hall is painted nineteenth-century brown and the walls are hung with very faded red flock paper. Against the columns of the gallery are plinths supporting white marble busts of Pitt, the Russian Czars, Walter Scott and the Great Duke, etc.

The Gallery is long and low—'matey' Gerry calls it—the walls covered with prints pasted upon a ground of gold leaf. Rather attractive, but G. wishes to cover these walls with damask, without however injuring the prints but so as to allow room for family portraits, for elsewhere there is singularly little space. At either end of the Gallery are brown painted columns, forming screens. The ceilings are covered with Edwardian lodging-house lincrusta. To the north is a small room with niches. The walls are hung with a delightful, flowery, 1850 gold and cream paper. In front of the fireplace is a special device of the Great Duke, namely a curious brass rail, with rings for curtains, to keep off excessive heat. The drawing-room has a rococo ceiling, and the same wallpaper as in the previous room. In it are some Boule cabinets and commodes by Levasseur and pictures acquired by the first duke. The dining-room is shut up, all the Apsley House pictures being stored there for the war, and valued at a million pounds, so G. says. The library is of Lord Burlington date. In it are the Duke's library chairs as seen in the conversation piece by Thorburn of this room, hanging in the Small Cabinet Room. Beyond it a billiard table and Regency lights for colza oil, very pretty, and beyond again the Great Duke's private rooms and his original bath. These rooms G. is going to make his own. The bath is very deep and satisfactory. A curious feature in this house is the water closets in each room, put there by the Great Duke inside great 1840-ish cupboards of maplewood.

After tea Gerry took a rod, and fished in the lake for perch with a minnow, but caught nothing. He cast with much ease and abandon. When I tried I found it difficult, and made rather a fool of myself. After dinner, at which there were no drinks except beer, he showed me his grandfather's collection of gems and intaglios, mounted on long, gold chains. When held against the oil lights some of the stones were very beautiful. A few are ancient, some Renaissance. G. is fussy over his key bunches, everything being carefully locked up. He has a butler, cook and two housemaids, and a secretary, Miss Jones. The last has meals with him during the week, and nearly drives him mad with her archness. 'Aren't you naughty today?' she says. She is unable to type, so when he wishes to despatch a letter not written by himself, he types it and gives it to her to sign.

Sunday, 16th April

Called at 7.30. Gerry motored me, the cook and a housemaid to Mass at Heckfield Park chapel. He called for us after Mass. Very good of him, for he went to his own church at 11. After church we unpacked in the attics brown paper parcels tied with string by fingers of the Great Duke's time, and not hitherto opened. This was very exciting. We blew away the dust and undid the knots of string, never cutting. Regency wall sconces emerged.

After luncheon we motored to Silchester and looked at the Roman walls which the Ministry of Works began repairing before the war, or rather taking down stone by stone, and re-building with new mortar. In other words the walls are no longer Roman fourth century but English twentieth century. G. is a most companionable and delightful person to be with, full of enthusiasms, abounding in historic anecdotes, and often very funny.

After tea we finished the tour of the house, upstairs. Everywhere brown paint is peeling off woodwork, where the door panels have not been scratched to glory by Duchess Maud's dogs. She can have had no house pride at all. Baths have been put into bedrooms, with naked pipes clambering up walls into the ceilings; and steam has made the wallpaper hang in tatters. The upstairs is really very grubby. The prints in nearly every bedroom and landing become a bore, but since most of them were stuck on by the Great Duke's own hands, G. thinks it would be an act of impiety to remove them.

Monday, 17th April

Gerry motored me to Reading in his little car which takes hours to start up. At Bristol station Eardley Knollys met me, and we drove to Westbury College, a poor sort of property which the Trust would not accept today. It consists of an old square gatehouse with fifteenth-century vaulting in the tower, and a large tumble-down white Georgian block adjacent. Then to Blaise hamlet of nine cottages, called Vine Cottage, Circular Cottage, Rose Cottage, etc. We compared their present condition with the early nineteenth-century lithographs of each, which we brought with us. After lunching in Bristol at the Mauretania restaurant, in a room which was once an old ship's dining-room of 1907 — Edwardian classical, black and gold — we motored past Sutton Court. Scouted round the outside and decided that the house, which I had seen before, was not good enough to accept. At Wells walked over our Tor Hill, and at Glastonbury up our Tor Hill to examine the fifteenth-century tower. Drove to West Pennard barn. It is not of outstanding importance, though a decent little building. I did not like the tiles the S.P.A.B. have used instead of stone slates; and their roof timbers looked flimsy and unconvincing. We visited Glastonbury barn, which is far finer, with its double tier of Gothic purlins and braces. To Bridgwater and stayed comfortably at the Royal Clarence.

Tuesday, 18th April

Today — Bridgwater Church; Coleridge's cottage at Nether Stowey; Holford village. Given luncheon by a Mr. Mantle, eccentric tenant, looking like an Italian organ-grinder (but without monkey), very friendly; Dunster Castle; Minehead, tea with Mr. Gunn, genteel and no less friendly, one of our architectural advisers; Holnicote House; Exmoor; Lynmouth, staying comfortably at the Lyndale Hotel. Had an abortive interview with a ghastly business man who owns some

49

land we covet and won't consider an offer we have made. I don't altogether blame him.

A gorgeous morning. E. and I walked up the valley to Watersmeet. Into the bottom of this precipitous gorge the sun seldom penetrates even in mid summer. Today the sky seen through the green canopy of trees was brightest blue, far brighter than when seen from the top of the gorge. Curious. At 11 we were back at Lynmouth. Motored up the hill and down again to Woolacombe, where we lunched with the American Army in a one-time hotel. Delicious American food. Only the Adjutant, in his shirt sleeves, entertained us. We felt rather a nuisance and unwanted. However we gorged. Bearded the Rev. Allfield in his filthy dog kennel of a villa. In the rain proceeded to Baggy Point. Talked to our farmer who complained of the damage done by the American troops who use it as a range for every sort of explosive. Barnstaple; no tea, only cake in the car. Walked up Kipling Tors, another poorish property. It was pelting with rain so we had no view. East Titchberry Farm which is really remote and wild. E. is most conscientious with his farmers, and on the best of terms with them. Soaked, we dined at the Hoop Inn sparingly, for there was little food. Nevertheless they produced a bottle of very good claret to warm the cockles. Stayed the night at Bideford, my room overlooking the river and old bridge. I sat in my Regency bow window before going to sleep, and pondered upon the vanity of sublunary appetites and torments.

Thursday, 20th April

Hatherleigh; Lydford Gorge; Tavistock. Drove over Dartmoor which is very desolate and full of terror, and to me not very appealing. Widecombe Moor Church House—bad plate glass in the windows. The good features, the stout ceiling beams of the lower rooms, and the sparkling granite of which the whole thing is built. One wants to suck it like barley sugar. The church has a low oak screen to the chancel, with painted panels of saints. Fifteenth century I suppose. One peculiar panel of Abraham sacrificing Isaac with reprehensible detachment and complacency. En route to Exeter we got stuck in a very long military convoy moving towards us. We thought the Invasion had surely begun. But we are always thinking this nowadays.

Nancy Mitford lunched with me at the Ritz, and we sat at a table by the door. We were chatting very happily when at 2 o'clock Emerald came in with Bertie Abdy, who having had an operation has gone grey from the intense pain within one week. Emerald told us how Nancy's grandfather, Lord Redesdale, behaved. 'My dear, he used to accompany King Edward to Paris, where they went wenching together.' At 2.30 I left for the R.I.B.A. library, for I am contemplating an article on Decimus Burton. Then caught the 4.45 for Oxford to stay with the Harrods.

Walked from Oxford station to the Harrods' house in St. Aldate's. Dear Billa rushed down the stairs and we embraced on the doorstep. She said I had not seen her since 1938. I cannot think why not, and this visit has reminded me how very devoted to her I am. We started with a large glass of sherry. Then Roy joined us. He is quiet, and has attentive good manners. If I knew him better I might like him very much. He soon left for some college function, and Billa and I dined alone, deliciously, with the candles lit, though it was full daylight and the sun shining. We gossiped in great content.

After breakfast in bed I went to Mass next door, in Bishop King's Palace where Ronnie Knox used to be priest, but now Father Vernon Johnson, who today was ill. As it is the first Sunday of term, the chapel was packed. After Mass we walked to Christ Church garden. The garden was a dream, and we sat on a seat like an elderly married couple, while the two Harrod children played. The elder boy is handsome, with jet black hair like Billa's, and the longest black eyelashes I have seen. His features resemble Roy's. The younger boy has a squint, and wears an eye shade. At luncheon we ate enormously, with the result that I felt languid for the remainder of the afternoon. We walked round the university, looking first at the naked Shelley memorial, to which Billa is devoted. The base of the sarcophagus is typically Victorian, and the glistening figure rendered beautiful with the submarine light from the dome striking it. I think the walls, instead of being boring 'Elizabethan' panels, should be painted with sea urchins, fishes and jellyfish, to give an enhanced submarine effect. On re-thinking, I am not sure that Shelley ought to be commemorated with a great body and that drooping penis, for one does not associate the too ethereal poet with the gross flesh. And this beautiful figure, although far from gross, is physically alluring. Then we strolled through my old college, Magdalen, where the quadrangular cloisters have been renewed, stone by stone, and did the round of Addison's Walk. The meadows were covered with fritillaries.

At 7 Roy took me to dine in Christ Church hall, at the high table. By the time we sat down most of the undergraduates had finished their dinner and gone. Roy says that today they all eat in hall, are all serious, and impecunious. There is none of the plutocratic gaiety of the old days. He thinks there never will be again, for the state subsidizes undergraduates now. I sat next to Roy and the Dean, and opposite Dundas. We had a very full and heavy dinner, with strong red wine, so that afterwards I felt worse than ever. When dinner was over, the Dean rose. We all followed him, carrying our napkins according to custom, down a circular staircase, to the Common Room where the port was freely circulated round the table. I sat next to David Cecil. It is difficult to reconcile his Dresden china appearance with his ever accelerating loquacity, twinkling of eyes, twisting of long fingers, and loose limbed jerkiness. Rather disconcerting. I felt like a slow-witted bull beside him. He talked of Hatfield and the state kept there when he was a child; also of the terrifying intellectual level of the conversation, and the devotional atmosphere. I imagine there was something a bit forced about both. Roy complained about the declining population — 'Now the rot has spread to the lower classes,' he said. Now he is talking rot, I thought to myself, but did not say so.

Billa very funny when we got back. She said that breeding was hell, and Roy must not suppose that she was going to do any more. Talking of pederasty, Roy said that the late King George V when told of Lord Beauchamp's trouble, exclaimed, 'Why, I thought people like that always shot themselves.' 'Heavens,' said Billa, 'I do hope the poor darlings won't start doing that. It would be like living through a permanent air raid.' I caught a 10 o'clock train to London which did not reach Paddington till midnight. The last tube had gone, so, carrying my bag, I walked home to Chelsea.

Tuesday, 25th April

Eardley and I walked to the Belgrave Square canteen to lunch with Sibyl Colefax, who when she is not animated — and this is seldom — is an old woman, rather bent. She does not often allow this evidence of her age to be revealed. At 4 I met the Eshers and Hubert Smith at Osterley Park gates. It was a ravishing day and Esher commented on the beauty of the shrubs and blossom in the suburban gardens. We motored round the park, and Esher's view was that it did not matter whether one could see building development from the house, if the house was to become a museum and never be inhabited again. Smith and I dissented from this pronouncement.

Wednesday, 26th April

At 10 started off in the car for Oxford. Gave two soldiers a lift there. Called for Billa at 12.15. She produced a glass of red wine which after a slight hangover from last night I was not really in need of. We drove to Faringdon. It was a day of unexcelled loveliness, the apex of spring-tide, warm sun and no wind. We had the roof of the car open, B.'s raven tresses swirling above her head and practically lassoing my neck. At Faringdon House Jennifer Heber-Percy was sitting in the sun, on a swing seat, against the curved retaining wall. There were small chickens running around. This frightened Billa for she hates birds. We talked until 1.45 when we lunched off chicken (she doesn't mind eating them) and rice. Lord Berners, wearing a green knitted skull cap and yellow bow tie, was positively cordial. He is a considerate host. Robert [Heber-Percy] came in to lunch from driving a tractor on the farm. He was wearing a pair of battle-dress trousers and a yellow aertex shirt open at the neck. Very bronzed by the sun, youthful and handsome. He is the *enfant terrible*, all right. What a curious family they were, sitting round this large round table. But they know how to live. I thought how enviable their ménage.

After luncheon I picked up Mr. Leigh Wyatt, the Pleydell-Bouverie agent, and motored him to Coleshill. The Army is in partial occupation of the house, and has through an explosion destroyed one of the gate piers and part of the wall at the office entrance. The elder Miss Pleydell-Bouverie, who is kindly, shy and stooping, looks as old as her mother seemed to be in 1936. The younger, also unmarried sister lives in a cottage in the park, and is a potter. They told me how desperately anxious they were for the N.T. to own the place, but that because of their father's settlement, they could not give any part of it away. The 5,000 acres of the estate cover a beautiful area of England. Since the Bouverie family have always been conscientious landowners the estate is in good condition, although the sisters are very poor.

I left at 4, motoring past Great Coxwell barn, which must be the finest barn in England. I thought if this estate can be acquired, then I ought to try and get the Buscot and Faringdon estates protected by covenants. The three would form a wonderful block.

At Faringdon found Berners alone, Billa and Jennifer having gone for a walk. He showed me round the downstairs of the house, for the Army is in occupation of the bedroom floor. Whereas the stone flags of the hall floor are worn down by generations of feet, the hard black marble ribs are not. Lord B. thinks some of the seemingly late eighteenth-century doorheads are in fact nineteenth-century and should be removed; but I am not so sure. The house is attractively untidy in an Irish way, with beds, but beautiful ones, scattered in the downstairs rooms. Much confusion and comfort combined. Jennifer's baby Victoria playing on the floor like a kitten. Lord B. said that this afternoon one of the Negro soldiers — and the place is stiff with them — accosted him in the garden with the request, 'Massa, may I pick just a little bunch of flowers for our colonel?'

After tea I motored Jennifer and Billa to Kelmscott Manor. Since we didn't have an appointment the tenant would not let us in. In dudgeon we walked round the garden, Billa being frightfully caustic and urging us to pick the flowers. She kept saying, 'These flowers are madly Pre-Raph. Do you suppose William planted these? Did Rossetti really sit on this seat?' I pointed to a garden house and said, 'That's where Queen Elizabeth went to the loo when she came to tea with the William Morrises.' 'And Queen Victoria stood outside, keeping *cave*,' Billa said. We drove to the church and found the Morrises' tombstone. The little church is the prettiest imaginable. Robert accompanied me in the car back to London, eating a chicken leg in his fingers, and wearing a dark blue pullover. Then he had indigestion, and consumed quantities of soda mints.

Thursday, 27th April

Took the 10.10 from St. Pancras, arriving Stockport at 2.30. It was a balmy day when I started, and cold on arrival, with a cutting wind. An alderman met me in his car and motored me to Dukinfield. There I was shown round the town hall, a hideous building entirely lined inside with shiny yellow, lavatory brick, and windows of opaque stained glass in tulip patterns. We then inspected Dukinfield Old Hall. It stands in dreary surroundings, on one side an ungainly factory, and on the other a canal, filled with detritus, and tall chimneys. The ancient hall is of brick and timber construction, for long in decay and now divided into four tenement dwellings. I went inside them all. Apart from a few stout beams and a fleurs-de-lys plaster ceiling in one dwelling, there was nothing remarkable. The house is worth saving because of the scarcity of old buildings in these industrial parts, and I think that if the Corporation will do it up under our super-

54

vision, the Trust should hold it, provided we are involved in no expense.

The alderman took me back to his bungalow for tea. To my surprise his daughter was carving a ham, but although I do not care for sweet ham and had already eaten adequately in the train, I simply had to say 'yes'. These local worthies are all the same. They attach the wrong values to old houses, such as Domesday origin and absentee ownership by some medieval baron, which have little or no consequence whatever in relation to the architecture.

At 5 o'clock I met Mr. Hobson, my host of the forthcoming night. He called for me at the town hall in a large brown Ford car and whisked me away from this gloomy district into the recesses of the Pennine Chain, as far as Hayfield, where his house, Park Hall, is. Here I stayed. Mr. Hobson is a massive, florid man of about 60 from Belfast, with a strong Irish brogue, completely self-made. He told me he came to England with £5 in his pocket to seek his fortune—just like my great-grandfather, Sir Joseph Bailey, who walked from Yorkshire to South Wales barefoot in 1790. This, I must confess, was the only thing about him I liked. His wife, English, grey haired and very sweet and kind, spoke with the strongest cockney accent. The house, built c. 1770, is of no interest or distinction outside. The inside has been reconstructed by the Hobsons in the most appalling style. He has wainscoted all the walls with unvarnished walnut in giant linenfold pattern. There are deep friezes of lincrusta, painted a sort of clown yellow; door surrounds inlaid with mother-of-pearl. The front door has had a V-shaped window inserted, with 'Please ring' engraved in gold. The 'lounge', as they call it, is furnished with several base French pieces and 'easy chairs' in Tottenham Court Road leather, complete with bronze ashtrays attached to tails of grey suede filled with lead, daintily displayed over the arms. The walls covered with 1880 Royal Academy conversation pieces, though in my bedroom I found a Copley Fielding. There were Carrara busts on marble pedestals of insipid girls with forefingers coyly pointed at their lips, and on their heads lace caps crocheted by Mrs. Hobson.

The site of the house is very fine. The valley in the middle of the property of seventy acres is so precipitous that you imagine the property is far larger than it is. The Lantern Pike looms on one side. Eccles Pike can be seen from the house to the left. Behind the house are the moors. The estate is densely wooded, which is unusual, for there are few trees in these parts. The crescent-shaped stable block must once have been rather interesting, but Mr. Hobson has made it into four or five separate dwellings. In fact in a mild way he is a bit of a speculator, for he has also built five cottages which he lets to Manchester business folk. The house too contains flats. He has built a heated swimming pool to which thousands resort in the summer, paying an entrance fee and buying teas. I found it difficult to decide whether the Trust ought to accept this property on account of the land.

Friday, 28th April

It is bitterly cold up here. I was called early. Breakfast at 8.15. We began with sweet grapefruit from a tin, eggs and bacon and the lot. These sort of people always press one to eat more than one wants — a tiresome conventional politeness — so that one has almost to snap to be allowed any respite. After toast I was offered custard trifle in a glass.

Saturday, 29th April

Went to the Dorchester at 5.45 and found Emerald about to step into a taxi. We drove to the theatre, Emlyn Williams's *Druid's Rest*, an enjoyable Welsh play, the small boy acting quite unselfconsciously as only children can. In the stalls a friend of Emerald's was sitting behind us, Jim Thomas, a Cabinet minister of some sort, Welsh, about 40, personable. He came back to the Dorchester and dined with us. The three of us sat round a small table till 12.20 when I rose to go. They gossiped about political friends which rather bored me. Thomas is an intimate friend of Eden. He says the Prime Minister depends on Eden to such an extent that he consults him over every issue, and Eden is worn out by this strain on top of all his own duties. J. Thomas motored me to Victoria for I was to firewatch in the office.

Sunday, 30th April

I filled the car with the Polesden pictures I had collected yesterday from the National Gallery. Drove to the Oratory, and then fetched Nancy and Milly her pug. At Polesden we ate sandwiches on the south verandah. Nancy even sunbathed in the afternoon. When I had finished my work we wandered in the fields, picking cowslips (nearly over already). N. at her sweetest and happiest. A heavenly day.

Tuesday, 2nd May

Caught an early train to Guildford where Hubert Smith met me in the car. We drove past the N.T. cottages in Ockford Road, Godalming

—not very interesting—of timber construction upon a raised causeway. Stopped at Eashing Bridges, built supposedly in King John's reign. Tanks have been over the bridges, but this has now been stopped. The arches have the look of incredible antiquity. The plain wooden rails in place of parapet are becoming loose, the military traffic having run into them. We passed Witley Common, which Hubert says can never be reinstated—it has been turned into a parade ground with tarmac roadways and brick barracks—to Tennyson's Lane and Boarden Door. Ravishingly paintable they looked today, these Surrey trees and faint misty blue downs. We motored on to Black Down, newly acquired, with distant, seemingly infinite views, for it is over 900 ft. high in parts. Then to Slindon, near Arundel, where we ate our sandwiches in the agent's house.

This property belongs to Mr. Isaacson, an old man of 88, who offers it with 4,000 acres. We motored all round the estate. The park with semicircle of beech trees and carpets of bluebells was a dream of beauty. We drove to the Downs at the north extremity of the estate, with a view towards Bignor. Then to the house, which is a travesty. Originally Elizabethan brick with flint courses, it underwent extensive Georgian alterations outside and in. The present owner mistakenly removed nearly all of these after the last war, inserting bogus ceilings with plasterine ribs. The main façade is practically re-built with 'Jacobethan' bays where none existed before, and windows of plate glass in lieu of sash. The only good features left are the seventeenth-century screen in the hall, and the overdoors, the pretty eighteenth-century wrought-iron balustrade of the staircase and rococo plaster ceiling above it. The other main staircase was partially boarded up, but I think the framework is modern, with Charles II panels inserted. Of their genuineness I am not sure. There is a little Regency temple with Trafalgar balcony around it, which the soldiery have burnt out. The big house has troops in it, and is sadly knocked about. The dirt and the dreariness of the surroundings are what one has come to expect in these circumstances.

Wednesday, 3rd May

Went at 12 to see a Mr. Hunter at his office in the Strand. He is, I believe, chairman of some newspaper firm, very business-like, steel-grey hair, brown suit, well groomed, the Roderick Jones type, only nice. He began by criticizing the N.T. for its slapdash methods. This surprised me; then he disclosed that the secretary had made three appointments and failed to keep any. Since he is a benefactor and gave me therewith a cheque for £1,750 my predicament was to pacify him without seeming disloyal to the secretary. A tangled web again. However, we made friends, and he is asking me to luncheon to meet his architect, whom he wants to erect a tower on Black Down in memory of his wife. I am not sure about the tower.

An American officer lunched with me at Brooks's. He criticized his superior officer, for which I piously rebuked him, and expressed a terror I have seldom seen across the face of any man, lest he might be dropped as a parachutist in the forthcoming invasion. I sympathized deeply, imagining my terror if I were faced with the command, but again piously begged him to keep such apprehensions to himself, lest other people, not so charitable as me, might interpret them as cowardice.

Thursday, 4th May

Martineau and I lunched at the Park Lane Hotel with Lord Braybrooke who has recently succeeded two cousins (killed on active service), inheriting the title and Audley End. He is a bald, common-sensical, very nice business man of 45, embarrassed by his inheritance. At his wits' end what to do with Audley End. Who wouldn't be? We discussed how the N.T. might take the house over. It was arranged that Martineau and I would visit the house with him in June. It is requisitioned by the Army and used for highly secret purposes, so that even he is not allowed into the rooms except in the company of a senior officer. Consequently he hardly knows the way round his own house. Two lots of death duties have had to be paid on the estate. When the present lord was only 21 he was heir presumptive. Since then however he never expected to be in the running again.

Friday, 5th May

During the luncheon hour, to the National Gallery. A lecture on Beethoven by Ivor James, the cellist of the Menges Quartet, which afterwards played Beethoven.

Jamesey met me at Brooks's, and we dined excellently at the White Tower—soup, coquille St. Jacques, and veal. I was sure these two courses were illegal, and felt guilty. James in addition had asparagus, and both of us had pudding. We drank Algerian wine. J. was extremely tired. He is over-worked. His War Office hours are 8.50 to 7 p.m. every day in the week, but one. He is in love with no one; and, worse still, no one is in love with him. Truly he is in a bad way.

58

Lunched with Eddy, who was in spanking form. He spied across the room a young officer, tanned darkest brown and wearing a kilt. He was sitting opposite me. Eddy made me change places before I realized his intention. Having reseated himself he said, 'You had better put your spectacles on.' I said, 'That's a bit late in the day in view of your extraordinary behaviour.' He talked of his lack of heart, yet not lack of feeling. He also said that whereas he considered disqualifications in himself to be a crime, he would consider the same in others to be merely a pity. James joined us at the end to judge the Blickling 'Holbein' of Henry VIII which I had in the car, outside. John Pope-Hennessy, whom I had invited, did not turn up.

Geoffrey Houghton-Brown called at 2.30 and we walked in Regent's Park. The walk was spoilt by the bitter cold and my new shoes, which cost me £6.10.0. and are agony. We searched for Decimus Burton buildings. Clarence Terrace, Cornwall Terrace and Holme Villa are his. These terraces have suffered grievously from the raids. Large pieces of plaster have flaked off and the shoddiness of Nash's methods is revealed. I said to Geoffrey I often wondered if an objective person like the Pope thought the English deserved to win this war; and I was pretty certain that, since it had dragged on so long, it would not matter in fifty years' time who had won it. Geoffrey said that Bobbie Harris, who has just returned from Italy, told him the Italians so hate us that they walk out of buildings when the British enter. Bobbie said the only people who may like us after the war are the Germans.

Nancy at dinner wore a little Queen Alexandra hat, with feathers on the brim, pulled down over her eyes, and was looking very pretty and debonair.

Wednesday, 10th May

After a meeting of the Polesden Lacey executors I went to the Kennets'. They arrived at 6, for he had been delivering a speech in the House of Lords. K. gave me tulips and lilies of the valley, her olive branch. This was our first meeting since the row in February outside the Albert Hall. Adorable woman.

Thursday, 11th May

Captain Hill came to see me in the morning to suggest the N.T. buying 4,000 acres of the Clumber estate from the Duke of Newcastle, to whom he now acts as agent. The area covers the park lands alone, the house having been totally destroyed. When I was last there, the house still stood, though gutted.

At about 4 I left in the car for Warwickshire. The sun was brilliant and with the roof of the car open I was drenched in sunshine. I shall soon become as brown as Eddy's officer, and then where shall I be? Admiring myself in the looking-glass, with my spectacles on? Stopped at St. Albans Cathedral. Its over-restoration is a disaster. It was one of the cases which brought the S.P.A.B. into being during the 1870s. The Early English style was actually substituted by the criminal Lord Grimthorpe for the Norman. Gilbert Scott never committed an offence like this. There was a service in progress as I tripped down one aisle, my brown shoes squeaking most horribly and shamefully. It must be the way I walk that makes all my shoes do this after a time. I arrived at Packwood House at 8 precisely, and there was Baron Ash on the drive awaiting me.

Friday, 12th May

Baron kept me up till 1 a.m. with woes, but I was down for breakfast at 8.30. During the morning we walked round the garden and down the avenue as far as it extends, the continuation of it having lately been given to the N.T. by Baron's brother-in-law. Baron is very distressed by the condition of the yews which have not been clipped or tied back for two years. He is right in stressing that the Commonwealth yew garden is of prime historic importance. With one gardener and two land girls it is impossible to look after the yews properly. Besides, if the land girls worked at them the Ministry of Labour would promptly take them, the land girls, away.

At 12 I left. Looked at the Children's Field, Knowle, a miserable little property—merely a flat field. There is nothing more to be said about it. On my way I passed Grimshaw Hall, that horrid, little, over-restored house. Stopped to eat some stale sandwiches in the porch of Castle Bromwich church.

At 2, according to plan, I reached Bloxwich, a suburb of Walsall, and went to the office of Messrs. Wiggin & Co. Old Mr. Wiggin received me and told me he was chairman of a family business of stainless steel, founded by his father. He was immensely proud of it. Showed me brochures of hideously designed coffee pots, thermos flasks, etc. A fortnight ago he bought Moseley Old Hall from the colliery company which has owned it, and is touchingly pleased. His life's ambition has been to own this house. He does not want to live in it, or to make it into a show place, but to restore it with the best expert advice, keep it as a place to take his firm's distinguished guests to, and in short, to gloat over it. I suggested covenants with the National Trust. He was delighted with this idea. One by one he summoned his two sons and two brothers, to each of whom in turn I had to explain the meaning of covenants. The old man was slow of speech. He appealed to his family to approve his motives and intentions point by point, delivering himself of a sort of inspired sermon. He reminded me of some Old Testament prophet addressing a tribe. It was a curious party and I was struck by the earnestness and sincerity and public spirit of this very worthy family, clustered round the revered autocrat, the patriarch. Then a brother and a son motored me to Moseley. To my pleasant surprise the old Hall is still in remote country, surrounded by and approached through lanes. Unhappily there are several fields of colliery pit heads and pylons in the near distance. The curious purple brick case stuck on to the outside in the 1870s is rather appealing. Of course I should prefer to see the half-timbering revealed, if it were at all possible, which I doubt. The Hall is a farmhouse which is nice. The interior has scarcely altered since the time when Charles II took refuge in it after the Battle of Worcester. It is a pity that the secret hides have lost their secrecy, their door slides having become hinged and handled. But they survive. The attic chapel, Father Huddleston's chamber, the King's little square black hole in which he crouched, are intact. The place is redolent of papistry, monarchy and sanctity.

I left at 3.30 for Boscobel, which is similarly farm-housey and unspoilt. It belongs to Lord Bradford. The oak tree, the garden mound are there, and the hide which Father Owen constructed as ingeniously as he did the ones at Moseley. The woman who showed me round explained that the pointed lancet and latticed windows painted on the chimney breast were Papist signs that here priests could find sanctuary. Hitherto I had deplored what I took to be bogus attempts to feign the real things.

Arrived at Weston Park at 5 precisely, hoping to look cool, the heat being terrific. I was given no opportunity to wash. Having rung the bell I was conducted by a young nephew straight into a room on the right of the hall where Lady Bradford was standing before a tea-kettle. She did not hear me enter, for she is deaf. She looked like a French *châteleine*. Lord Bradford very territorial and patrician. Both charming, with wonderful manners towards the stranger. After tea I begged to be allowed to see the pink French tapestries in the drawing-room. They are in superb condition. Lady Bradford walked me through the tunnel where, she told me, Queen Mary knocked her hat right off, to the Temple of Diana built by Paine. It has a superb plaster ceiling like the Osterley temples, and a circular room at the rear with painted Etruscan ceiling panels. The central ceiling of the China Room has just collapsed, smashing all the china. There are Chinese Chippendale chairs made for the room. We continued round the lake. A temple has been built on the verge of it by Gerry Wellington. Lady B. said The Cottage was also built by Paine. To me it looked later.

Saturday, 13th May

Slept very soundly, and up early. Went to the office, put away the car and caught the 10 a.m. from Liverpool Street, having foolishly gone to King's Cross by mistake. Arrived Ipswich at 12.15 where Marshall Sisson met me and drove me to Swanton Morley. We stopped at the White Hart Inn at Scole for a drink. Sisson says there is no finer inn in the country. Caroline Flemish gables of red brick. We ate sandwiches in the car and reached Swanton Morley a little after 2.30. Found Colonel Jack Leslie with old Mr. Bullard, a brewer, the local rector and others. The purpose of this visit is very strange. Colonel Leslie had given a plot of land in the village, on which it was supposed once stood the cottage lived in by the ancestors of Abraham Lincoln, and demolished fifty years ago. With great ceremony Lord Zetland received the deeds from Ambassador Winant in February. Several plans were considered for a memorial on the site, one of which was a replica of the demolished cottage. With all this sentiment I disagreed, too strongly according to Matheson, from the first. Sisson, who was sent on our behalf to investigate the site soon after the gift was declared inalienable, suspected that it was the wrong one. By comparing a seventeenth-century map recording Lincoln land with an up-to-date twenty-five-inch ordinance, his suspicions were confirmed. Finally Leslie and the other local enthusiasts admitted that a mistake had in all innocence been made. It transpires that two-thirds of the old Lincoln house does indisputably exist in the present Angel inn, belonging to Bullard. There is even a small sketch of it on the old map. Bullard is prepared to give us a strip of freehold at the back of the inn. It is very important that eventually we should acquire the inn itself, which he won't surrender. Why should he? It retains a magnificent central cluster of octagonal brick chimneys and several beams with original moulds and stops. All the Lincoln fields marked on the seventeenth-century map survive today, with the same demarcations and hedge boundaries; even the lanes and ponds are the same. The Trust is left with a useless plot of land, an old chicken run of no beauty and less historic interest which it **can** never get rid of except by special Act of Parliament.

Sisson motored me back to Ipswich and I reached London at 10.30.

Dined with Alvilde Chaplin at 55 Park Lane. Left rather early for firewatching in the office, where I slept beautifully on my camp bed without sheets. Such a deprivation does not worry me in the least. Alvilde had been to see Ethel Smyth three days before she died. She was living in great discomfort, almost in squalor, and lay on an iron bedstead, looking like Wagner.

Lunched at the Savoy with Mr. Hunter, the donor of Black Down, and was exactly on time. It was just as well for he remarked upon it. He is an autocratic tycoon. He had his architect to meet me, a man with, I suspect, no taste at all. We discussed the tower Mr. Hunter wishes to erect on the Down in memory of his wife. He wishes it to be higher than the Leith Hill tower, and to be made of such durable material that the trippers cannot disfigure it by cutting their names.

The three Pope-Hennessys have great family pride and are very united. Dame Una said to me, 'Can't you write a book and join us?' I thought, even if I could write a book I wouldn't be permitted to join them, however much I might want to. Speaking of Lord Hartington's marriage they all declared it was a mistake to marry out of one's station, that people like us should not marry dukes and dukes' daughters, it was shocking. The Dame said, 'The Kennedy girl will never be able to take her place.' I could see that Jamesey was amused.

Took the 4 o'clock train to Lincolnshire and reached Gunby Hall in time for dinner. The old Field-Marshal gave me a warm welcome. He loves to talk about Gunby, its history and problems. He and Lady Massingberd are true county squirearchy, with a high sense of public duty towards the estate and the neighbourhood. They live in easy austerity, no wine, but good, solid food, and enough of it. They have a butler, his wife the cook, a pantry boy, two housemaids, a chauffeur, and lead a feudal existence on a modest scale.

Friday, 19th May

This morning I motored in a hired car to Harrington Hall, seven miles away. It is two miles from Somersby, just off the wolds, and very remote. Belongs to some people called Holiday Hartley. In 1927 the house was to be sold in lots by auction. In the morning a Major Rawnsley bought it, but so late that the auction had to take place just the same. The staircase had already been sold, and Rawnsley had to buy it back. He could not buy the sundial over the porch, and so had to have a copy made. Rawnsley sold Harrington to the Hartleys for £1,500, on condition that if they parted with it they would give an option to purchase either to the Rawnsley family or the National Trust. It is beautiful, romantic, and finely situated. Originally early Tudor, with a high brick Henry VIII central porch. The rest is Charles II. The oak staircase is better than the Gunby one, yet similar, with arcaded, fanlighted doorways leading to it. There is a walled garden immediately behind the house, and behind that a wood with the remains of an oblong canal, longer than the Gunby one, and a lime avenue. A remarkable feature is the raised terrace garden, 'the high hall garden' of Tennyson's *Maud*, which was written with Harrington in mind. Maud's 'little oak room', alas, has had the early Renaissance and linenfold wainscoting removed. The Hartleys offer the house and fifty acres of park to the N.T. but without endowment.

In the afternoon I walked round part of Gunby estate with the Field-Marshal. After dinner he talked about Churchill. Said that he must have learnt much from his study of Marlborough, for Marlborough also had remarkable contacts with crowned heads, and leaders of countries when he dashed around Europe. The Field-Marshal said that he and Weygand and Pétain were the sole survivors of the Council of the Allies held in 1918 when the fortunes of the allies were at their lowest ebb. Churchill, then Minister of Munitions, came over to France and asked what he could most usefully do to help. The Field-Marshal said 'Keep an eye on Pétain. I suspect that he may let us down.' The Field-Marshal greatly admires Montgomery, who is no relation, and Alexander even more. He says Alexander has never put a foot wrong.

Sunday, 21st May

Nancy asked me to lunch. I willingly accepted, but I should have stayed at home and worked. She has just bought for £40 a huge Dresden china clock which she thinks lovely. It is not eighteenth century, more likely 1840s, and the face even later. Alas, it won't go, and we pushed the pendulum, shook the clock and propped it on paper wedges, to no avail. She walked Milly and me round St. John's Wood, looking at houses. How charming some of these streets are. I left at 3.30 and worked at an article on my return.

At 7.30 to Harold Acton's flat in Chesterfield Court, where Norman Douglas was. We drank whisky till 9.45 and dined at the Ritz Grill. Norman Douglas said he was 21 in 1890, so he is well over 70. He has straight white hair, is thin, has a mottled face, slightly beaky features. I would not say a particularly striking face on first meeting. He laughs intermittently, explosively, and talks a lot of bawdy. He told us he had written about the destruction of London buildings in a recent number of *Life and Letters*. Until this war he had not been in London or England indeed, since 1916. Hates it, and the cold of it, and the restraint, the bad food and the puritanism. Is delighted to be able to talk to the Italian waiters in the Ritz grill in their own language. Has no idea what has happened to his house and belongings in Florence. I accompanied him in the tube to Gloucester Road, for he is afraid of having fainting fits, to which he is prone. He asked me what they did with the earth they dug out in excavating the tubes. I had no idea, but Eardley tells me a lot was sent to Mill Hill. Douglas said that in Florence he cultivated the reputation of being a bear in order to avoid social persecution by the wrong people. We shook hands warmly at Gloucester Road. He said he would ask Viva King to bring us together again.

Monday, 22nd May

To the George Inn, Southwark, at tea-time, and met Forsyth and the painter to consider some light cream Forsyth was trying out on the gallery balusters. I emphatically disapproved of this colour, and voted for retention of the existing chocolate brown as enhancing the Dickensian gloom of the Inn. Voted for the walls behind the galleries to be painted the same yellow as the distemper on the adjoining range of buildings, of which the Inn forms part, the woodwork of this range to be painted chocolate likewise, so as to preserve the uniformity. Was pleased that both Eardley and Forsyth agreed in the end, and so this decision was carried.

Tuesday, 23rd May

At 9.30 Eardley and I set off to look at Lord Hambleden's estate over which he has given the Trust covenants, entirely through Eardley's efforts. We looked over Culham Court, now used as a nursery school. It is a compact, small house, very well planned. Neat entrance hall. All the vaulting of the passage ceilings is delightful. Two drawing-rooms preserve circular relief panels over the chimneypieces. The eastern drawing-room is green with gilded gesso panels, pretty and apparently contemporary, though E. thinks they may be by Lenygon.* If so, they are well done. Some bolection-mould mantelpieces have been inserted. They of course are wrong and make me suspicious of the rest. The house might have been built by Sir Robert Taylor. The out-side is a very pretty pink brick. It is a pity that the trees have been allowed to grow so thickly along the reach of the river, and that there are too many conifers round the house.

We motored in and out of the drive of Greenlands. Walked down the azalea ride of Great Wood. Were shown over Hambleden Manor by the tenant, a lady who drives round the garden in a swift, silent electric chair. This house was built in 1604 with three pointed gables of knapped flint on each elevation. In 1814 an additional wing with elliptical bay formed a Regency ballroom. More recently a bad billiard-room has appeared. The house has been over-restored by rich people. Walked across to Kenricks, which, formerly the parsonage house, is of red brick, *circa* 1720. The outside rendering having been removed, leaves the brick rather blotchy. A little stiff and dull inside.

Wednesday, 24th May

After a Georgian Group meeting Puss Milnes-Gaskell lunched with me. She was looking sad. She said that Fitzroy Maclean was to have travelled in the same aeroplane as her son, Charles, which crashed, but that circumstances made him too late, and he had to take the next. I asked her whether Queen Mary would accept the Presidentship, if asked, and she seemed to think she might, and would not be too adversely influenced by Lord Harewood. So I have written to Lord Zetland. I would like Queen Mary to become President of the National Trust, because she is the only member of the royal family interested in such things. Puss told me she was in Partridge's shop with the Queen. Partridge showed them a bed cover of seventeenth-century crewel work, telling them he had already sold the hangings of the same stuff. Puss recognized it as having come from her old home. Mr. Partridge pressed her to accept the bed cover as a present. Puss resolutely

* A fashionable decorating firm in the 1920s.

protested until Queen Mary turned on her, and said, 'Constance, never refuse a firm offer. I never do.' Thereupon Puss had to accept.

After luncheon we walked to Prunier's where David Lloyd, his wife and mother were lunching. The two Ladies Lloyd were arguing amicably about the lot of poor women having to look after their children. The younger was saying, 'I think our class do not realize what hell it is having to look after children all day and every day.' Blanche replied, 'But then our class are not accustomed to it, my dear.'

I dined at Emerald's, and sat next to Lady Juliet Duff and Mrs. McEwen, a sweet, gentle woman. Her husband was there, one of the Government Whips, a high Tory; Rory Cameron, in the U.S. army, a new friend of Emerald's; Daisy Fellowes, wearing a mantilla and looking remarkably, deceptively demure, and beautiful. She is a sparkling conversationalist, with a distinctive, corn-crakey voice, and French intonation. It was an enjoyable dinner. Lord Sherwood came in afterwards. He is supposed to have great success with women, but looks a runt with a large nose. He talked republicanism, is against kings, etc., and yet has accepted a peerage, which is an inconsistency. Drawing-room politics ensued. Emerald was not at her best, and kept harping upon Chips Channon, saying, 'I think Chips longs to have a grand passion, and doesn't know how to. The trouble is he hates women. Now, Jim, what do you think?' as though I had any views on the subject. She said a few funny things, such as, 'Robert Byron's father used to poke his daughters with a sadistic fork,' and, 'Women today are so unromantic, so—un-succulent.' She surprised us by saying she had once been asked to stand for Parliament for Mells, apparently meaning Stroud.

Thursday, 25th May

I went off in the car at 4.30 and arrived at Wickhamford at 7.45. Mama looks much older, is very thin and very lined. I hate this, and I hate to see her on her hands and knees dusting the floor and polishing the boards. It is moreover quite unnecessary.

Friday, 26th May

This morning Mama talked to me about her will. She has made several odd codicils. She wishes to be buried a day after her death; there are to be no wreaths at all on her grave; there is to be no lead lining to her

67

coffin because it is unfair on the bearers; she is to be buried in her best nightdress, and not in a winding sheet tied up at the head like a bonnet, as old Mrs. Someone-or-other was in the village, fit to make you split with laughter. These clauses in her own inimitable layman's wording were very funny, as she solemnly read them out to me.

I motored to Overbury, picked up Thurstan Holland-Martin and drove him to Tewkesbury. He showed me the cottages and buildings round the Abbey which his Trust intends to buy if we will provide some money from our Cathedral Amenities Fund. I do not absolutely share his ideas for I see he is a vista-maker. But I do think his Trust should be helped to acquire the dwellings lest a chain store purchases them in order to put up something beastly. Thurstan wants to pull down some Georgian dwellings of little intrinsic worth, and to reconstitute some medieval overhangs and fronts.

I returned to Overbury Court and lunched there. Mrs. Holland-Martin has become very old, small and bent. She still has that deep, capable voice which I remember from early childhood days, a voice which frightened me to death during tennis tournaments, when she umpired. Woe betide whoever partnered a son of hers, and let him down in a boys' double, which I invariably did. For this reason I simply dreaded being paired with Thurstan. Sitting on a stepladder Mrs. Holland-Martin would boom out, 'Pull up your socks, young Lees-Milne.' Oh, the agony and dread. And Mama told me this morning how at the beginning of the war she and other Worcestershire ladies were being drilled by Mrs. H.-M. I said, 'Are you sure you were drilled?' 'Yes, of course,' she said, 'and I went on parade with my shooting stick, and while we were forming fours, it got entangled in Josey Duncombe's shoe-laces and brought her crashing to the ground. And you know she is over 80. And Nell gave me the most terrible dressing down in front of the whole platoon.'

Today Mrs. Holland-Martin was absolutely docile and friendly.

Saturday, 27th May

All morning in the Polytechnic with Miss Paterson and old William Weir, arranging 260 designs by competitors for the West Wycombe village hall. This lasted till 2.30. We took Weir back to Cheyne Walk and gave him an odd meal of tea and eggs. Weir reminded me that he had been a pupil of Philip Webb, who had been a pupil of Edmund Street. He has a great regard for Webb for having dissociated himself from Street when the latter embarked upon the Law Courts. But I admire the Law Courts.

I crept into Westminster Abbey through the west door during a service. After the oven-like heat of outside the charnel cool of the inside was refreshing. There was a procession of dean and canons in beautiful copes, and choirboys in Elizabethan ruffs, singing a hymn. On my way from the cloisters to Dean's Yard I noticed for the first time a high marble monument to an Admiral Cornwall, *circa* 1750, a cliff-like structure hung with reliefs, and encrusted with shells, sea urchins and rocaille ornaments. It is jet-black with dirt, and would look wonderful if cleaned.

Monday, 29th May

The hottest day I remember. With my four windows wide open, and in my shirt sleeves I dripped, while compiling a memorandum for the National Trust. I nearly died of the combination of heat and work. Thus occupied all day until dinner at the St. James's Club with Charles Fry. Batsford's are going to produce the official book in celebration of the N.T.'s fiftieth birthday.

Tuesday, 30th May

Had a great shock this morning, for the Gas Company telephoned to say my cheque to them had bounced. I rang up the bank at Evesham who were sorry and said I was £200 overdrawn. I am terrified lest other cheques may be returned. I wrote to my father in desperation and shame. Now he has always implied, like King George V about buggers, that men shoot themselves for such a disgrace. As for the other offence I dread to think what he supposes they should do; slowly roast themselves to death on a spit, I daresay. Oh Lord, he will be furious.

Visited Pierre Lansel, who in Piccadilly the other day begged me to see him. He said it was madness not to continue my treatment a little longer, and in proof of his wisdom showed me a graph of my blood behaviour, nodding in a knowing way. It meant nothing to me, and I was too alarmed to ask for a detailed explanation. Besides I can't possibly afford the treatment, and daren't risk a cheque bouncing off him.

Dined at Emerald's. Nancy, Joan Moore and a don called Denis Rickett, terrifyingly incisive, intellectual and All Soulsish. Emerald was in sparkling form. Venetia Montagu came in at 11.30. She is a very clever, well-informed woman, with a masculine and independent mind. Denis Rickett told Emerald that she had an astounding knowledge of the classics. It is true. Talk was of George Eliot and English novelists. There seems to be no novel that Emerald hasn't read, and, what's more, remembered.

Wednesday, 31st May

This morning I tubed to Totteridge to see a house called Darlands and 100 acres, making a real island of country in a horribly built up area. The house, dating from 1930, is built by Guy Dawber in decent red brick, with a sloping tiled roof. A well laid out garden. I thought it one of the best houses of this period. It does not quite verge on the arty, which the best houses of 1910 tend to do. The bailiff took me round the property which Mrs. Kemp, a biscuit manufacturer's widow, wishes to leave to the Trust. I favour covenants, for I don't think the place would be of much use to the public.

Returned in time to lunch with Nancy at Gunter's. Alvilde Chaplin and Hamish there. Alan Pryce-Jones joined us for coffee. Nancy said that last Sunday *Reynolds' News* reproduced a Spanish caricature of King George and Queen Elizabeth in bed. The Queen was saying to the King, 'George, why do you look so low this morning?' and the King was replying, 'Because I have it on the best authority that Winston means to swap me for an old destroyer.'

Dr. Vaughan-Williams came into the office this afternoon. I did not realize until after he left that he was the composer. He came to announce that his brother of Leith Hill Place had died this morning, leaving the property to him, and that he wished to give it to the National Trust. He was not wasting much time. He is an elderly, stout man, handsome and distinguished, not at all practical. He was wrapped in thought and had a distracted manner. He kept rubbing his hand through his untidy white hair. In shaking his hand I noticed how soft and resistant it was, as though he were frightened of injuring it.

Thursday, 1st June

Lady Cohen asked me to luncheon at the Greek Club to meet Lady Luke. I supposed she must be the Bovril Lord Luke's wife, until she said, 'I am afraid I am only a common knight's wife.' I liked her for this.

At 6 I called for Loelia Westminster and took her to Wilton's, where we met Anne and Esmond Rothermere, and ate dressed crab and drank sherry and white wine, as a preliminary to a charity film, *This Happy Breed* by Noël Coward, a kind of continuation of *Cavalcade*. It was in colour, and quite horribly and insidiously sentimental, so that I had constant lumps in the throat and wanted to cry, while realizing all the time that my lowest emotions were being played upon. Loelia had paid I don't know how many guineas for each seat. At Ciro's afterwards they were talking of a party the other night which cost £75, and how disgraceful it was of someone or other only to have contributed £10. So I quickly thought I would not even make a gesture of contributing to this entertainment, for had I proffered £5 it would have been accepted as though it were 5d. Nonetheless I felt rather uncomfortable. But they are all so vastly rich, and I am so rat poor.

Lord Rothermere is very tall, with a mouth like a cupid's. He seems to think the Invasion will be a walk-over, 'for the Germans cannot stand much more of a licking'. He talked of the embarrassment caused by Mrs. Roosevelt's public statement that Churchill was sixty years out of date. I said I supposed we would hear nothing of it owing to the strict censorship of the British papers. He said the censorship was too rigid; so much was bottled up that when a news item was released it often made more noise than its importance justified.

Friday, 2nd June

Trained to Hatch End, arriving punctually at 10. Lord and Lady Braybrooke waiting in their car, and Anthony Martineau already arrived. They motored us to Audley End.

Audley End is at present used as a military college. The principal state-rooms are closed to the soldiers and stacked high with furniture. The rooms lately in use have been most carefully protected by the Ministry of Works, even the stair treads being boarded over. It is a very secret place and only with difficulty was permission granted us to see round. We went all over, through the back regions, into practically every room and on the great lead roof, which looked in good order. It is of course a huge house, although three-quarters of it was demolished 200 years ago. It is certainly extremely important, being on a par with Blickling and Hatfield. The hall screen was once painted white, and I wish it were again. Vanbrugh constructed the grand staircase at the other end of the hall. I was fascinated by the Walpolian Gothick chapel. The eighteenth-century rooms on the south side, painted and decorated by Rebecca, are of poor quality and mean size. It is interesting that successive alterations in the eighteenth and nineteenth centuries were done with much care to reproduce the Jacobean

71

style, notably in the design of windows and bays, and ceiling plaster-work, much of which is indistinguishable from the original. The Great Hall and the Fish Saloon are very impressive. There is an early nine-teenth-century flavour in the paintwork of the rooms. The portrait copies in the Saloon are atrocious. Some Adam suites of furniture are good of their kind, but there is a deal of indifferent stuff in the rooms, which makes Audley End a true English country house, and not a museum.

We drove across the road to the circular Robert Adam temple where we had an excellent picnic luncheon. A noble view of the house from up here. The beautiful, undulating park is by Capability Brown, and could never be mistaken for nature's accident. The stable block is supposedly late sixteenth century, but looks early sixteenth to me, although there are no depressed arches discernible. An Elysian Temple, Lady Portsmouth's column and Brettingham's Temple of Concord complete the park features. Lord Braybrooke can barely find his way about. He is very keen to preserve his inheritance by means of the National Trust. He is willing for Mrs. Van der Elst to rent from the Trust, but he will not sell to her. We looked at Abbey Farm, and the almshouses which the Royal Historical Commission ranks high.

I returned by train to dine with Margaret Jourdain. The train was crammed, and I stood in the guard's van, almost dead with fatigue, my legs aching. Margaret was alone. She read me extracts of the William Kent letters she has found and is publishing. We discussed the possibility of a joint book on Kent, and also of editing the Bennet Langton papers, now at Gunby. She is a wickedly entertaining woman, and can be cruel about people less well informed than herself, notably poor old Clifford Smith, whose ignorance she never tires of exposing. She says Ivy [Compton-Burnett] will not come back to London, she is so afraid of bombs. We talked a lot about Ivy's books and the unreality of the characters. Margaret says Ivy lives in the past, and nothing after 1914 has any reality for her.

Saturday, 3rd June

Went to Dickie Girouard's nuptial Mass at Spanish Place. It was solemn and moving, and lasted one hour and a quarter. Billa Harrod was sitting in front of me. We went together to the Dorchester reception given by the bride's mother. We found Nancy there and the three of us tucked into chicken mousse and tongue, washed down with cider cup. Then chocolate and cocktails, which we had not been offered before. Billa could not restrain her greed, and ate and ate. Nancy says

72

Peter Rodd tells her the invading troops are penned up like prisoners in barbed wire enclosures awaiting the signal; that Peter actually knows which beaches they are to land on. He keeps appearing and disappearing, stressing how frightened he is because he has already participated in two invasions, saying good-bye for ever and warning Nancy that a widow's pension is very small.

Sunday, 4th June

Dined with James and Constantia Rumbold at the Allies Club. Talked of poverty and overdrafts, and of the impending invasion. Both of them knew beforehand the date of the North African invasion, but denied they knew anything about the forthcoming one.

Tuesday, 6th June

Miss P. woke me early at 7.30 and we breakfasted soon after 8. Consequently she missed the 8 o'clock news in her bedroom to which she usually listens. I left for the 9.30 at King's Cross, bought a paper and read of the capture of Rome without destruction, which was cheering. Hubert Smith met me at Grantham at 11.55. It was bitterly cold. He asked me if I knew anything about the Invasion. I said I knew nothing. Had it begun? He said the 8 o'clock news intimated that it had. I was filled with mingled emotions, apprehension over the outcome, anxiety for my friends, regret and guilt that I was not participating, relief that I was not. Hubert Smith drove me to Grantham House, where we were received by the two Miss Sedgwicks, old women of the churchy, godly sort. They are very north country, abrupt and spinsterish. They expected me to stay the night, and seemed cross when I said I must leave in the afternoon. In actual fact there was nothing for me to do, and my visit was a waste of time. Their wireless would not work, the battery having perished, so we heard no news at 1 o'clock. Had a rhubarby luncheon, rather nasty. Miss Marion left for a funeral, and Miss Winifred took us to look at the property the other side of the river. It rained and was depressing. Never before have I been so conscious of the fatuity of my work, fiddling while Rome burns – though, thank God, the actual Rome is spared. After tea and a rock cake at 3 we left.

A long, straight drive of a mile brought us to Harlaxton Manor. The butler at the lodge said he dared not show us the house without a written letter from Mrs. Van der Elst. I hadn't got one, I explained, but the agent said I might see over. The butler accompanied us to the back premises and telephoned to London. Meanwhile Hubert and I looked at the outside. The date 1837 is carved on the parapet of the porch. The stone of which the house is built is a beautiful bronze yellow, almost like Stanway's. The design is meant to put one in mind of Burghley. The pavilions and gate piers of the forecourt are as baroque as Vanbrugh. Mrs. Van der Elst has made ghastly, insipid white marble statues peer from bushes and sit on pinnacles. The butler was away so long that Hugh and I went to look for him. We walked for miles in a rabbit warren of back passages. Mrs. Van der Elst has suggested that we should sell Harlaxton for her, and with the proceeds endow Audley End, which she will rent. The butler finally reappeared, having spoken to Mrs. Van der Elst. She refused categorically to allow us to set foot inside the premises. I was made extremely angry by this treatment.

Hubert motored me to Oxford. I ate a sandwich at the Randolph. Just before Oxford we saw about 100 aeroplanes towing gliders, evidently returning from France. All day I have felt excited and longed to have news. On Didcot station waiting for a train I met Willy Teeling, now M.P. for Brighton, and travelled to Paddington with him. He said he must get to his constituency since his constituents felt safe if he were there. No harm in this, but he is yet another example of a man whose head the 'House' has turned. He told me Lord Vansittart complained to him at Denham that since the P.M. took office he had never consulted him or addressed a word to him, but systematically cut him.

Wednesday, 7th June

National Buildings Record photographic exhibition at the National Gallery. Those provided by the Warburg Institute of the detailed bosses, tombs and effigies in Westminster Abbey are superb. The heads of the early Plantagenet kings and queens must be portraits, they have such character. Equally revealing are the Warburg photographs of St. Paul's, taken of views one never can see oneself, such as the drum of the dome from above, the window heads of the turrets.

Had tea with old Mr. Rhys-Williams of Merthyr, a strange, unappetizing old man who told me he hated his eldest son, whose mother had turned him against his father, and when they lived under the same roof treated him as though he were an idiot. But he hounded them both out of the house all right, and will never speak to them again. I asked him if he had other sons. He said, 'Yes, but my second son is not mine really. It's sad in a way.'

I trained to Rochester in the afternoon to look at the Old Hall. From the gate of this rambling old place, close to the Cathedral and opposite the Castle, the owner, Miss Shinkwin (Dickensian name), came bustling forth, accompanied by several cats and pekingeses. Elderly, dumpy, she was wearing a too light summer frock, silver ear-rings and finger rings. She had dusty dyed hair and stockingless legs. I was disposed to dislike this Pomeranian lady, but she was so good-hearted, enthusiastic and kind that I soon took to her. She spoke in a curious, high, exaggerated drawl. The Old Hall is a muddle of wings and gables, and basically early Tudor. The inside suggests a second-rate antique shop with its pickled walnut 'chiffoniers', 'davenports', 'chesterfields', Knole settees and lampshades made of parchment deeds. Miss Shinkwin has within ten years unveiled square yards of very perished wall stencilling and one complete room of mid-Tudor painted panelling, of a conventionalized flower device which is in fair condition. But there is so much revealed timbering, which never ought to have been revealed, that my enthusiasm quickly flagged. Even so, Miss Shinkwin is beginning upon two more rooms, scraping away to disclose more painted, or stencilled wainscot. Above one chimneypiece she has brought to light two allegorical figures of Justice and Truth in pre-Tudor dress, reminiscent, she declares, of Sienese primitive paintings.

Harold Nicolson dined at the White Tower. Stuart and his friend Robin Brewster, just come from America, joined us. We were in a very noisy upstairs room and I could barely hear one word Harold uttered. He was, I think, tired and trying his utmost, as he always does, to entertain us. Not a highly enjoyable evening. Brewster is a set, earnest young man with fanatical, sunk eyes. Stuart says he is the 'last Puritan', as well as immensely rich. He is buying from Agnew's a Watteau for £5,000. He hardly spoke, and looked cross and difficult. He left us after dinner, and Stuart and I accompanied Harold to King's Bench Walk. Harold was intrigued by Brewster's reticence, and asked about his private life. Stuart knows nothing of it, although he is one of his oldest friends.

Friday, 9th June

This morning I trained to Leatherhead with Christopher Gibbs and his wife Peggy. They have grown to look exactly like one another — an infallible indication of a happy marriage. We lunched at Christopher's parents' house, Goddards, one of Lutyens's earliest domestic buildings, full of oak timbers and ingle nooks. Although I can see how well designed, and well executed every detail is, nevertheless I do not care for a contrived 'olde worlde' flavour. Christopher motored me to Leith Hill. We picked up Roland Vaughan-Williams and passed Tanhurst, his house on the edge of the Leith Hill slope, with splendid views. The house is square, early Georgian. We continued to Leith Hill Place, likewise on the slope, a short distance away. His cousin the composer, Ralph Vaughan-Williams, was waiting for us. This house is likewise fairly small, and was built about 1730 for a General Folliot. It has two flanking wings with pedimented gables, very wide and rather Kent-like. The south side is faced with Portland stone. The windows have nice period surrounds with pulvinated friezes. Inside there is not much decoration, apart from a decent feature or two. The composer remembers his father removing the exterior roof balustrade and inserting the dormer windows. He showed us what had been his nursery and his bedroom when he was a boy. He wants the house to be used as an institution, which is a pity, for it is just the sort of house that would let privately. There is a large walled garden, with trees, shrubs and an azalea walk, which is lovely. Unfortunately the whole property is destitute. It is offered without endowment.

The composer is a very sweet man, with a most impressive appearance. He is big and broad and has a large head with sharply defined features, and eyes that look far into the distance. He has shaggy white hair that is not long. Slender hands and fingers with square-ended, or rather bitten nails. He is very courteous and when it began to rain in the garden, offered to go into the house to fetch my burberry. I had some difficulty in preventing him. He is longing to disembarrass himself of his responsibility for the estate. When asked by Christopher to resolve some estate matter, he replied, 'We will let things continue as before, for the present.' In the car he told me that when young musicians came to him for advice he always discouraged them, for he said that those who seriously intended to make music their career would always do so willy-nilly. He has a quiet, dry humour which expresses itself in very few words. He laughs in a low key.

Sunday, 11th June

All day I read, and slept, for I feel worn out. Dinner at Alvilde Chaplin's promised to be, and was, fun, for Nancy, Emerald, Harold Acton and Palewski, General de Gaulle's *chef de cabinet*, a bright, cheerful man, were there. Emerald asked a lot of inadvertent questions, such as how many French troops there were in France now. Palewski is staunchly loyal about de Gaulle, says he is charming but shy, and does not wish for power. We have heard that so often. There was much criticism of Americans and Roosevelt for their non-recognition of de Gaulle, and pusillanimous reasons given, namely their wanting to wait and see which way the cat jumped before committing themselves to his support. I said to Palewski, surely the reason is that Americans think de Gaulle stands for authoritarian power, or what in their democratic eyes is authoritarian power. If de Gaulle no longer favours the old *laissez-faire* democracy which brought France to perdition in 1940, then I was all for him. A good deal of talk about French literature between Harold and Palewski, who is a cultivated man. Few fireworks from Emerald. She did say, 'What is the use of handsome husbands? They soon become less handsome, and in the end they are nothing but an incubus.'

Wednesday, 14th June

Lunched with Sibyl Colefax and Mrs. Gladwyn Jebb at the Canteen. Sibyl said Lord Bruntisfield told her the aeroplane brought down on Monday night near Liverpool Street station was a pilotless one, a kind of rocket. For the present the Government are not releasing the news. She said no one in authority expected the war to be over for a very long time. I walked away with her, and we took a bus as far as Bond Street. In the open she appears very tiny, round shouldered, old and pathetic.

Stuart told me that in his office the American soldiers speak with surprise about the familiarity of English girls, none of whom decline to sleep with them. They are convinced that all English women are tarts, and despise them accordingly, just as English soldiers despised the French girls during the last war.

Thursday, 15th June

To the Courtauld Institute for Kenneth Clark's lecture on Cézanne. A great crowd. It was a brilliant lecture, delivered with that purring ease which I admire in him so much, yet with haste, and packed with meat. Slides of Cézanne in black and white are not wholly satisfactory.

John Fowler dined at Brooks's. He told me some horrifying stories of how American troops behave after dark. One night this week John and two friends were walking home at midnight through the Green Park. One friend stopped to pee behind a tree, while the other two walked on. He took a long time so they retraced their steps. They found him on the ground, pouring with blood, having been assaulted, knocked down and stamped upon by two drunk G.I.s. The rest of our conversation was about art in our time, and how general depreciation of quality as well as lack of time for rumination drove us to being preservationists, and thus un-creative.

While I was in bed, very tired, the siren went. There was severe intermittent gunfire throughout the night until, indeed, 9.45 a.m. when the all-clear sounded. This is unprecedented since the early raids. I heard one aeroplane roar overhead extremely low.

Friday, 16th June

I lunched with Philip Frere, who is working at the Ministry of Aircraft Production. He told me that last night 140 pilotless planes came over. They are guided by radio and when they land their bomb load of 2,000 lbs. explodes. This is like an H. G. Wells story. It is almost inconceivable. Some of these things have landed in Surrey, some around and in London, doing great mischief. Morrison in the House of Commons has disclosed this information today. Frere talked of Lord Lloyd, and how he first met him. Lloyd told him before his death that Darlan gave him a signed pledge that he would not surrender the French fleet to the Germans. After G. Ll.'s death they looked everywhere for this document, but it has not yet been found.

L.H. brought her son to see me. He has just returned from South Africa. She has always gone on and on about his exceptional good looks and wonderful intelligence. He appeared extremely sallow, with no back to his head, a long cadaverous face and a Hitlerian black moustache. To all my enquiries about South Africa he was unable, or unwilling to stammer one word. How mothers deceive themselves. I trust mine does not sing my praises to strangers. Somehow I think not.

At midnight the sirens went. I was very tired, and did not get to sleep till 5. Intermittent gunfire extremely noisy. Shrapnel clattered on to the road, and the looking glass in the kitchen fell off the wall, breaking into a thousand fragments.

Saturday, 17th June

Worn out all day, but recovered marvellously in the evening. Worked in the R.I.B.A. library this morning, and Brooks's library in the afternoon. I am always happy in Brooks's stuffy, dingy, Victorian library in which silence is accentuated by the relentless tick of the old, stuffy clock. I love the old, stuffy books on the stuffy brown shelves, books which nobody reads, except Eddie Marsh, and he falls fast asleep over them. The very atmosphere is calculated to send one asleep, but into the gentlest, most happy, nostalgic dreams of nineteenth-century stability, self-satisfaction, and promise of an eternity of heavenly stuffiness, world without end. How much I adore this library, and club, nobody knows. May it survive Hitler, Stalin and all the beastliness which besets us.

I had to return to prepare tea for Nancy in Cheyne Walk. When we had begun Stuart walked in. Talk was of little else but the pilotless planes. They came over again all evening. We kept rushing to the window to look for them, but were always disappointed. I have only seen plumes of smoke across the river where they have landed. I believe they are hardly ever shot on the wing either by our fighters or by anti-aircraft guns. Nancy cracked very bad taste jokes about them, implying that she welcomed them as a hilarious diversion during these dull days. She said Palewski, who accompanied de Gaulle to France this week, was deeply impressed by the quiet, reverential way in which the General was everywhere received. Montgomery, he said, was tactful, and on greeting him apologized for being too busy to escort him, and so let him be on his own, which he, Monty, knew was what he wanted.

Nancy agreed to dine with James and me. When she and I were outside Bridget's flat in Mount Street, suddenly Michael Rosse in battledress, and wearing a beret and thick, fleece-lined waterproof, approached us round a corner. He had unexpectedly come up from Wanstead with his brigadier for an hour and a half. The whole Guards division is there, and have not yet gone to France. They wait like caged swans, for the north wind to drop before they can sail. We accompanied him into Bridget's flat. I talked to him while he had a bath. He said that in a few days' time a huge offensive would be launched, but that unless things went very wrong, his company would not be in it. He wants Bridget to tell Anne this, for he dares not do so on the telephone, and letters are censored. He warned us that all trunk calls are listened in to. He was very cheerful, and yet looked sad. I felt extremely sad. He was so matter of fact and unsentimental that I was much moved. Nancy and I said good-bye to him in Mount Street.

We met James outside Rules restaurant, which was shut. So we dined at Simpson's, Nancy dashing to the window whenever we heard a rocket. She made us laugh a lot. Told a story about the tart in Curzon Street who, when asked how the war was treating her, replied that for a reserved occupation, £700 a week tax free, plus emoluments from the Government for reporting the indiscretions of soldier clients, was so satisfactory she only wished she could open a second front. After dinner we walked along the embankment. We watched two boys, who had clambered on to the subsidiary bridge at Westminster, throw large planks from it into the Thames until a policeman chased them away. This amused Nancy. James and I put her into a bus at Victoria and wandered round Pimlico until I went to the office for firewatching. We held a conference in the warden's post and agreed that those of us who could sleep should do so, and those who could not, should from time to time patrol the streets after gunfire. I of course am one of the non-sleepers. This night turned out to be worse than the previous ones. Nevertheless I felt far safer downstairs in Eardley's company than at home, and slept better than on Thursday and Friday nights.

Sunday, 18th June

At Mass at 11 there was a great noise of gunfire and a rocket. In the afternoon Stuart walked in and said that a rocket had landed on the Guards Chapel during service this morning, totally demolishing it and killing enormous numbers of Guards officers and men. Now this news did shake me. After dining at the Churchill Club we walked through Queen Anne's Gate, where a lot of windows with the old crinkly blown glass panes have been broken. In St. James's Park crowds of people were looking at the Guards Chapel across Birdcage Walk, now roped off. I could see nothing but gaunt walls standing, and gaping windows. No roof at all. While I watched four stretcher bearers carry a body under a blanket, the siren went, and everyone scattered. I felt suddenly sick. Then a rage of fury against the war welled inside me. For sheer damnable devilry what could be worse than this awful instrument? We heard another go very close over our heads, and explode. I left Stuart in St. James's Park underground, and walked to Victoria. On getting out of the bus in Beaufort Street I heard and saw my first rocket. It was rushing overhead at great speed northwards. Half an hour ago, while writing this, I heard another, and saw one out of my west window, like a dagger with a flaming beacon at its tail. Then the engine cut off, and I watched it dive over the World's End. In a second the windows rattled, and a thin plume of smoke rose to the sky. There was a faint, distant sound of wailing. Dame Una tells me that today they have destroyed Tyburn Convent and the Charing Cross bridge.

I lunched with Lord Esher at Brooks's and discussed a number of N.T. problems with him, including M.'s feud with Mr. H. Esher said it was utterly useless his arbitrating in specific disputes where the trouble was irreconcilable incompatibility of temperament. There was nothing any man could do.

Another fearful night. Nothing dropped in Chelsea that I know of, but before midnight one just across the river made a hideous clatter, and the house shook like a jelly. The guns have ceased firing now because they merely bring the rockets down—when they hit them—to explode in the streets, just as they do if they fall of their own accord, which is sometimes in open country. In fact, for the same reason the balloons have been removed to open country outside London, as well as the guns, where the barrage to the south of the city must be terrific. Whereas previously I cursed the guns for the ceaseless noise they made throughout the night, now I find that without them I am more frightened. Quite irrationally I feel let down. The lack of guns strikes me as an admission of failure in defence. Instead I lie awake for hours and hours, my ears waiting for the sound of rocket planes. Here in Cheyne Walk we have distant trams, trains, motor vehicles and river traffic which one mistakes at first for a plane. There are also the factories across the river, where a horrid ghostly warble is released every single time a plane is approaching. It warns the workers before the sirens blow. This too is distracting. During the past week the sirens have ceaselessly blown, and there is a raid quite as often as there is an all clear. This night I was awake until 5. Miss P. is very good but nervous, and whenever she hears a plane will get up and sit on the stairs. I put on my gumboots and in my dressing-gown walk about the road, watching the fingers of the searchlights prodding the planes and catching them in their beams. Tonight I talked to an old man in a bowler hat who is night watchman on the boat moored on the embankment immediately below this house. He took me into his cabin, which had a blazing fire in the gate. One or two others, wardens and so on, congregated there. We all talked about the bombs and the war. It was very cosy and intimate, like being inside Peggotty's up-turned boat on Yarmouth sands. I feel I need never be lonely with these nice people so close.

Thursday, 22nd June

Jamesey rang me up this evening, and I went round to his flat. We moved to the garden of the inn next door, which he has only just discovered. We sat on the terrace drinking cider and gin till we were quite tipsy. Then, rather fearfully, staggered up the hill to dine with Dame Una, who hates drink, especially if it is 'brought home to her', as J. puts it. She has rocket bombs on the brain and can talk of nothing but first-hand atrocity stories of the appalling things that have happened to people. James can hardly bear it any longer. He and I walked away and upset ourselves very much by studying in a morbid manner the dreadful chaos at the sharp angle of Kensington Church Street, where a rocket has fallen. Widespread devastation has been caused to several houses. Gaping holes reveal people's pathetic little pictures still clinging to walls over an abyss.

Friday, 23rd June

Very tired and gugga this morning after a bad night. At 10.15 to a sub-committee of the Georgian Group in Keeling's house. After Keeling and Alfred Beit left, Dame Una and Acworth and I stayed on talking. I proposed there and then that we should urge the House of Commons Amenity Group to invite the chairmen of the C.P.R.E., the N.T., the S.P.A.B. and the Georgian Group to attend a meeting. The Amenity Group should stress its concern about the lack of co-ordination among these bodies, and persuade them to get together and eventually amalgamate. Acworth and the Dame agreed. We shall prepare a statement to be sent to Keeling for him, Strauss and the other M.P.s to digest in the hope that they will convene a meeting of Abercrombie, Zetland, Esher and Wellington.

Tonight after 11 o'clock, against a velvet purple sky, a rocket plane sailed over Lots Power station, a huge red flame issuing from its tail, and a dimmer light gleaming at the fore. There was a flash over Hammersmith way, and a second or two later an explosion which shook my windows. After dinner Miss P. and I fixed up a bed for her downstairs in the disused dining-room, where she certainly feels safer and cosier.

Saturday, 24th June

A very fine day, and free from fly bombs. I went to Emerald's at 5.45. She and I waited downstairs for Mrs. Corrigan, who bowled up in a small car. Bogey Harris joined us and we four motored to the Saville Theatre to see *The Gipsy Princess*, an old-fashioned, newly hashed-up musical comedy. I thought what a strange party we were, these three old Edwardians and me. I sat next to Emerald who praised the singers without stint, and talked rather loudly of sex. She said she did not, could not understand the need for it, and asked why people did it, dear? If one loved someone one did not think of sex, which was quite incidental. I could hardly subscribe to this argument. Then she asked me in what way animals behaved differently. She knew very little about them. Horses, she supposed, had to be severely controlled, it was very terrifying.

We dined in Mrs. Corrigan's suite in Claridges. She is a young 60, on first sight well preserved. But everything about her appearance may be false. Certainly her chestnut hair seems unnatural. Her smooth face is rather mask-like. She wears two of the largest pearls on one ring I have ever beheld. She is very rich and very generous. Everything she does is in great style. Everyone is lavishly tipped. We had a delicious dinner, and a white wine like nectar. There were pats of butter like cricket balls, and peaches. She dispensed the food and wine and would not suffer any assistance. If one offered to help she got quite cross. Emerald kept whispering to me, 'I don't suppose you will like her. She is not cultivated.' But I did. She seems to have eminent good sense and is outspoken. But she is incorrigibly social, and a great malaprop. She said of Lord Londonderry, 'Charlie has three balls on his cuisse.' She is a little disingenuous, and angles for compliments by telling stories to her own credit. Apart from that venial failing her manifest virtues appealed to me.

Monday, 26th June

Today was meeting day. I did not get home from the office till 10.30, and then wrote letters. At midnight the siren went, and I put on my boots and watched the fly bombs from the embankment. Because of clouds the beacons from their tails lit up the sky in a weird, uncanny manner. A number came over. I went to bed soon after 1 a.m., and fell asleep. At 2.30 I was woken abruptly by a terrific concussion, sat up in bed, and heard a cascade of glass, plaster and broken woodwork. But the house stood up. I was intensely alarmed, and went down to Miss P., now sleeping in the disused dining-room. I did not know whether I should find her alive or dead, since not a sound came from her direction. She had been awake, heard the plane approaching and covered her head with a pillow, which with the rest of the bed was strewn with fragments of powdered glass. A tiny muffled voice came from under the bedclothes. I said, 'Don't move an inch until I can see what's happened.' My feet were crunching glass on the floor. I found the torch. Her bed looked as if buried under a snow drift. I removed the glass as carefully as I could and disinterred her. She was not even scratched. Neither of us was hurt a bit. The bomb had fallen in the river opposite Turner's house, which has already been blitzed, and 100 yards from us. We walked into the kitchen, and even in the dim light could see the air filled with clouds of dust. A cupboard had burst open and disclosed a chimney belching a heap of soot. The only window in the house not broken was my bedroom one. My big room was inundated with glass fragments, which had shot across the room through the blinds and curtains, which were cut to ribbons. Nothing of furniture or objects was broken. All rugs inundated with soot and muck. The back door was blown across the passage. Window casements and wooden surrounds torn out, and the poor little house terribly shaken. Oddly enough this bomb killed no one.

Tuesday, 27th June

We made some tea and went back to bed. In the morning surveyed the damage. We did not go to the office, but put all our furniture in the middle of the room, packed away china and covered the lot with the torn curtains. There is nothing else we can do until the Borough send men to render first-aid. Meanwhile there is a howling gale driving rain through the open windows. The house is quite uninhabitable, but I did have a bath this afternoon, oblivious of the fact — of which I was informed later — that, since the bathroom windows were out and part of the wall was down, an admiring crowd watched my naked form drying itself. Good Eardley took pity on me and is having me down to the Bothy for two nights. Raymond Mortimer there too, and very kind and solicitous. The only encouraging factor is the excellence of the news in France, Italy and Russia. Raymond jubilant over it.

Thursday, 29th June

Lunched at the Ivy with Acworth and Dame Una to discuss Acworth's admirable draft letter to be sent by the three of us to Keeling, M.P., for him and the other Amenity Groupers in both Houses to address to the chairmen of the principal societies. The siren went during luncheon, and Dame Una made stately preparations to dive under the table at the first sound of a robot plane. I repeated Nancy's hairdresser's remark while indulging in an orgy of bomb experiences, 'And I came into her room, and what did I see? A spongey mass of blood and feathers.'

84

I dined at Sibyl Colefax's Ordinary. Met Chips Channon in the Dorchester beforehand, and had a drink. He said New York was quite pre-war, but Washington rather bustling. Everyone there thought the pilotless plane a fiction. It was too terrible to be true.

Emerald came in very late and tapped me on the shoulder, saying I had been a success with Mrs. Corrigan. Apologizing and having a word with everyone, she caused her usual consternation. She walked down Park Lane with Chips and me. She has absolutely no fear of bombs and will not leave her rooms on the top of the Dorchester.

Friday, 30th June

Rick Stewart-Jones has been very kind getting the Borough men to work on my house. They were plumbers with the most rudimentary ideas of carpentry. I tipped them £1, so they plastered over the holes in my ceiling, a thing they are not allowed to do. The filth of the house is indescribable, and only my bedroom is a refuge. A bomb in Battersea this evening blew out the makeshift windows they put in this morning.

Saturday, 1st July

All afternoon, planes came over. For the first time I am feeling despondent and dispirited. Miss P., having tidied the house up a bit, left for the country. I am glad for her poor old sake. The workmen are still in the house, and the head workman was almost as drunk as I was last night. I induced him to go home. What a life this is! How wasteful too, for I cannot read or write, having nowhere to do either.

At 6 I met James at Kings Bench Walk, and we tubed to East Aldgate. We walked down the Commercial Road to the river. God, the squalor, the desolation and the dreariness of the East End! Poor inhabitants. We passed one beautiful church, burnt out, which I said must be by Vanbrugh. J. identified it from his pocket guide-book as St. George's-in-the-East, by Hawksmoor. The pinnacled square towers like those of All Souls gave the clue.

We were smartly dressed underneath, but wore over our suits dirty old burberries buttoned up to the chin. Went into a pub for a drink, and a robot came over, nearer and nearer, exploding a few yards away. The pub keeper turned us out and shut the door, saying he had had enough for one day. We wished him good luck. 'All the best,' he said. We wandered through Wapping, to Wapping Old Stairs where Judge Jeffreys was captured trying to escape to France dressed as a sailor. Then to the *Prospect of Whitby* on the water, with its rickety galleries built over the river on piles. Found Philip Toynbee there with a pretty little girl, a Communist. We sat together on the gallery drinking beer and eating sandwiches, watching large boats struggle up the river, pirouette in front of us, and retreat into the docks. From here Jamesey saw his first robot. It scurried through the clouds at a great rate, and seemed to be circling and not going straight. By 9.30 the inn was full, and a piano and a clarinet were playing hot music. Women sang into a harsh microphone, sailors stamped, and peroxide blondes and the worst characters of London danced like dervishes, sang and swilled gallons of beer. It was a strange, gay, operatic scene. J., who was looking forward to meeting his romance of two nights ago, was bitterly put out when the romance turned his back on him and was frankly rude. Philip said he did not know life yet, for the masses were incorrigibly fickle and perfidious. Philip has much charm, affability and the novelist's enquiring, curious, humorous mind. He is 28, dark with what are, I think called pronounced features. I guess he will become a great writer.

Slept in John Fowler's Anderson shelter on the top bunk, which was very luxurious, although there were as many as five of us in the shelter. A noisy night, but quieter at dawn. Incessant jokes and hoots of laughter non-stop. In fact we laughed ourselves to sleep. Nobody woke before 10.15.

Sunday, 2nd July

Tonight for the first time I slept in the basement of 93 Cheyne Walk, Mrs. Gaskell's birthplace, where this morning with John Russell's help I moved my bed. John Russell and another young man sleeping in the same room. Not very comfortable because there is no light to read by, and I cannot go to the loo in the middle of the night. There isn't one downstairs, and the girls sleep in the passageway immediately outside our room. It was a very bad night indeed. Every ten minutes the factory warning warbled across the river, and two or three planes came over at a time. There were many loud crumps. I hardly slept a wink.

Monday, 3rd July

Raby, the permanent head of the Ancient Monuments Department of the Ministry of Works, lunched with me. He is a dry old medievalist, and not easy to talk to. Firewatching in the office tonight, and my hour

of vigilance in the street was 5 to 6. Eardley called me. It was the best
night we have had, and I am mightily refreshed.

Tuesday, 4th July

I went to Chawton, near Alton. Travelled from Waterloo in the same
carriage as Sir Edgar Bonham-Carter. What a wise and yet diffident
man he is. Owing to a robot having fallen on the line near Wimbledon
the train was one and a half hours late. I lunched quite well at the
Swan in Alton, and walked to Chawton House. The village of
Chawton is long, straggly and attractive. At the Winchester road
bifurcation is the house Jane Austen lived in. It is now divided into
three workers' tenements. Chawton House is approached by a straight
drive, with the church rebuilt in the 1870s and full of older Knight
monuments on the right, the attractive stables on the left. The house,
not very large, is irregular, with a tall porch of white clunch and flint.
It is mainly Elizabethan, having been built by a Knight and altered in
the mid-seventeenth century. The south front is rosey red brick, the
rest flint and brick. The windows are lately restored. The situation on
rising ground is salubrious. The lime avenue to the south was planted
under Jane Austen's direction, so Mrs. Knight told me. She is small
and pretty with gold red hair, and has a beautiful little boy. She took
me over the house, which is full of old wainscoting, and has two Caroline staircases. There are some good Mortlake tapestries, framed in the
panelling, and one sixteenth-century panel which must be very rare
indeed. It is a pleasant, happy old house, in which Jane Austen spent
much time, particularly in one large oak-panelled room on the first
floor, which she constantly referred to in her letters. The place belongs
to Mrs. Knight's husband, who is serving in India. She is merely playing with the idea of the N.T., and there is no indication that her
husband will do anything. He is descended from Jane Austen's brother,
who was adopted by the last Knights of Chawton. They took a great
fancy to him, his father and mother having settled in the village. At
present Barnardo children occupy three-quarters of the house. Mrs.
Knight says they are very undisciplined and destructive.

Wednesday, 5th July

Had a rather curious luncheon with a man called Campbell Stuart,
editor of the *Sunday Pictorial*, with whom I have lately been having
acrimonious correspondence about a gross mis-statement his paper
made on our announcement of the Gunby Hall acquisition. He is a

young middle-aged, rather brash, extremely affable, nimble-witted man. His sandy hair is parted in the centre too exactly to look natural. I liked his friendliness and abrupt plunge into the issue in hand. I explained to him the Trust's motives in the preservation of beautiful houses and estates. He expressed much ignorance about the Trust and aesthetic matters generally. Thought Blenheim too ugly for words and was surprised that the Trust should want to own any eighteenth-century buildings. I boldly told him that I thought his paper had behaved scurvily. He ended in asking me to write an article for the *Pictorial* about the Trust.

We talked of other matters. He despairs over the future for, he says, no plans are being worked out by the Government. Except as a fighter, Churchill is a disaster. He lives for war and killing Germans, as though they were pigeons. He is a man of no ideals, no principles; is an opportunist surrounded by yes-men, most of them insincere and of little integrity. Aneurin Bevan he thinks one of the few men in the Commons of undoubted integrity, and he is too temperamental. Eden is a flabby, middle-aged man, unhappy with the Prime Minister. He thinks that only men representing the professions and trades ought to sit in the Commons; that there should be no 'professional' M.P.s on the other hand; that the House of Lords should consist of life peers only. He says no naval battle takes place that is not directed by the Prime Minister personally from the Admiralty, whither he rushes the moment there is an engagement. I said, 'Churchill may not be a good man, but surely he is a great man?' He said, 'Not a great man in the way Lloyd George was; but undeniably a great personality, which is another matter.' Lloyd George cared passionately for good causes, but, alas, today, he is becoming senile and he forgets things.

C. Stuart said he often has to attend press conferences in Downing Street, and these invariably end in a flaming row. Churchill loses his temper and dismisses the press, who no longer can resist the temptation of baiting him. They taunt him by inferring that he cares nothing about the future, and enjoys the war like a game of chess. He fears Churchill will certainly try to remain Prime Minister when the war is over and the country will re-elect him. He does not foresee a swing over to Socialism after the war, but a tempered form of dictatorship. All Churchill's closest associates are unscrupulous, opportunist, fascist, crooked or vicious men; and he went through the list.

Campbell Stuart thinks Frank Pakenham the ablest of the younger aspirants towards rule. He thinks that possibly a new radical party may emerge from the Liberals, who must first of all drop their Whig element.

I got to King's Cross punctually at 9.30. The train for Peterborough was not scheduled to leave until 10.30. Even so, only through a 1st class reserved seat becoming de-reserved, did I manage to get a seat. The corridors were crammed. On my return I had to stand all the way from Peterborough, having just squeezed through a door. At Peterborough I caught a bus which did not take me as far as Cotterstock. Started to walk, and was picked up by Lady Ethelreda Wickham, who had driven to meet me.

She is 80. Her father, she told me, was born in 1792, the same year as Shelley. She is very upright and active, though a little shaky on her feet. She drives a high-powered car and smokes innumerable cigarettes. She is very broadminded when one discounts the fact that she hates all foreigners. She is wonderfully well bred, and says good-bye in that dismissive, indifferent manner of the upper classes of the old school.

Cotterstock is a compact, small manor house in the village, dated 1658, thus built during the Commonwealth. It has a large scrolly gable behind and above the porch. It is set in an ocean of lush, low-lying meadows, with Fotheringay in the distance. The inside has nothing very remarkable. On the top floor is an oak-lined room with slanting ceilings where Dryden wrote much of his verse. The house was at that time, I think, Vane property. Lady Ethel motored me back to Peterborough and I walked through the Cathedral. Struck by the Gothic iron stoves with little doors of ogee shape; and of course by the great beauty of the fan vaulting of the ambulatory.

I drove Stuart to his rooms where he packed his books and various clothing into a big, blue kit-bag for me to store in Cheyne Walk during his absence.

I had tea with Nancy in her garden, which is a wilderness of rank grass and chickens. She talked about Skittles, the Victorian tart kept by the present Duke of Devonshire's great uncle, to whom the present Duke paid £2,000 a year until her recent death when, so he told Nancy, he discovered that Lord Coventry had settled a like sum upon her. Nancy boasts that she is not the least frightened of the fly bombs. In bed at night she beckons to them, 'Come on, come on,' and then waves them away with, 'Go on, go on. And they always do, my dear.'

I left in the car soon after 10 in pouring rain. I arrived at B. House precisely at 1.30 in time for luncheon. When I told Stuart where I was going, he laughed and said, 'Lord — has the worst reputation in the world. His taste is Lascars.' Well, I thought, then I am all right. He is a natty, foxy little man with blue eyes and a boyish figure and boyish hair cut, though well over 60. A young American with a baby face was staying. He disappeared after luncheon. Lord — took me round the grounds and then round the house which has thirty-six bedrooms. In one we came upon baby face fast asleep in an enormous bed, just a turned-up nose projecting over the top sheet. In every room a delicious smell of rose water, or furniture polish, I was not sure which, mixed with that sweet mustiness of calf-bound books. Lord — inherited B. from his mother who lived here until her death. She had no commerce with her children, and would not see a soul. She never left the house. She slept all day, and prowled around the house all night. I was bound to tell my host that I much doubted the Trust being able to help him. He was very nice about it. I left before tea.

After dining alone I walked in St. James's Park in the rain and the sunshine, then doubled back to the Travellers. Found Harold Nicolson who had also been dining alone. He wanted to know if I was frightened of the buzz bombs. I said, 'Quite honestly I am when I hear them near me. But not when I see them. And the moment they are gone I do not give them another thought.' Harold says we shall be in Paris in three weeks, and on the Rhine in mid-September. How can clever people be so stupid? Soon Harold left for firewatching at the House of Commons. When there is a raid he sits on the top of the Victoria Tower pressing bells. He says it is immensely exciting.

So many of my friends have already gone, or are about to go overseas that I feel extremely restless and dissatisfied with my sheltered life. Went this afternoon to the Red Cross Society and spoke to the secretary about a possible job in France. Felt idiotically shy and secretive, not wanting the other people in the interview room to hear. To my surprise he said that if I could pass my medical test, and could get the sanction of the Ministry of Labour, I might go as an officer with a unit in three weeks' time. Alas, I could not possibly leave before 1st September when Matheson returns. And could I pass the medical? Nevertheless was quite pleased when the secretary said other units were bound to be going later.

I dined at Emerald's. Gladwyn Jebb was there, and Lady Kenmare, very beautiful, with sweet melting blue eyes. She has lost four husbands, all by death. Also Lady Kitty Lambton, magnificent, eccentric, with dark glowing eyes, very wild, and a tumble of grey hair. She was gay and teasing. When she left Emerald complained, 'She is not sequential in her conversation. She does not make sense. She is a descendant of Nell Gwynne,' as though that explained everything. Emerald not in her best form, and abusive of the waiters again, which is agony. She said it made her angry when her friends praised the food at the Dorchester. She said American food used to be so good and is now atrocious. 'It is all so distracted and dejected, you cannot enjoy it.' I thought she was somewhat distracted and dejected tonight.

Saturday, 15th July

Got back from Buckinghamshire in time for a late dinner at Brooks's with John Fowler. At 9.30 Stuart walked in. He said, 'Well, I do go tomorrow. I have come to say good-bye. It was in this room that we met in 1938.' There was little to say, and what I did say was fatuous, 'Yes, I was sitting in that chair by the door.' 'No,' he said, 'you were standing against the fireplace,' which was scarcely more pointful.

Sunday, 16th July

Found a message from Nancy asking me to lunch with her. We ate in her funny little garden, or non-garden as she rightly calls it. She told me that her upbringing had taught her never to show to others what she felt. I thought how lamentably my upbringing had failed in this respect, and how too perfectly in her case, for there is a vein of callousness in her which almost amounts to cruelty. All Mitfords seem to have it, even Tom, who has never directed it at me, though I have seen him turn it upon others. And I have blanched at the spectacle.

Monday, 17th July

Had another interview with the Red Cross who raised further difficulties as to my chances of going overseas, in that the Ministry of Labour, even if they released me from the N.T., might re-draft me into the

Army. I know this to be impossible. A great pity I can't go with the first unit in three weeks' time.

We had the Country Houses Committee in the afternoon. Every time I thought I heard a buzz bomb I warned Esher, who is slightly deaf, and without shame he threw his papers before him and dashed to the door and the staircase; then laughed at himself. After the meeting Lord Carlisle said he wanted to see me and talk about Naworth, and I must go there.

On walking past the Ritz I heard Nancy give a cry; and there she was with Tom, back from the Mediterranean after two and a half years' absence. He almost embraced me in the street, saying, 'My dear old friend, my very oldest and dearest friend,' which was most affecting. He looks younger than his age, is rather thin, and still extremely handsome. We went up to his suite in the Ritz—how civilized and pretty after the Dorchester and modern jazz hotels. There he telephoned Harold Acton and Bridget, bidding them to dine this evening. Rather cross with me because I simply would not cut the Girouards' dinner party.

Before firewatching I dined with Bridget in her flat. She has not slept properly for six nights. She began by not minding the bombs: now they have got on her nerves. Besides, she has a new job at the Foreign Office, eight hours a day, six days a week, and nothing to do. She sits mending stockings and reading novels, and the dragging of time nearly kills her. When I left she went to Claridges where she has taken a room for the nights, since Lord Newburgh, in whose cupboard downstairs she has lately been sleeping for safety, has returned to his flat. It is true that her bedroom in Mount Street has a huge plate-glass window immediately opposite the bed.

Called at James's flat at 7 and we drank gin and lime in the pub garden. How I hate the taste of gin. Unquestionably J. and I are no longer the confidants we used to be. I do not care for his arrogance and vanity. In order to take him down a peg I foolishly told him that the Kenneth Clarks disliked him and me—I included myself. I was sorry too late, for J. harped on this. Moreover I have broken an elementary rule of social conduct by repeating what a third person has told me.

A very noisy and frightening night. Buzz bombs, three at a time, coming over, and incessant explosions on all sides. Sirens never cease blowing, and they get on the nerves more than the bombs.

Friday, 21st July

Cold east wind, and sunless as usual. Bombs very bad. One at breakfast blew out the linen windows in Miss P.'s bedroom. Everyone much excited by the abortive attempt on Hitler's life and inclined to attach too much significance to the revolt, calling it civil war.

Monday, 24th July

Arrived Paddington at midday and met Mr. Parker of Bewdley. We lunched with Geoffrey Sturt. Our endeavours to protect the banks of the Severn between Bewdley and Stourport make little progress, alas.

I dined at Emerald's in the Dorchester. The party consisted of Freya Stark, the heroine of the party, Nancy Mitford, Lord and Lady Londonderry, Oliver Stanley and the Duke of Devonshire. I sat next to Emerald and Lady Londonderry, who is very tall and masculine, dressed as a brigadier in khaki. She told me that this evening's flying bomb made for Londonderry House, but on seeing it it swerved to the left over the Park, and exploded near the Serpentine. Lord Londonderry told Nancy the same story three times over. He is very handsome and patrician. He told me how he snubbed Sir Charles Trevelyan once, and was so amused by his story that I thought he was never going to stop laughing.

The Duke of Devonshire is ferociously anti-Catholic. He said, 'I am a black Protestant, and I am proud of it,' and told several anti-papal stories. His ancestor Lord Richard Cavendish, whose portrait by Landseer hangs over his bed here in London, was cut off by his family and sent to India as Bishop of Madras because he stayed at Hatfield, a Tory High Church household. This Duke's own father looked askance at his son's marriage with a daughter of Lord Salisbury for the same reason. When this Duke left Eton his father, very embarrassed, felt he must give him a pi-jaw. He said, 'Don't take to strong alcohol. Don't take to women. Some men may think they need women before they marry. It isn't true. And above all, *don't* ever go inside the Carlton Club.' He said he had just received an indignant letter of remonstrance from Gerry Wellington because Debo Cavendish, his daughter-in-law, has given her son at his christening the name Morny, a diminutive of one of the Wellesley titles, Mornington. 'How would you like it,' Gerry wrote, 'if I christened my grandson Harty or Burlington?' Nancy said, 'But Debo christened him after her favourite jockey. She has never even heard of the Duke of Wellington.' Emerald expostulated, 'You should have put this duke of only a hundred years creation in his proper place. You must have courage, Eddie.' Lord Londonderry interpolated, 'I too am only a peer of mushroom growth.'

Emerald said Tom [Mitford] was very rude the other night to the Chilean Paz Subercaseaux about Papists, calling them aliens, and saying it was quite out of the question his ever marrying one. Paz, slightly nettled, with two eligible papist daughters of her own, asked, 'But if you were staying at Arundel, would you consider the Duke of Norfolk an alien?' 'Certainly,' Tom replied. The Duke of Devonshire then said, 'Quite right. Papists owe a divided allegiance. They put God before their country.'

Tuesday, 25th July

Talked to Mr. Batsford about the Trust's Jubilee book. Conversation soon turned to the flying bombs, how they were getting people down, and how terrible living conditions were in parts of London. Streatham, Wandsworth and Battersea are the worst hit. It is thought that less is done to relieve people living in Tory districts than in red ones, like Battersea.

Took the train to Henley and Eardley motored me to the Bothy. After dinner we sat on a table by the river, watching stream after stream of heavy bombers, with lights at the tips of their wings fly south-westwards. The roar was like that of Niagara waterfall. We could barely hear each other speak. Hundreds passed.

Wednesday, 26th July

We motored to Somerset. A showery but not un-beautiful day. Climbed to the top of Lardon Chase and admired the view across the Thames. At Figsbury Ring we walked along the outer rampart of this curious prehistoric site. It is remote, with a distant view of the tip of Salisbury spire. But the remoteness is spoilt by some hideous half-timber villas along the main road, which never should have been allowed. We had difficulty in passing a long convoy of tanks on heavy lorries, bound for the coast. They were flying the Croix de Lorraine, and so must have been Free French troops.

After lunching in Salisbury we drove to Trafalgar. This great red-brick house lies beyond Longford, in the same valley, on the same river, surrounded by beech trees. It was built in 1733 by John Wood, with a Grecian portico added by Revett in 1760, as were the two connecting pavilions. A niece with a distinctly off-centre accent welcomed us. Presently there was a hurried puffing sound, and in bustled Lord Nelson. He is 87, the great-nephew of 'the Admiral' as he refers to his forebear, as small as Nelson, with white flowing hair and a large mouth. His spare build, peculiar shape of head and features are identical to the Admiral's. With a little mutilation, an eye out here, an arm off there, he would be the very incarnation. He was most hospitable and genial; in full possession of faculties; but eccentric. He has a trick of picking at one's coat as he talks. We liked him immensely. He showed us round. There is a picture by Rigaud of Nelson aged 22. There are several miniatures and relics, and some furniture from the *Victory*. He has not however got so good a Nelson collection as Nelson Ward and others. There is much fine French furniture. The interior of the house is splendid. I particularly admired the ingenious oval stair-case, the central hall which is a cube with plaster ceiling and a fireplace carrying a bust of Inigo Jones. The old man walked us round the outside. He almost cried when he asked why the world was indulging in an orgy of cruelty. He said the best trait in the Admiral's character was his capacity for affection.

We gave him a lift to the main road and left him waiting for a bus. If we had not done this he would have walked the three miles to the nearest bus stop for Salisbury.

Eardley and I proceeded to Montacute where we had tea with the Yateses in the King's Arms. At 7 Lord Aberconway motored over to make suggestions for improvement to the gardens. He advocated turning the north garden into a formal kitchen garden. E. liked this idea. I not so keen. There are 600 Negro troops at Montacute. They smile and say, 'Hello' in an engaging manner.

Thursday, 27th July

In the morning we went over the house. Then drove to Muchelney to look at the Priest's House, which is a good little property. The church has a barrel nave roof with painted panels of *décolletes* angels with pendulous bosoms, of the time of Charles I. I returned to London by train, in time for a scratch meal at home before firewatching in the office.

Rose from my camp bed at 6. Breakfasted at the Great Eastern Hotel and caught the 8 o'clock train for Colchester. Here Sisson met me and motored me to Caister. We ate sandwiches, sitting on the grass-covered outer wall of the Roman city, Venta Icenorum. He shares my disquiet about the future. He says it is fruitless caring for good buildings, for wars will continue, and there will be underground architecture only. We looked at the site of the Anglo-Saxon cemetery over which we are offered covenants. It is a detached spinney on a hill, from which all finds have been exhumed. It was a hot day and I felt tired. Got back in time to dine with Harold Acton and Roger Spence.

I went to bed soon after 11 in our cellar. At 12.15 a bomb fell with great noise. The basement was filled with fumes, so I guessed the bomb had been pretty close. Got out of bed, put on gumboots and burberry, and walked into the road. Even in the clear light of the moon I could see a cloud of explosive steaming from the river in front of me. This fly bomb had cut out its engine, and recovered twice before finally falling. As I watched I heard people in the street shout, 'Look out, another's coming!' and they rushed down to their shelter. I was left transfixed, and knew there was no time to descend into my basement, down the rickety area steps. So I looked at the light of the bomb coming straight at me. Then the engine stopped, and I knew we were in for it. I lay flat on my face on the pavement, as close as could be to the embankment wall. I heard the bomb swish through the air. It too fell in the river, only closer than the last, and sent a spray of water over me. At dawn I met a policeman picking up a fragment of the bomb from the road. It was over a foot long. It must have hurtled over my head. I could see that all my windows and the window frames at no. 104 were out again. I saw poor Kiki Cruft at the gate of no. 97. She had been alone in the house and was rather startled. I talked to her before returning to my basement. This time I had experienced the familiar phenomenon of not registering the actual explosion of the bomb, because it was only a few yards away. I attribute it to my preparedness and the automatic instinct of tautening the whole body, including ears, to resist it. I remember hoping that my outstretched legs, which seemed so far from my cowering head, would not be cut off.

Saturday, 29th July

Left home early this morning for Paddington, and caught the 9.10 to

Leamington. There was a vast crowd waiting for the train to draw in; and a still vaster crowd the other side of the platform waiting for the Plymouth train which, when it came, caused an astonishing spectacle of women, children and old men fighting with their fists to cram themselves into the apertures at the end of each coach. When our train approached I was amused by our crowd ducking down to pick up their bags and eagerly rising again, all in one rhythmic movement, as though they were a trained chorus in a pantomime. It was like wind rippling over a stream. I tried not to belong to the crowd.

At Leamington Hubert Smith met me and motored me to Bewdley, complaining of the awful manners of the accountant who is 'evacuated upon' him at Polesden Lacey. We lunched with the Parkers at Tickenhill. She is a dear little brown body, like a clever dormouse. In the afternoon motored round the Ribbesford estate, and was distressed that my uncle had sold it in lots after the last war.

Hubert dropped me at the Sandys Arms, Wickhamford. I talked to Maggie at her kitchen window. She had soapsuds up to the elbow. I was fascinated by the way they dried on her bare arms, first they gently burst one by one, and then they left little broken rings of dry grey scurf. Parents delighted to see me, and my father very gentle and kind.

Tuesday, 1st August

Called upon the Labour Exchange who encouraged me to suppose they would not obstruct my efforts to re-join the Red Cross. I asked James to meet me at Brooks's at 7. On arrival I ran into Tom, and drank with him. When James was announced I told Tom he must be polite, for I understood he hated him. He was polite, but I saw it went against the grain.

Wednesday, 2nd August

An S.P.A.B. meeting, and many items of great interest to me. Went to Brooks's at 6 to talk to Tom. He said he must marry and asked my advice which of his girls he should choose. I said, 'Let me know which are in the running?' So he began, ticking them off one by one on his fingers. He told me, with that engaging frankness with which he always confides in me, the names of those he had already slept with, and how often, those he rather loved and those he merely liked, until I stopped him with, 'But all this sounds most unromantic to me. If I were one of those girls and knew how you were discussing me, I

97

wouldn't dream of marrying you.' 'Oh, but they don't know,' he said, and roared and roared with laughter.

Tom also told me that Professor Lindemann (Lord Cherwell) was in disgrace with the P.M. for having made light of the flying bombs before they actually arrived. He saw Winston Churchill when he was in Libya, and the P.M. gave him news of his sister Decca, now married again and living in America. When in America the P.M. sent for Decca, and told her he felt sure she would be glad to know that her sister Diana was now much happier in prison because she was reunited with Tom [Oswald] Mosley. Decca said very abruptly, 'I don't want to hear her name mentioned.' He then offered to get her a job on Lord Halifax's staff. Decca answered, 'I wouldn't touch him with a barge pole.' The P.M. felt very snubbed. She is as fanatically Communist as ever.

Thursday, 3rd August

This morning I went to the Red Cross who told me they might be having a meeting of the selection board, to be followed by a medical examination next Wednesday.

Grandy Jersey, who called at the office, is very busy dealing with the flying bombs. He assured me that more than half those launched are destroyed by us; but that they will definitely continue until the war is over. The Germans are able to establish new bases within a few days.

Saturday, 5th August

Went to an indifferent revue. Standing in the street after the first act I was accosted by a familiar voice. It came from Patrick O'Donovan in battledress, back from Normandy three days ago. I barely recognized him, for he was wounded in the face. It was caused by his standing up in his tank, and being practically decapitated by a wire stretched across a village street. He broke the upper part of his jaw. He was sensitive about his appearance, and kept his hand over his mouth when speaking, for his teeth were painted gold in hospital for some reason. We went off to eat together. During dinner he said he was wretched not being in Normandy, which he loved. He said that every night he used to sleep under his tank in a slit trench; that German tanks were better than ours; and that German prisoners were very demoralized. He was sure the war would be over in two months. The most offensive things on a battlefield were dead cows, which swelled to enormous proportions, and burst. The stench was appalling. He was seldom frightened.

98

In burying the dead the troops found it very difficult not to break down, so services were made as short and informal as possible. No hymns and no bugles. He was constantly weeping over dead friends.

Sunday, 6th August

My birthday, and the less I think about it the better. Only members of the family remember; for I suppose they are the only people to whom one's existence does matter just a little.

Went to Mass in Warwick Street and lit candles for friends. Candles may help. At least they can't hinder. Caught an afternoon train to Kelvedon, and walked two miles in great heat to Felix Hall. Since I was last here before the war, the centre block has been gutted by fire, and the two late eighteenth-century pavilions have been demolished by Geoffrey Houghton-Brown. He now lives in one large room reconstructed out of old bits and pieces. It gives the impression of Crowther's shop. In the room where I slept, the walls were panelled with early wallpaper brocatelle, dated 1812, which Geoffrey salvaged from one of the demolished pavilions.

Monday, 7th August

This morning Geoffrey, one of the guests and I bicycled six miles to Layer Marney church. In addition to the famous terracotta Renaissance monuments, a superbly beautiful mural painting of St. Christopher on the north wall arrested my attention. The wavelets of the water and the little fishes were meticulously linear. The gravity of the saint's head, turned to one side, was most moving. The house was empty, so we walked up to it and pressed our noses against the windows. There have been horrible recent additions to the tower, a bad adaptation of the barn and a contemptible garden layout. If the place were mine I would pull down practically everything, leaving the great, perpendicular tower standing in a naked meadow.

Wednesday, 9th August

Lunched with Anne Rosse in Bridget's flat. Bridget, Dmitri of R. and Harold Acton there. Anne provided vodka, a ham with cloves stuck in it, hock, peaches and cream. And she called it a picnic. I went back at 4 to talk to Anne alone for an hour. I told her I might be going to France and she seemed genuinely sad, which touched me. She writes to Michael and he to her every single day. She is tremendously proud of him, and if anything happened to him, it would, I firmly believe, kill her.

I had a letter from Esher this morning – rather a chill and formal one – merely saying that the Committee could hardly oppose my going, if (underlined) I should pass my medical test.

Rick called at 1.30 at night when I was fast asleep. I was woken by a loud peel of the bell. He stayed till 3.30, and we ate cake in the kitchen. He leaves for the Middle East on Monday, and gave me all sorts of directions what to do, if he did not come back. They are all going.

Friday, 11th August

Mr. Hobson of Sotheby's lunched with me in order to talk over his ideas about museums. He is writing a book on the subject, and wants restrictions on the export of works of art to be lifted. He claims that it does not matter in which country works of art are kept, so long as they are properly cared for; that there are too many in this country; and that those which remain will eventually be mummified in a museum. He believes that a museum curator should be, not a stuffy expert, but a Reinhardt with a dramatic sense. In many respects I agree with him, but by no means in all. There are very many English works of art, for instance, which I would hate to see leave this country. Hobson is a big, burly man, deaf with an efficient apparatus.

I had a long talk with Eddy in Brooks's. He is suffering from a cist on his lip and large blemishes on his forehead. 'It is my anaemia,' he says. He has learnt to despise the buzz bombs. 'They are just incredibly silly.' Yet he feels worn out. I suppose even we civilians are suffering from war weariness to some extent.

Saturday, 12th August

Bought *The Golden Bowl* at Heywood Hill's shop on my way to lunch with Osbert Lancaster at the Holborn Restaurant, a marvellous 1870 building of every known expensive marble. We drank Algerian wine although it was too hot a day. Osbert bubbling with gossip. He explained Nancy's indifference to bombs as being a consequence of steeling herself to an indifference to Peter's misbehaviour.

I finished *The Hotel* in Brooks's – not a good novel, although Eddy recommends it. I found Ralph Jarvis at dinner, and ate with him. He is just back from Rome, which he says is not at all knocked about. Naples is no more damaged than London; rather less so. Frascati has gone; and every village on the road from Naples to Rome gone.

Damnation. He spoke favourably of the Vatican. It was fascinating he said, watching its cautious reaction to Stalin's feelers towards the Church in Russia. The Vatican wouldn't commit itself, suspecting that Stalin's intentions might be purely expedient. 'Of course they must be,' I couldn't help saying.

Sunday, 13th August

To Mass in Cheyne Row. Was wonderfully devout and well disposed to the world in general; gave my seat to an old man, and stood myself. I took Bridget to Polesden. While I sorted things she lay on the grass in the sun. Like others she was enraptured with Mrs. Greville's visitors' book. It is odd how people can be fascinated by lists of signatures and dates, and nothing else. We had a picnic luncheon and tea on the terrace.

Drove back in time to dine with the Rodds, at Claridges. Peter ordered drinks and left me to pay for them. This I did, but was determined not to be similarly stung with the expense of the dinner. If Peter had not been present it would have been more enjoyable. As it was, he interrupted every time one of us tried to speak. He made irrelevant remarks which were nonsense. He is a hopeless character. He puts Nancy on edge, and makes her pathetically anxious not to displease him. Now why should a husband put a wife under such an obligation? I walked home with Bridget.

Monday, 14th August

Eardley and I motored to Bristol. We lunched in Marlborough, having had a puncture and changed the wheel ourselves, getting covered in oil and dust in the process. Picked up an architect and drove to Thornbury. Sir Algar Howard took us over the castle. I was cross with Eardley for hating the place and saying that the Trust should reject it on the grounds that it was badly restored and hideous. I agreed that the mid-Victorian interior was deplorable—the only decent things being the green Morris wallpapers. But the outer walls are genuine and the side facing the church has the glamour of stage scenery. Besides, the twisted brick chimneys and the clover leaf windows of Henry VIII's reign are of the highest importance. Pugin greatly admired and drew them. The garden the Howards have made is simple, orchardy and Pre-Raphaelite. Admittedly no one could possibly want to live in the gloomy, ill-conceived warren, which Salvin made out of the ruin. The castle ought in my opinion to be made back into a ruin.

It was an extremely hot and sultry day. At 5.30 we had high tea, which portended nothing more to eat till breakfast next day, a depressing prospect. Eardley and the architect drove away, and I was left to stay the night. Sir Algar and I walked in the garden. He told me that new peers and knights and even commoners sought grants of arms now in wartime as much as they ever did. All the College of Heralds' books of reference are stored in the castle.

With eagerness we—the Howards and I—listened to the news at 9, anxious to learn whether the German Army had been enveloped and annihilated in the pocket near Falaise.

Tuesday, 15th August

Eardley called for me at 10.30 and we motored to Lacock. We lunched off delicious goose in the Abbey. I think Miss Talbot is one of the noblest and most exemplary benefactors we have had to deal with. She has a number of lonely, white-haired octogenarian ladies lodging with her. While we were in the village with the agent, an old shopkeeper said that at noon a special announcement told of a fresh invasion on the Riviera. We rushed to the Abbey and made the old ladies turn on the wireless. Somehow this news falls rather flat after D-day. One cannot be keyed up all the time.

The pictures in the Abbey are in a deplorable condition; so is the furniture, stacked together without dustsheets. The English have become an untidy, as well as a grubby people. And still they maintain an overweening and quite unjustifiable sense of superiority over all other nations, firmly believing that foreigners never wash.

Wednesday, 16th August

Stayed last night with Eardley at the Bothy. En route near Devizes we were slowed up by a troop of German prisoners. We felt ghoulish staring at them. They stared at us just as hard, but with impassive, expressionless faces. They showed no sign of either chagrin or relief, poor brutes. First came the officers, then the men, all hatless. They were a fine looking lot, bronzed and with only a day's growth of beard, and had presumably been captured some twenty-four hours before. Among them were a few very young boys, and some quite old men. They marched well and made an impressive spectacle. A few feeble looking American soldiers, physically infinitely their inferiors, were in charge of them, holding rifles with their fingers on the trigger.

Depressed by receiving a letter from the Red Cross that after all they will not accept me.

At 11 I had an interview with W. S. Morrison, the Minister of Planning. An upstanding, grey-haired, middle-aged man, handsome and efficient. A strong Scotch accent. He advised against the N.T. pressing for the insertion of a clause in the new Bill, to protect its inalienable properties from possible acquisition by local authorities. He said Parliamentary Counsel assured him that the Trust's powers were already adequately protected by our Acts of Parliament, and that a general clause would arouse the hostility of several government departments. He spoke sympathetically of the Trust's work, and said Parliament generally favoured us. This was gratifying, but not wholly satisfactory. Morrison's face is arresting. His mouth is chiselled like that of an Alfred Stevens model.

Saturday, 20th August

James and I accompanied Dame Una — to whom I gave all my eggs — to Peckham by bus. The objective was to look for the house where Dickens kept his mistress and where he began writing *Edwin Drood*. She says, were it not for income tax amounting to 75 per cent, she would undoubtedly make a fortune from sales in the United States and here.

Our expedition was a failure. It rained hard, we lost our way, and were confused by the bus routes. The Dame's earnest enquiries of local inhabitants for the house of Dickens's mistress evoked astonishment, and made J. and me giggle uncontrollably. His amused, placatory indulgence of her as though she were a child put her in a bad humour. We never found the house which he and I believe was either demolished before the war, or even disappeared in the recent raids. We were horrified by the devastation of this part of London by flying bombs. I think, without exaggerating, that two-thirds of the buildings in Peckham and Camberwell have been destroyed or irredeemably ruined.

Sunday, 21st August

A terrible morning, dark with torrential rain, like a non-stop stage storm scene, and constant sirens and flying bombs coming over very low and noisily. I stayed half lying in bed, half running to the shelter on the stairs, and half (this makes one and a half) telephoning to Bridget and the Pope-Hennessys to ask for news of those bombs I heard flying over me. Bridget said the windows of the shops opposite her flat in Mount Street had all gone, and seven ambulances were passing as she spoke. Dame Una said what an infuriating bore it would be to be killed now that the Americans are actually in Paris, and the bombs must cease in a few days' time. This is inspiriting.

At 4.30 I went to Bridget's flat where Tom was. Together we went to Nancy's for tea. Then we walked to look at the damage caused by a flying bomb which settled this morning on the roof of Lansdowne House flats, at the corner of Berkeley Street. In the neighbouring streets all windows were blown out. Shop windows have strewn their contents on the pavements.

Tuesday, 22nd August

At 6.45 I went to see Alan Lennox-Boyd. He was in his bath and I sat with him while he washed and washed, I have seldom seen anything like it. It makes me suppose I must be very dirty. Alan said he had no news of Francis (his youngest brother) who has been missing since D-day. Alan was with him from 6–7 on the eve of D-day, for both knew that afternoon what was about to happen. It appears that Francis was among the first to leave soon after midnight. The trap of his aeroplane failed to open the first time they were over the target. Upon returning again over the target the trap opened unexpectedly, and Francis fell through a little while before the other paratroops. He has not been heard of since, and it is supposed he fell behind the enemy lines. Alan still believes he may either be a prisoner or in hiding, but it seems unlikely to me. Francis was one of the most sensitive, fastidious, delicate men I have ever known. A. is a spontaneous and generous man. He poured figs and peaches into my hands on parting.

Alan said that the percentage of fly bombs brought down over England out of the total number launched, was actually forty-four, not counting those brought down over the Channel. That the production of seven fly bombs corresponded in cost and time with that of one Spitfire. That a straightforward kind of German rocket may start at any moment. One school of thought estimates that the weight of each may indeed be less than that of the old fly bomb, which contains one ton of explosive; the other school predicts that it may contain seven tons of explosive.

Tom and I dined at Brooks's. I asked him pointblank if he still sympathized with the Nazis. He emphatically said Yes. That all the best Germans were Nazis. That if he were a German he would be one. That he was an imperialist. He considered that life without power and without might with which to strike fear into every other nation would not be worth living for an Englishman. I absolutely contradicted him. Told him I was unrepentantly pacifist, and would prefer to live in a country of tenth rate power, provided there were peace and freedom of action and speech. The sweet side of Tom is that he never minds how much an old friend disagrees with him. But woe betide an acquaintance.

At luncheon I practically had a row with Eddy over the Vatican and his indictment of the Pope. Now here are two friends I love, and profoundly disagree with.

After the S.P.A.B. meeting I picked up Marshall Sisson and motored him to Dedham. At Colchester we digressed to visit Bourne Mill, a charming old property of the N.T., only spoilt by the ugly villas built along the road since we acquired it. The strange little conceit, built in 1591, was doubtless intended for a fishing lodge. Its extravagant curved gables and Flemish finials are appealing. In the early nineteenth century it was converted into a mill, when the hoist was added. For long now it has been derelict, but the admirable Sisson showed me his plans for its conversion into a dwelling, without any alteration to the elevations. The mill machinery may have to go, which will be a pity.

I like the Sissons immensely. He belongs to the same type as Alec Penrose—has very good taste and sound views; is quiet, anti-social, dry-humorous, scholarly and contemplative. He is a liberal-intellectual, or intellectual-liberal. His chief passion is architecture. He is besides an incurable pessimist and an avowed anti-philistine. She is positively no-nonsensical, enlightened, well-read, willing to be amused and clever. She is an invalid who walks with a rubber-tipped stick. They are childless and devoted, each the complement of the other, I would think. Obviously no troubles are allowed to detract from the harmony of their easy-going, cultured, marital life. Shermans, their house in Dedham High Street, opposite the church, is a gem. It is a red brick, 1730–40 doll's house, perfectly symmetrical, with a sun-dial on the front. The inside is set curiously askew on the axis, so as to fit into an awkward site. Everything has been sacrificed to the remarkable little text-book façade. Plain wainscoted rooms, appropriately furnished. For dinner we had duck and hock. Sisson is a pacifist. He deplores tyranny, slavery, and is sceptical about the outcome of this war and the future peace. He is a Spenglerian too. Excellent and delightful couple.

Thursday, 31st August

During the night—and I slept ill—there was a distant siren. I heard several flying bombs. Five of them exploded fairly close. The last was very close and made the house rattle like a dice box so that I thought windows must have broken. For a minute my heart beat faster. Then I recalled that I was in the country, away from London, and felt, quite irrationally, that I was safe. It was odd to hear these sounds away from London.

This morning I motored Sisson to Blickling. A glorious day in a world of ripening corn, with harvest sheaves stacked under a blue sky spangled with fluffy white clouds. We lunched at the inn with Birkbeck, the agent, and in the afternoon went round the house and garden. I had to indulge in rather too much consoling and jollying of Miss O'Sullivan and Miss James. The latter wishes to leave, and I must take no steps to prevent her.

Sisson is convinced that the Blickling garden layout dates from about 1700, a thing I always thought might be the case, but was not sure about.

Friday, 1st September

A crisp, chilly morning, with that whiff of melancholy in the air. Autumn is well on the way. I would not mind if only I felt well, clear-headed and un-drugged. Sisson took me to Flatford Mill which the N.T. has acquired. I love Constable, but I do not love this place. It has been made a travesty of the totally unpretentious, rural, domestic scene of one of England's greatest painters. Today the manor house is too picture postcardy for words. Willy Lott's Cottage is abominably whimsy inside. Sisson favours whitewashing or white painting all interior beams, I am glad to say. I concur with nearly all his ideas. The Mill itself is still relatively unspoilt, and the island garden, with fat box hedges and old apple trees is full of charm. We drove to Thorington Hall. It has a rather neglected look, and the furniture inside—well! The house has had evacuees, and not been inhabited as a private house since the war, which explains much. I left the Sissons after luncheon, and drove to Paycocke's, that hideously over-restored house in Coggeshall. The tenants' bogus French furniture most inappropriate. Sisson and I would like to whitewash all the harsh new brick nogging on the street elevation. Back in London in time to take Bridget out to dinner. Sweet tonight like a lioness on her off day, and just as provocative as that beautiful dangerous creature.

Saturday, 2nd September

Pouring wet day, so I read the *Chartreuse de Parme*, and revelled in it. After tea I packed and went to Send for the weekend with Loelia. I do like her immensely, although her world is not mine. During Mass the Pope's letter to Londoners was read by the officiating priest. There has been too much criticism of the Pope lately. Why can't Protestant England understand the dilemma he is in? Why does it suppose that he should only care for the souls of two million British Catholics, and cast into utter darkness those of twenty million German and Italian Catholics? Why are we so arrogant, so obtuse a race?

Monday, 4th September

Matheson is back. At 11.30 we drank coffee at the Grosvenor Hotel, and then lunched. We talked for hours about the Trust and what had happened in his absence. He was almost touchingly appreciative. Yet our talk was unprogressive and went round in circles. I cannot fathom his mind.

After dinner I called on the Kennedys. The General had last week been flying over France and tearing round France in a jeep with Montgomery, whom he and Catherine hero-worship. General says the devastation of the towns and villages and farms in the battle zone is truly appalling. He thinks there will be no armistice with Germany; that the Nazis will never negotiate, and that guerrilla warfare will proceed indefinitely in Germany. He says that our destruction of the flying bombs averages 90 per cent of those launched (I don't believe it), for by mathematical calculation and precision we have mastered them; and that no more can be launched, now the Pas de Calais is captured. Holland is too far away for launching, he says.

Tuesday, 5th September

Met Loelia and Lady Diana Cooper in the Ritz. Lady D., as she shook hands, looked at and through me with those legendary blue eyes which petrify. She does not know me and those goddess eyes were presumably assessing the strange worm which had dared rise on its tail from the mock Savonerie carpet. Her beauty is rather divine than human. Not a line visible. Her hair, celestially golden (again mythological) all curled and thick, had, she said, just been permanently waved in Algiers by a child of nine. Loelia lunched with me alone. She told me some particulars of her marriage. In the 1930s the Duke lived like a prince. Eaton was more like a town than a house. She had acted mistakenly in not leaving it as it was, a period piece of the 1870s. Instead she endeavoured to bring it up to date by making it less ugly and more liveable, in fact spoiling it. She thinks she will go down to posterity as a vandal. But she was very young, which excuses her. The first dinner party she presided over numbered seventy-five guests. Eaton could house 100 guests, each with a servant, and still there was room for more. Red carpets were put down each time she and her husband left the house, and red carpets were put down at the station. When they got off the channel boat, other passengers were made to stand aside. Since she loved flowers the Duke marshalled an army of gardeners to bring them into her rooms in barrow loads. A botanical institute was provided for her. She had two maids. The Westminsters seldom stayed more than two nights anywhere. Life was spent in planning where to go next. The Duke always intended to stay for ever, but never did, for the moment he arrived anywhere, something annoyed him and he had to move on. Since Loelia suffers from sickness in aeroplanes and on boats she was perpetually ill. Whenever she admired a piece of jewellery or a motor-car belonging to another person, a duplicate would be given to her. Yet jealousy and bad temper made her life a misery.

Loelia's married life is a definition of unadulterated hell. Two yachts, three houses in Scotland, one in London, two in France, one in Venice, besides Eaton and goodness knows how many more in the English country, contribute to it, without the spoilt and good-for-nothing lord and master. Loelia said, 'Of course, when I married him I was a poor girl who made all her own clothes.'

As we left the Ritz the porter told us that the Germans had surrendered. We were greatly excited. The news was in the *Evening Standard*. But is not confirmed. The *canard* was started by the Belgians.

Friday, 8th September

Perishingly cold east wind, and sunny between showers. I can't think why I record such information which will be of no possible interest to a single soul tomorrow, or the day after. I motored to West Wycombe and met Lord Esher. He extends his hand in a studiedly polite, keep your distance way, which I appreciate. We walked down to the village and were conducted by Captain Hill to the proposed site for the Village Hall. Hill was quite truculent, for he loathes Esher, Helen Dashwood and me. Yet he kept taking me aside in order to mock their (and, presumably, my) undemocratic, antiquated ideas. I was constrained to tell him that I shared their ideas unreservedly. He made a noise like what I imagine the word 'pshaw' in Ouida's novels is meant to sound like, and cast such a look of malevolent contempt upon me that I took a step backwards. Esher of course grasped the situation at once, and in his quick way teased Hill madly by associating him with the most outrageously revolutionary opinions. Instead of feigning amusement Hill, silly ass, went purple, and earnestly, and gravely rebutted each charge. I do love Esher.

Sunday, 10th September

Bridget accompanied me to Sussex. We stopped at a pub and drank ginger beer and ate sandwiches. At Bateman's the hospitable Parishes gave us coffee, port and figs. Most of their windows were blown out and some upstairs ceilings brought down by the buzz bomb which fell thirty yards away. Mr. Parish, who was expecting me to bring an agent, was delighted with Bridget who indeed made every effort to please. We drove on to Brede. Clare Sheridan was dressed in green with a coloured bandeau floating above her head like a halo. We had tea in her little wooden house. She showed us her new carvings, one pine figure of Mary the Immaculate, a young woman with child, and another of Queen Emma, looking remarkably like Clare, who believes herself to be the reincarnation of that remote sovereign. Clare is anxious to give Brede Place to the National Trust if she can thereby forgo Schedule A tax and all rates. Her wish is to caretake and live in a small part, using the greater part as a gallery for her sculpture. I thought Clare was more magnificant, eccentric and enchanting than ever. On parting she said to B., 'You are very beautiful.'

Monday, 11th September

Grandy Jersey told me that his department was warned last Christmas Eve to expect 1,000 flying bombs to be launched by the Germans in one day. The day to be chosen would be a foggy, dark one in mid-winter. London would have had no warning. The terror and chaos would have been without precedent. It was entirely due to the R.A.F. straffing the bombing sites that this little scheme came to nothing.

At about 6 a.m. I with thousands of others in London was woken up by an explosion like an earthquake, followed by a prolonged rumble, which at first I mistook for thunder. The explosion was followed by a second. Both, I learnt later, were caused by V2 rockets which other people have heard before. I am told that quite thirty have so far been dropped on different parts of the country. This morning's are said to have fallen at Chiswick. They have greater penetrative but less lateral destructive power than the V1's. They are very exciting and not frightening at all, for when you hear them you know you are all right.

This morning Lord Londonderry called at the office to discuss Londonderry House, of which he owns the freehold, and its entire collections — it contains six Lawrences at least. He was very charming, friendly and diffident, saying, 'No, no, it cannot claim to be a great London house,' which I suppose is true. On the other hand so many of the greatest have already gone, and their collections are dispersed.

Johnny Philipps lunched at Brooks's to meet Professor Richardson. Johnny delighted with him, told him all about Picton Castle and asked him to help restore it after the war. The Professor recounted quips and jokes he made with George V when building the Jockey Club for the King at Newmarket.

People in the street stop one to discuss the V2, which thrills us all. James gave me further confirmation of its authenticity this evening, while we were drinking at Simpson's. He said the press are not allowed to release news of it, so that the Germans may not learn where it has fallen. The rockets are released from mobile emplacements along the main roads, inside Germany. James has met a French girl cousin, witty, intellectual, beautiful, with whom he has fallen madly—he thinks— in love.

Met Eardley with the car at the canteen, where we lunched with Nancy and Bridget. Then we motored through Maidenhead to Shottesbrooke Park. It belongs to Miss Smith, a descendant of the Vansittarts who owned the place. She lives in a cottage under the shadow of the church spire. The house is used as a hospital for Free Czechoslovakian wounded soldiers. It is a Jacobean house of red brick, altered inside in George I's reign, and outside in the early nineteenth century. The prevailing flavour is of the later period. Inside there is a good deal of George I work left, oak staircase, panelled rooms, cornices, and rococo plaster-work. The park is flat and uneventful. I would not recommend it for a property, but the lady offers covenants. Neither of us liked her much. She is a charmless horsey lady, with down on her jowl. She has some good pictures, one of the Medici family that came from Horace Walpole's collection.

Sunday, 17th September

I am staying with my Aunt Doreen Cuninghame in Stow-on-the-Wold. After tea, or rather after several cups of coffee and slices of cake at the kitchen table, I went for a walk. I started down the hill to Broad-well, a secluded little village. I noticed sadly how the grey stone tiles of the barns and farm buildings are falling, and breaking. They will not be replaced. Just beside the old church is an enchanting house, Broadwell Manor, of yellow Cotswold stone. It has a classical façade of late seventeenth-century date. A notice by the gate invited entry at a charge of 2d. for the Red Cross, so I walked into the garden. I soon found that this ideal house faced due north, the south and back side having an ugly, sloping roof, and no windows. It thereupon ceased to be my ideal house. A pretty, simple garden full of yellow autumn flowers, and a stream purling somewhere out of sight. Through the front door I spied a Georgian oak staircase and other elegancies. The church contained mural tablets to the Leigh family (of Adlestrop), then as now lords of the manor. I found Anthony Bailey's grave under a rough headstone. Proceeded across fields and past hedges of massed brambles to Maugersbury. Was told which was the Baileys' house and found Mrs. Bailey sitting in a garden hut, looking the same as she did twenty-five years ago when I first met her, and wearing a thick black velvet band round her throat. She and the Colonel seemed pleased to see me. They talked of Chris, and told me how he was shot through the lungs in North Africa. His colonel sent a messenger with a white flag to Benghazi to beg the Germans for medical assistance. They captured the messenger and sent no assistance. The parents presume Chris died of his wounds. This was two years ago. Anthony was killed flying, owing to a fighter plane cutting in just as he was landing his bomber.

Bussed to Cheltenham; changed into another bus to Gloucester. Bought photographs of Wickhamford church from Sydney Pitcher, who has an amazing collection. Walked round the Cathedral and marvelled again at the lavish beauty of the Perpendicular cloisters, surely the best in Britain. Met Eardley at the New Inn where we lunched. We motored to Monmouth. Here we climbed up the Kymin hill on foot. The Trust owns the summit, including the Round House, built by a Duke of Beaufort as a folly, where Nelson lunched at a small mahogany table, now the Trust's property and used by the old couple who inhabit the house, with rain-water pouring through the roof. There is a quaint temple close by, erected to the memory of Nelson's admirals, with tablets commemorating them, now painted white but formerly the respective colour of each admiral, with his name in gold lettering. There are distant views from the temple in all directions. E. and I visited the Nelson Museum in the town, the collection bequeathed by Lady Llangattock. It is one of the largest collections of relics of a single historic individual I have ever beheld. The room itself is ugly, and the contents are not attractively arranged, or well maintained.

We drove on to Llanwern, Lady Rhondda's house, which was occupied by troops in 1939. It is now empty, spoilt and desolate. It is a George II house, rectangular, with an unsightly well in the centre. It is built of grim red brick and stone dressings, but has no pediment, parapet, or ornamentation of any kind outside. Indeed it is a plain, forbidding house, of unsympathetic texture. Within, however, there are much good early Georgian wainscote, rococo plaster ceilings and bold rusticated doorways with ogival heads. Structurally the house is still sound, although pipes have burst and water has been allowed to seep on to the floors and lie in pools. Unless the house is given immediate attention, it will quickly disintegrate. The garden is in desperate plight. So too are the park and trees. The surrounding country is beautiful, but Newport is stepping perilously near.

Tuesday, 19th September

Eardley and I stayed last night in Cardiff, not an agreeable city. At 11 I went to the Castle and was shown round by Lord Bute's house-keeper. It is astonishing that in these days one great nobleman can own a vast dwelling house and hundreds of acres of carefully kept gardens and park right in the middle of the capital of a principality. Lord Bute rarely comes to Cardiff more than once in two years. In peacetime the

Castle ruins are open to the public, but not the grounds. The Norman keep is on a high mound. Surrounding the whole castle enclave is an earth rampart, under which a Roman wall has recently been discovered. It is this wall that Sir Cyril Fox raves about. The present Lord Bute has constructed a crenellated wall on the outside of the rampart. The Castle proper is, inside and out, the most hideous building I have ever seen. The core may be early medieval. It was made Nash-like and pretty about 1800. Its present appearance dates from the 1870s. William Burges was the architect who entirely reconstructed it. There are Arab rooms and rooms wainscoted in pitch pine, inlaid with looking-glass between the crenellations of the dados. There are a few pieces of furniture and several family portraits of interest. There is a private chapel of unparalleled hideousness—encaustic tiles, embattled chimneypieces, coffered gilt ceilings. The old housekeeper, a Papist like all who serve this family, was very proud of the Castle, which she keeps spotless and polished.

I met Eardley in the National Museum. Sir Cyril was in London. We admired the way he displays the exhibits. We had tea in Tenby, an enchanting Regency town, perched above a sickle of golden sands. We watched the duck swimming in and out of the waves with enviable abandon. The N.T. has a boring little property up a back street, called the Old Tudor Merchant's House. It has a monstrously large chimney, some Gothic windows and fireplaces of the rudest kind. The thick cob walls, painted and stencilled, are now covered with hoarding to protect them from the evacuees who use the house as a clearing centre. I bought a tea pot for 10/- because the nob of the lid was off, and E. a picture frame and Bristol vase at an antique shop. Spent the night at the Ivy Bush in Carmarthen. Good solid food.

Wednesday, 20th September

Was made very cross this morning. I telephoned Picton Castle to make sure that John Philipps was expecting us, to be told by the housekeeper that he was still in London and was expecting us to stay next week. So instead we booked rooms in Tenby and drove off to Dolaucothi. Lloyd-Johnes was away, but we found his factotum, an old estate workman, whom E. familiarly calls David. He is a charming character, with perfect manners. In these remote parts the Welsh are very hospitable. For instance, when this morning we called at a cottage up the valley to fetch a key to see over a neighbouring house for sale, the cottage woman, who could hardly speak English, invited us to luncheon. Dolaucothi House is not a show place, but a sunny, cheerful, early nineteenth-century house, of moderate size, made symmetrical by the addition of two square, blank walls, to complete the main façade. The result is fairly satisfactory when viewed from the front, but slightly absurd from the side. There are two projecting bays at either end. The whole is painted a cheerful yellow. But the situation is low and oppressive. The estate is in a poor way, and the land overgrown with thistles and bracken.

We lunched at the Dolaucothi Arms off fried eggs and thick slabs of home-cured bacon. I drank tea; Eardley beer. The meal was given us by the landlady who would not allow us to pay a penny. The Dolaucothi valley is renowned, but I thought the lower part where the house and Pumpsaint village stand, was too enclosed. When we drove up the valley, it broadened and became singularly lovely like a Scotch lowland glen, with sheep grazing on the horizon of the hills.

We stayed the night at Tenby, in a little old-fashioned Inn on the front. There was nowhere to sit after dinner, so I went to bed at 8.30. Alas, there was no reading lamp.

Thursday, 21st September

E. and I very cross with each other this morning. He could not get the car to start. I pushed him in it down the hill. He said I ought to have continued pushing while he put the car in gear. I did, but it wouldn't move. I said, it was all very fine for him sitting pretty at the wheel while I sweated my guts out. He said he was trying with might and main. 'It is I who am struggling, and suffering,' I said querulously. Finally we got off. I read the half-inch map wrong and directed him in the opposite direction to the right one. But E. is never cross for more than five minutes, if that. At Manorbier there is a disfiguring aerodrome with huts. We could not enter the castle which is closed. The outside is very overgrown with ivy. We drove past Carew Castle, and down a long, bad drive to Slebech, a cardboard Walpole castle on a mere, romantic, but empty and dilapidated. It belongs to John Philipps's brother-in-law. We called at Picton Castle for letters. The house is now a military hospital.

In a field overlooking St. Bride's Bay and the blue sea beyond we and the agent of the Trust's Pembrokeshire properties ate our luncheon of a loaf of bread, margarine, honey and tomatoes. Walked to the Deer Park at the tip of the cape opposite Skomer Island. We watched seaplanes practise bombing in the bay. Interminable discussion between E. and the agent whether or not we would erect a water ram for Farmer Codd. His wife, in eager expectation that we would, gave us a great tea of luscious bread and butter in their parlour. On this hot day they had a roaring fire, and we nearly died of the heat, and the flies. Nice, friendly people.

Motored towards the setting sun, visiting more N.T. properties and protected coast line. We stayed at a farmhouse, called Lleithy, under the dark hulk of two mountains, near St. David's Head, which Graham Sutherland paints. Given lovely fresh farm food. Slept in a large feather bed. One sinks and sinks until one is drowned in prickly, stifling asthma-inducing plumage.

Friday, 22nd September

To our chagrin the weather has completely broken. All day it poured. St. David's Cathedral was completely empty, and for an hour we were the only visitors. It is built on a slope so that to walk from the west to east end one climbs a hill. Gilbert Scott restored it well. The interior is uncongested and austere. The bones of St. David are preserved in a casket behind a grill, and would of course be venerated if this were a Catholic cathedral. The Ministry of Works have taken over Cilgerran Castle from us and installed a uniformed official with a peaked cap. He says he is lucky if he has one visitor a day. Reached Dolgelly and stayed at the Golden Lion.

Saturday, 23rd September

Motored in the rain to Dolmelynllyn, a spectacular property on one side of a valley. The house perfectly hideous, with a gable of carved wood, fashioned out of an Indian bed. We walked up to the waterfall, Rhaiadr Ddu. Lunched excellently off lamb, apple pie and cream at the Tyn-y-Groes Inn, and drove through mountain valleys to Conway. Aberconwy is greatly improved by loans from the National Museum of Wales. Arrived Bodnant at tea-time.

The house is large, Victorian and not distinguished, but the gardens are world-renowned, and superbly sited, with a view across the Conway tidal river towards the mountains—Snowdon behind the range in front of us. Lord Aberconway walked us round the gardens after tea. Milner, the Victorian landscapist, actually began them for Aberconway's grandfather. There are terraces and two large pools on two levels, the lower bounded at one end by a yew stage with wings, and at the opposite end by a Kent-like edifice, moved here in 1939 from Gloucestershire. It is called Pin Mill. It is hung with French seventeenth-century arabesque Poitiers tapestries. An upstairs room retains its contemporary wainscoting, and the parquetry floor comes from a demolished house in Whitehall Gardens.

Sunday, 24th September

Lord Aberconway, our host, is solicitous and affable. He is a man of much versatility and shrewdness. A great gardener, he has wide business interests, steel, ships and aeroplanes. This afternoon he conducted us for two hours round the remainder of the garden. We walked slowly through the Dell, a steep narrow valley with a stream, lined with rare conifers to which he is much attached—macrocarpa, sequoia, Atlantic cedar, and firs of all sorts. He particularly likes *pinus insignis*. There are too many conifers for my taste. I like them to be interspersed with hardwoods as at Stourhead. We returned through a stretch of rare gentians, now in bloom, with little water sprays laid on to each batch. There is a long, tunnelled pergola of laburnum. The glasshouses contain cactuses, some very exotic tropical shrubs, and plants with giant spotted leaves.

After tea he took us over the house. The best things are the carpets. An expert comes once every two months to mend them. There are portraits of his grandfather with scientific instruments by Ouless, his mother by Tissot, and paintings by Cranach—and conversation pieces by Rankin. He has bought and inserted many early and late Georgian chimneypieces. The architect of the house was Ould, who built Wightwick Manor and Hill Bark, Cheshire. I could not have liked Lord A. more for his kindness, politeness and intelligence.

Monday, 25th September

The beginnings of what I know will be a bad cold. E. and I were up early and left by 9. At breakfast Lord Aberconway was as polite as ever. But he had the businessman's Monday morning face on, and was I could see anxious to dismiss us and get down to answering letters.

Today, after trying twenty times unsuccessfully to buy razor blades, I procured *one* at the twenty-first shop.

We motored across Telford's Menai Bridge and inspected the N.T. field, by name Cae-glan-y-Mhor. Then to Beaumaris, for I wished to see the outside of Baron's Hill, built by the architect of Attingham. It is spoilt by an addition on the west side. We drove right across Anglesey to another N.T. cliff field at the extreme northern point, Dinas Gynfor. It is an unimportant patch of a large unspoilt area. After a puncture we crossed to the mainland and reached Vaynol at 1.30.

116

Michael Duff, extremely friendly, welcomed us. He is taller than me and as thin, and carries himself straight and proud. A very handsome man with melting eyes like a dog's. He gave us an excellent luncheon somewhere in the back regions of this house, which is a military hospital. Michael speaks Welsh and makes his local speeches in Welsh, which is a great credit to him. I have been astonished during this tour how universally Welsh is still spoken by the middle classes as well as the peasants, but seldom if ever (except in Michael's case) by the upper classes.

We left at 4 for Segontium the Roman fort. Museum well kept, but the site overgrown with nettles. No one to cut them, and no money to pay if there were someone. Continued down the projecting arm of Caernarvon to look at a dreary bit of land offered us on the coast. My cold getting worse. We stayed in Harlech.

Tuesday, 26th September

I slept badly, my cold much developed in chest and throat. Eardley came into my room ashen grey to announce that he too felt awful. We agreed to cut short our tour and return home, or rather to his Bothy.

Wednesday, 27th September

Lay in bed all morning. E. has invited me to stay tonight and the following night. Saintly of him, in the, I should say in my, circumstances. In the afternoon we went to see old Mr. Mackenzie of Fawley Court, who may give us restrictive covenants over his property, which lies between the Greenlands estate and Henley-on-Thames. With the greatest effort and by sheer willpower I prevented myself from sneezing and spluttering over this ancient man. But when the effort is no longer called for the bottled up rheum explodes worse than ever.

Thursday, 28th September

E. and I motored to London early. He dropped me at Cheyne Walk. I immediately had my hair cut and washed. The washing may have been a great error. Miss P. gave me luncheon at home and I caught the 2.10 from Paddington for Much Wenlock.

Carried my bags across the fields to the Abbey. Mary Motley greeted me. She lives in this large house with four children, all boys, a nurse and an old general servant. Several women and girls come in at odd hours of the day. Loo, her husband, is as yet away. By dinner-time I was not feeling at all well.

Friday, 29th September

Got up late for breakfast but felt so awful that Mary took my temperature which was over 100 and sent me straight back to bed, where I remained, dozing and reading—Trevelyan's *Social History*, just out, Fynes Moryson's *Itinerary*, Harrison's *Elizabethan Times*, and Sir John Reresby's *Memoirs*—until

Sunday, 1st October

when I got up for dinner with a temperature of nearly 100. Met Loo for the first time in years. I had never been at all on his beam, and considered him a philistine. He doubtless considered me a cissy. But by midnight I really liked him. When we first met this evening he neither addressed a word to me, nor smiled. I was determined slowly and cautiously to break down this animal suspicion. And I believe I succeeded. He talked of rockets and aeroplanes. He is manufacturing rockets at this moment. He so impressed me with his ability to reckon speeds and revolutions with mathematical precision that I thought to myself, 'The man is perhaps one of the geniuses of our time. He is certainly wonderfully in line with scientific inventions. Unlike the stuffy, escapist intellectuals among my friends he is positively contributing to an ultimately better world, for he intends to turn his dreadful instruments of destruction, the moment the war is over, into instruments of benevolence and succour.' We drank a lot, and after dinner were on the best of terms. He complained bitterly of the restrictions upon big employers, and inveighed against the Government for their ignorant interference with business, and pandering to the voters. He abused the workers for responding only to harsh treatment and rejecting offers to participate with management.

Mary told me this morning that Loo began with nothing. He borrowed £200 and set up his inventions with that capital. Now he has a turnover of £750,000 a year, and yet his actual spendable net income is £800.

Loo says that the German rocket, V2, goes eighty miles into the air, and descends forty feet into the earth, where it explodes. It does less damage than the V1 on the whole. Its range is longer than the V1s. It is launched in Holland.

Yesterday morning the Motleys left, and I have had two glorious days entirely to myself. I cannot express my gratitude to these good Samaritans for their kind treatment. I only wish I could stay here for ever. I must go somewhere else, and don't want to return to London before my month is up. I rang up Pitchford last night. Sir Charles Grant was away, and Lady Sybil answered. I understand her now — she is like a little girl with a mind as sharp as a razor's edge, and quite unaccountable. She said, 'Yes, I know who you are. You wrote afterwards to Charles and never asked after my leg, which I thought rather beastly of you.' I apologized and said I was sure it had quite recovered by now. 'It hasn't, as a matter of fact,' she said.

I could not make up my mind whether or not I was still ill. After luncheon I took my temperature. It was just under 100. I decided that I was still ill, and had nowhere to go to be ill in, except my kind Aunt Deenie's. So in despair I put through a trunk call to her at Stow-on-the-Wold. There was no answer. I thought again, and took my temperature again. It was sub-normal. This, I decided, was absurd, and to take it out of myself, I would bicycle to Attingham. This I did, ten miles there, up and down precipitous hills, in a piercing east wind. I felt very much better for it. Lady Berwick was alone and gave me tea. She was charming to me. Told me that, after all the cancellations, the Shropshire Education Committee were re-considering Attingham for their adult educational college.

Wednesday, 4th October

Left Wenlock by an 8.30 train to Shrewsbury. There I had to wait. I looked very closely at St. Chad's church by George Steuart. It is built on an oval plan. It has two narthexes, one with a delicate curved stairway and mahogany handrail leading to the gallery. The pews, beautifully shaped to conform to the oval, are preserved. A hideous reredos presented as a war memorial. I changed again at Crewe and reached Glasgow at 7. Could get into no hotel and motored round the town looking for a room. Finally found one miles down Sauchiehall Street near the Museum. It had a double bed and the landlady expressed surprise that I should want it all to myself. Horrible smells of yesterday's cooking, and the sheets of that coarse variety which cause one to fear what may lie underneath them.

To the Art Gallery where no pictures are hanging, and there is nothing to see but a few bits of machinery. I took the 12.15 to Oban where I was met by Aunt Dorothy and driven by her to Ardachy.

I am left much to my own devices, but this enables me to make progress with the chapter for my National Trust book. I am enjoying this visit even more than I did two years ago. One day I bicycled to Bonawe up Loch Etive where the road comes to an end, and a track follows the loch past the quarries, sharply to the north.

On Sunday I bicycled to Connel Ferry to Mass in Dunstaffnage's wooden chapel, which is exactly like a hen house, under the bridge by the edge of the loch. Another day we motored to Oban. Seated in the ring on wooden steps covered with spittle and manure from farmers' boots, we watched Highland cattle being auctioned. The highest price a heifer fetched was £82. I also went to a meeting at which Tom Johnston, the Secretary of State for Scotland, spoke to the farmers. He is a distinguished elderly man whom the local Conservative M.P. praises as the best Minister, though Labour, that Scotland has ever had.

Today we went for a hundred-mile drive round Argyllshire, pursuing land girls, of which army Aunt D. is chairman of a large section in the county. We started over Connel bridge, up the river Awe to Loch Awe. There we left the Glasgow road and struck left up Glen Orchy. The river Orchy, a galloping, chestnut-backed river. Past the Falls of Glen Orchy to the bridge of that name, and Loch Tulla. Through Glencoe which is weird, cruel and haunted, emerging upon Loch Leven. Along the east bank of Loch Linnhe, through Appin and back again to our Loch Etive. Lovely indeed it was, although visibility was bad. There is more romance in Scotch hills than in Welsh. In Wales you do not sense the eternal presence of Celtic deities. There is not the same terrifying passion in the way the clouds envelop the bare brown mountain tops. Yet as I watched the silver water tumble in lively ribbons from these bleak mountains, their tops wreathed in black cotton-wool-soaked clouds, I wanted to be away from them, and back in the friendly south. I can well understand how eighteenth-century travellers from England found them 'horrid', with nothing beautiful about them. Only an aggressive sublimity.

Thursday, 12th October

Left Connel at midday. I reached Glasgow at 4.30 and again could get no room in an hotel, so finally stayed in an apartment next to the house of ill fame of my previous visit. Was bored and had nothing to do. I waited for the London train, hoping that Geoffrey Houghton-Brown might be on it; but there was no Geoffrey and by that time it was too late for a cinema. Besides, it was dark and raining. I found a cheap restaurant where I ate and read my book. As I was finishing, a man two tables away got into conversation. He came across to my table and offered me a drink. We drank beer, which I hate. For an hour and a half he told me his life story, beginning at the age of 2 when he claimed he first remembered falling in love with his mother. 'Rather early?' I suggested. 'Not a bit,' he said; 'from that instant I knew that women were to be my line. I never looked back. And now I will tell you how my first adventures began.' I groaned. He took no notice, and proceeded. His first love affair was at the age of 5 with his pillow. His second at the age of 8 with his sister. His third at 12 with God knows whom. I rose from my seat. He pulled me down, ordered more beer and went on to the next infinitely boring adventure. After several more glasses he had only reached the age of 20—he must now be 60 years old at the least I calculated. I could bear it no longer and pleaded that my bladder needed relieving. 'Good God,' he exclaimed, 'fancy that. It's on the left there, and when you return I will tell you what I did with that photograph.' Mercifully he did not see me bolt through the door into the street, and run as fast as my legs would carry me. Now why do strangers have to persecute harmless individuals like me in this way?

Tuesday, 17th October

Today we had our monthly meeting and also the annual meeting. Lord Zetland announced the gift of the two Queen Anne Street houses, which we may make into our offices. As regards situation they would be very suitable.

During my long absence from London nothing has been done to my house. But today, twelve hours after my return, an army of builders have begun putting in glass to the windows, mending frames, the bathroom ceiling, doorlocks, etc. Thank goodness, but the mess is once again appalling.

To my intense surprise and delight the Committee have given me a bonus of £200 for my work during Matheson's absence.

Saturday, 21st October

Looked over 17 Alexander Place, which Geoffrey Houghton-Brown has just bought with a view to my fitting myself into it too. A nice little house but I don't see how it can easily be divided up.

Caught a train to Bradford-on-Avon and stayed the night with Mrs. Moulton at the Dower House. Had a long talk after dinner, when his mother had gone to bed, with Alex Moulton about the future, which promises apparently to be less black for his generation—he is about 24—than for mine. In actual fact I don't think this applies to me particularly because I have never known riches and pre-war luxury, unlike most of my contemporaries from Eton. I am not gloomy about the future for myself. He is a rather appealing young man in that he is very earnest, intelligent and already successful, with a fine grasp of business. The youngest of three children, he is the one who loves The Hall, and is about to return to work in his family business, Spencer-Moulton, at the bottom of The Hall garden. The works are screened by trees. He is determined to and undoubtedly will make money. He will be a conscientious manager, for he has enlightened views about the conditions of his workers, who number 700 Bradfordians. He is very proud of the proximity of the factory to The Hall, and rejoices in it. He is also determined to do his duty by The Hall. He is now going to live in the stables, which he is about to convert into bachelor lodgings, and eventually move into The Hall when he has made enough money. We went all round the house, which was heavily restored by his great-grandfather in the 1840s. The furniture which I saw the last time I was here has been sold since. The house has distinct academic interest.

On Sunday afternoon I drove over to Westwood Manor and stayed the night with Ted Lister. I enjoyed it but Ted will not go to bed till the early hours and thinks one offensive if one slips away before 3 a.m. John Leslie and Sir Orme Sargent dined. The latter is a tall man with a sloping forehead, nose and chin: all slopes. An agreeable evening with much Edwardian gossip and laughter. These three elderly gentlemen are given to story-telling. Have you heard this one? The hotel commissionaire saying confusedly to the lift boy, 'Take this lady up to P. I mean to letter P. I mean to letter P on the door' – and others of this calibre.

Lunched at the Travellers with Johnnie Dashwood, who calls all the waitresses, 'My dear,' and cracks jokes with them. They love him in consequence. Indeed he is the most good natured, jolly man imaginable. He is very cross with the Trust for suggesting that the West Wycombe account is overdrawn; says that our accountant and Hill both have tortuous minds, and that together their tortuosity is invincible. He has been in Rome, which is clean and gay; food obtained by the rich through the black market, and by the poor through excellent soup kitchens, so no one starves. All sections of the British, officials down to the common soldiers, hold the Italians in greatest contempt for having treated our prisoners so badly. The Romans pay no heed to the Pope, who, he considers, has not played fair, by them or by us.

Johnnie repeated the statement which I have heard before, that the Pontiff blessed the Italian troops at the outset of their Abyssinian campaign, but never blessed our troops on their entry to Rome to relieve the Romans of the Germans. Anyway he thinks the Curia a farce with its preponderancy of Italian cardinals. With this sentiment I heartily agree, and have always considered it the one irrefutable indictment of the Vatican set-up.

Had tea with Lord and Lady Esher at the Dorchester. At 5.30 Lord E. and I walked to Londonderry House. Lord Londonderry's secretary showed us round. Troops occupy all the state-rooms, which in their present condition are tawdry and unimpressive. The grand staircase is indeed grand, but from what I could see the architecture of the house is so-so. Of course with the return of all the furniture which belongs, it would look entirely different. It was odd to see at the end of the great gallery where the famous *Miranda* hung, an exhibition of worn motor lorry tyres. We went over the Londonderrys' reserved part where they now live, and which they call 'a flat', but which we calculated could be divided into five and possibly six expensive Park Lane flats. Lord Esher asked how many servants the Londonderrys employed before this war. The answer was, 'Twenty-eight in the kitchen, and sixteen in the steward's room.'

Lord E. and I agreed that Londonderry House should not be reserved as a museum exclusively; but that we should ask the Government if they would rent it from us for official entertainments. He thinks Benjamin Wyatt a mightily indifferent architect.

I lunched with Lord Carlisle in the House of Lords. Found him in the library, which was dark as pitch. Several other peers emerged from the half light. I thought what a seedy, drab collection of old crocks, and above all how out of date. Lord C. on the contrary is very spry. He has spent three years in Turkey; his wife is an A.T.S. General in India; his son is fighting in Italy. He may be sent on a mission to Yugoslavia in a few weeks' time. He talked of Naworth, which is, he believes, the king of all castles. His son loves it too. He may never live in it again, and wants the N.T. to have it. He suggests a school renting it. Asked me to come and stay there in a fortnight's time, which I shall enjoy doing. After luncheon the House sat, and I stood behind the Bar for a few minutes in the Chamber, which is now the Robing Room, smaller, cosier and more intimate than the old Chamber. There were the Lord Chancellor in his wig, the bishops in their lawn sleeves, and the stately attendants in boiled shirt-fronts and tail coats, with medals hanging round their necks on chains, which clattered against the starch. The peers, mostly decrepit, looked gaga in the dim yellow light, and remarkably nineteenth century. This is the best place in which to recapture nineteenth-century atmosphere. I love it, and would not have it any different.

Went to Mrs. Ionides's house in Twickenham at 9.30. Very foggy and so could not see much of the riverside scenery. Mrs. Ionides owns the grounds of old Orleans House, now pulled down, and Gibbs's beautiful Octagon, which she showed me. It is well preserved. She offers to leave it and eight acres, which adjoin Marble Hill, including a building which contains two derelict flats. She hates the local council, who wanted to pull down the Octagon, and who cheered when told that Radnor House had been demolished by a bomb. Before I left she offered to include her pictures of Twickenham, including a Zuccarelli, which K. Clark wants for the National Gallery. The offer is certainly a worthy one. She is a highly intelligent old woman, a sister of Lord Bearsted, and talks of 'ceows'. I liked her.

I rushed back to Brooks's and talked to G. M. Young about his contribution to the N.T. book, and read his chapter in manuscript. We talked of Robert Byron. He said Mrs. Byron was going through all his diaries and letters. He did not know if any monograph about Robert was to be published.

Met Major and Mrs. Fuller, their daughter Mrs. Boyle, recently widowed, and all trained to Uxbridge. We ate sandwiches in the tube. In a warehouse we looked at a set of four Flemish tapestries of biblical scenes, *circa* 1680, the colours extremely strong. Major Fuller had contemplated buying them for Great Chalfield Manor, but was disappointed with them. He thought the figures too large and too classical. But I feel sure they are good tapestries.

At 5.30 to tea with Emerald. Lord Berners gave us a white powder to sniff, which he said was cocaine. It smelled of menthol, and I liked it, but Emerald did not, complaining that it burned the membrane of her nose. She talked of trees, and asked, 'Are you intimate with trees? I know a man who is. He tells me that when they transplant them, they have to be given an anaesthetic for they feel the pain so badly.'

Friday, 27th October

Sir Cyril Fox, director of the Museum of Wales, lunched with me at Brooks's. He offers to give the Trust help and advice on our archaeological properties, and wants to do a tour of them with me after the war. We had a long, useful talk about the Trust's post-war problems, and about Cardiff Castle. To my surprise he admires it very much, particularly the Victorian work by Burges. Said Lord Bute is quite impossible, and will not make up his mind; nor will Lord Tredegar about Tredegar Park. In fact he said rather wistfully, 'The aristocracy are all the same. They keep to themselves, and are afraid of outside contacts. I do not expect them to fraternize with a mere ordinary citizen like myself, but they might discuss cultural matters with me on a common level.' I said that they were probably frightened of cultivated, highbrow people like himself – although no one could be more charming or less frightening than Sir Cyril – and they were deeply suspicious of city councillors, government officials and the Inland Revenue. He ought to understand that.

I took the train to Sevenoaks, and had tea with Lord Sackville and Mason (the agent) at Knole. Lord S. is always charming, and exquisitely dressed. Mason is down to earth and sensible. Lord S. agreed, as I thought he would, not to press for a 500-year lease, but to abide by whatever term of years the Court of Chancery decides upon. He said no one after Eddy would be able to live in Knole. I broached the park problem, about which Davidge the town planner spoke to me this morning, asking me if I would ascertain privately what Lord Sackville would accept in compensation. Would he accept £100 per acre, amounting in all to £100,000, a sum he believed the local authorities would provide? I did not need to put this question, for Lord S. advanced the view, which came as a surprise to me, but sensible, that if he accepted this sum, then he would benefit after income tax by £300 a year only, and Eddy would have to pay additional death duties of 40 per cent. Whereas by not doing so and keeping the parkland, which is unproductive, Eddy would pay only nominal death duties as he, Lord S. had done on succeeding his brother, and he would be able to threaten to sell parts if occasion arose, and thus bargain with the local authorities. If they then wished to preserve it from development, as they do now, they could purchase it from Eddy for an open space. After tea we walked in the garden, which is well maintained in spite of the war, and looked at the outside of the house. I had no idea how much glass was lost when the landmine fell in the park in the spring. Most of it has already been replaced with excellent new panes, and the injured mullions have been well restored. Incidentally £1,500 has been spent on the damaged roof, out of the war damage fund, at no expense to the estate.

Dined with Puss Milnes-Gaskell, who had Sir Hughe Knatchbull-Hugessen, just appointed Ambassador to Belgium, and Lady. He shrewd, she abrupt. He said that lunching at Buckingham Palace yesterday the Queen pointed out to him that they still had no glass in their windows, only cellophane.

Sunday, 29th October

Lunched at home, and worked at my chapter. Tea with Logan Pearsall Smith, who is getting very old, and breathless. Nevertheless he talks like a river. He is devoted to Stuart and read me some extracts of a letter from him, with which he is well pleased. He gave me his book of Aphorisms, in which he wrote my name. Afterwards I remembered he had given me one already. He said Sibyl Colefax was a genuine friend, kind and painstaking; that Emerald's ingenuous remarks about love were a pose. Nevertheless she was a brilliant talker, *the* most brilliant. Next time we met, he said we must have a 'serpent-talk' instead of a 'dove-talk'.

Monday, 30th October

Trained to Luton and walked to the offices of a rather seedy, be-pince-nezed solicitor. He took me across the street to tea in a bun shop, and told me he had a collection of Bernard Shaw books, press cuttings, theatre programmes and photographs which he wished to leave by will to Shaw's Corner. He is 42. Shaw is his absorbing hobby, and has been ever since at the age of 15 he read an article by Shaw against the last war in 1915, having overheard his father warn his mother not to let the boy see it. After school he left Birmingham, where his parents lived, and set up in Luton in order to be near Ayot St. Lawrence where Shaw lived. At the time he was so poor he could not afford to buy the newspapers in which articles about Shaw were published. So he copied them out in his own hand in the public library. He now knows Shaw, and constantly goes to his house. He also knows Lowenstein, who with his help is compiling a Shaw bibliography. He even learnt German in order to read a biography of Shaw in that language.

Got back from Luton just in time to pick up Jamesey at his flat, and walk to dine with the Moores. I sat next to Joan and Diane Abdy who is so defenceless one wants to hug her. She said she bought a lavatory this afternoon in a smart shop. The sales manager in a frock coat pulled, tweaked bits of paper, threw them into the pan, and flushed with absurdly exaggerated, genteel gestures. Joan played Mozart and Bach after dinner, exquisitely, poignantly. Drank too much. Damn.

Tuesday, 31st October

Several loud crumps from rockets during the night, which woke me up. Several more today. They are becoming worse, and will doubtless continue for the rest of the war. They say they come from inside Germany, even from the Tyrol. Nancy Mitford saw one descend in a ball of fire, like the setting sun. Even she had a cold sweat, and was riveted to the ground.

At 9.30 I accompanied Mike Peto to Mark Turner's office. Turner proposed that the Pilgrim Trust should buy Audley End; the Trust should let to Lord Braybrooke, and he in turn re-let to the Fyffes for their girls school. I doubt if this will work out. Matheson disturbed me by saying that Mr. Hobson of Park Hall thought I did not know what I was about. The truth is I knew only too well, but I could not tell him.

Dr. Tom Jones lunched with me at Brooks's. Very Welsh. A little old man with white hair, a pointed intelligent face. He knows everyone. His manners are abrupt. He seized the food himself and plumped the fish on to my plate. Now I would not dare do that if I were lunching with him. I liked him all the same. We talked of the N.T. and the Pilgrim Trust, which has tremendous power, of course wielded by himself. His shrewdness is by no means to be disregarded. He was, I think, secretary to Baldwin's Cabinet, and is a kind of perpetual power behind thrones.

Wednesday, 1st November

All Saints' Day does not mean so much to me as All Souls', for one day I shall be one of the latter, and never one of the former. Went at 12.30 to old Reginald Blunt's memorial service (for he died last week) in St. Luke's beautiful church, Chelsea. During the service I thought about the dentist; and at the dentist's this evening I thought about Reginald Blunt. I thought of his lifetime love of Chelsea, which in spite of his efforts the Chelsea Council persists in spoiling, while the Mayor draped in chains piously attends his service as a mourner. An odd world.

Mann of the Wallace Collection lunched with me and was more informative, and less bottled up than previously. I understand why he is a power in the museum world, for he is very positive and go-ahead. He thinks owners should be paid by the state to live in their ancestral houses. He disapproves of the institutional age ahead of us, and the inevitable lack of individualism that will accompany it. He thinks Raby a stick-in-the-mud. G. M. Young came to the office to look through files about N.T. manor houses. I went to Harold in King's Bench Walk. He talked with pride of Nigel's cleverness; and said he would stand for Parliament in a Highland constituency. Then I dined with Bridget.

Friday, 3rd November

I lunched at the Reform Club with Peter Watson, who said he would publish my architectural article in *Horizon*, if I amplified it a little.

Went to no. 40 Queen Anne's Gate, which with no. 42 has been given us by Mrs. Murray Smith, and is to be made into our new offices. No. 40 suffered a good deal when the Guards' Chapel was hit by a flying bomb. All windows are out; parts of inner walls down, doors wrenched off, and ceilings down. We expect to move into no. 42 next spring. The old lady was there, fumbling through old letters, and infinitely pathetic. I had been asked to choose from the furniture any pieces we might want, but she had changed her mind and would not look at furniture today. So the visit was rather wasted. However I saw over the house. No. 42 is charming. I think we should have the outside plaster removed; it would be an improvement. Matheson and I went to Twickenham to see the Octagon and Mrs. Ionides's land. Matheson wondered how we could afford to look after it. He is right, it will need capital outlay. I made a plea on behalf of Miss Paterson that she is grossly overworked. I hope he has taken this in.

Monday, 6th November

Received a letter from my mother that she has rheumatoid arthritis in her hands, which has made me extremely sad. Mothers wring the heart.

I dined at the Travellers with Harold Nicolson to meet a young poet and playwright, by name Michael Clayton-Hutton, aged 23. I took an instant dislike to him, for he is rather off-hand and hideously pleased with himself. Shaftesbury Avenue looks, moreover. Harold talked politics over port wine. He said Hitler told a friend of his, the Swiss Governor of Dantzig, that Hitler lamented there was no prominent English statesman to whom he could speak freely in his or our tongue. The Dantzig Governor asked what he would say to the Englishman. Hitler replied: 'Supposing it were Lord Halifax I would say—I offer your country the ports of Antwerp, Dunkirk, Le Havre, etc., absolutely, on the understanding that I take Poland and the Balkans without interference.' Harold said that when the Germans walked into Slovakia, he was with Winston Churchill and Lord Cecil. After serious discussion Lord Cecil left, saying, 'Well, Winston, I must go. Things are desperate. I feel twenty years older.' Churchill replied equally seriously, 'Yes, Bob, things are desperate. I feel twenty years younger,' and these words convinced Harold there and then that Churchill was a great man. It convinces me that Churchill enjoys war.

Tuesday, 7th November

Took the train to Portsmouth with Sir Humphrey Prideaux-Brune. We crossed the Sound in a launch to Gosport, and taxied to Rowner, where Sir Humphrey's family owned property from the fourteenth century until the 1920s. This Sir H. has bought back five acres round the old church and wants to hand them over to the National Trust. He was so nice, so enthusiastic, and has so great a sentimental attachment to the place that I had not the heart to tell him I thought it not important enough. With no endowment it would be an uneconomic property. Besides it has no national interest whatever. Sir Humphrey has spent thirty years in China. His wife who was ill in Switzerland in 1939 was caught there, and has not got away. He has not seen her all these years.

After dinner with the Darwins Esther Darlington drank tea with me, and persuaded me reluctantly to become Hon. Secretary of the Chelsea Society until the end of the war and Rick's return. Because of my admiration of Mr. Blunt and friendship for Rick I consented, but I shall have little enough time to be active.

Wednesday, 8th November

Nancy rang up to say that her father had a diamond necklace which all the West End jewellers valued at £1,000, but a pawnbroker gave him £2,500 for it. I took mine to Spinks this morning and they only offered me £400. Now I shall try Nancy's pawnbroker.

Thursday, 9th November

Took the morning train from Euston to Carlisle, arriving at 4.30. Read *Phineas Redux* all the way. At Carlisle took a bus to Brampton, and another to Naworth, reaching the drive gate in the dark and frost. Walked downhill to the Gatehouse, just above the Castle; and Lord Carlisle was there to greet me. This little house, formerly the estate office, is let to a Miss Mounsey Heysham, an old lady, and a Miss Chance, with whom Lord Carlisle stays when he is here. Since the war began the Castle has been first a school, Rossall, and then a military headquarters. Now the military have gone from the Castle and merely occupy a few huts in the park. Bitterly cold, and had it not been for my electric pad, I should have been frozen in the night.

Lord Carlisle is young middle-aged, stout, smiling, entertaining, and a very nice host indeed. This morning was clear bright, there having been a hard frost. We went all over the Castle. The surrounding country is idyllic. Scotch hills in the distance and few scattered farmhouses. The Castle is perched above two deep glens which unite at the foot of the 1881 wing. There is a square walled garden made by Belted Will about 1600. There are two detached, rugged buildings, the Gatehouse proper and the Bote House. The Castle walls are of beautiful gold and red stone, and date from the fourteenth century. Fairly discreetly added to one end is the Stanley wing, by Salvin according to Carlisle, but I should say by a later hand.* It makes the house enormous. The Castle is a rabbit warren of rooms, and uneven floors, and endless corridors. There is only one room that is actually old, namely Lord William's Library in his tower, where the stout fourteenth-century ceiling is preserved. It is of massive beams, with Gothic panels and fat bosses between. All the other rooms and the

* Actually by James Fergusson.

gallery are of Salvin's time, for there was a disastrous fire in 1840. The Great Hall is new likewise, the walls covered with very fine early Gobelin tapestries that belonged to Henry of Navarre, with his monogram and a crown in the cresting. Lord C. was offered £100,000 for them by the French Government in 1914. The war came and the offer was never repeated. Otherwise the Castle is completely empty, the furniture being stacked in the stables. The Army have treated the building well. It is undamaged, clean and kept heated. All the rooms, like those of most castles, lack shape and proportion, and are inelegant, with poky windows in deep embrasures. The open courtyard is certainly beautiful, with steps leading to the Great Hall. Lord C. loves the place and thinks it the best castle in the United Kingdom. Yet he is determined not to live in it again, and offers it without grounds, and without endowment.

In the afternoon Carlisle and Miss Heysham, aged 75, very crumpled, dotty and angelic, went after pheasants. A Mrs. Hamer and I, with a perambulator and baby, walked down to Lanercost Abbey, which embraces the parish church and the ruins given to the Office of Works. The Howards are buried in the ruined east end, which makes a romantic mausoleum.

Saturday, 11th November

I walked by myself round the Castle and into the gardens, and along the ravine in the morning. After luncheon, was motored by Lord Carlisle to catch the 3.30 train. Last night we had a long talk about the war. Lord C. said he was convinced that wars had nothing but a demoralizing effect upon troops and civilians alike. I agreed. I got home at midnight and drank quantities of tea and ate apples.

Sunday, 12th November

Had a glass of sherry at Brooks's with Tom, who walked in. He tells me he is soon off to Burma at his own request, for he does not wish to go to Germany killing German civilians, whom he likes. He prefers to kill Japanese whom he does not like. Tom makes me sad because he looks so sad, and because I am so deeply devoted to him.

Monday, 13th November

Meeting day. Esher asked Smith and me to lunch with him at the Grosvenor Hotel, in order to talk about his property, Watlington, which though delightful is not exactly a national monument, in spite of its one fine ceiling by Abraham Swan. The Finance Committee have in their good, considerate way, agreed to let me have the £200 they gave me, in kind instead of in cash, on which I would have to pay tax. So I may have £200 worth of the secondary Polesden furniture they lent me, not at probate value but market value.

Dining with Pam Chichester I met G. B. Stern. She was very talkative and cordial. She is a hugely fat Jewess, bulging everywhere. She has straight, cropped grey hair à la Gwen Farrar, a curious sight. She discussed schoolgirl books, but I am not well read in that branch of literature.

Tuesday, 14th November

Nancy's pawnbroker in the Strand has given me £525 for my necklace. Consequently I feel extremely rich.

Looked over Miss Noel-Hill's little house in Graham Street. It is tiny, with extremely tiny rooms. I could have had it there and then, and would have been tempted were it not for the Underground, which passes *above* ground just behind her garden wall.

Johnnie Churchill followed me into Brooks's. He said Midge Tweeddale died of galloping cancer of the lung which attacked and finished her off within a week. I liked her so much. He said that Mary his wife was a fanatical Protestant and was going to bring up Cornelia as one. I said I disapproved.

Thursday, 16th November

Attended a lecture at the Courtauld Institute by Anthony Blunt, on Castiglione. He delivered it extremely well, with no notes of any kind. K. Clark present and looked benignly approving, which is the greatest compliment a man can receive.

Saturday, 18th November

B. lunched with me, and for the first time was wearing a small black beret on one side of her head, which suited her. She talked rather pathetically about her future. Said she had never yet been in love with anyone who loved her. I asked if it irritated her having someone in love with her. She denied this. She said that her first affair was with X who wanted to leave his wife for her. Now she was glad he had not done so. He would have got on her nerves. Y was another suitor, but he was too noisy and boisterous. She would like to marry some-one with a small country seat, so as to have a garden, dogs and birds. She would marry Z if he showed any inclination. I observed that Z had neither seat, garden, dogs nor birds.

Listened to Delius in the Albert Hall. Aimless and soporific, without beginning and without end.

Monday, 20th November

My train to Newton Abbot was one and a half hours late owing to floods across the line. A taxi drove me eight miles down narrow lanes to Little Hempston Manor, seemingly miles from anywhere. It belongs to the Dundases. He is a first cousin of Lord Zetland. Being with this cosy, modest and by no means affluent couple, made me ponder on the near accidents of birth, and the advantages and disadvantages of primogeniture.

Tuesday, 21st November

They kept me talking till after midnight. I was very exhausted this morning. Little Hempston is a tiny, medieval manor house with forecourt. It is built round a minute central court. It has some six rooms in all on the ground floor, and six bed and dressing-rooms upstairs. The outside is of the simplest character. No one knows whether it is actually a manor house, or a parsonage. It has its original, very coarse screens, and screens' passage. A great hall with half-timber partition over the screens. The walls are of plaster, pink-washed. Over the far wall is a fresco of the Resurrection, date about 1450. The house itself is supposed to be fourteenth century. Most of the windows have been restored not too well by the late owners, who found it derelict and bought it from the Church. Though its general disposition is prac-tically untouched, some details have been altered with circumspection and even improvement. Yet the flanking barns of the forecourt still retain unsightly corrugated roofs. Little Hempston is situated at the bottom of a steep ravine, and the river Dart is just visible from the house. Dartington Hall is on the other side of the river. We went there this afternoon. It is a frightful mess. The great hall with its pointed windows is magnificent outside, but the new roof is too flimsy and the new screen of unvarnished oak inexact.

I felt really sorry for the poor Dundases. She told me she has not been away one single night since the war began, but has slaved in the house all these years single-handed, cooking, housemaiding and caring for a boy, aged 8, and girl aged 2½. Endless chatter about the house, of which she is intensely proud, being very medieval-minded. I liked him even better: a tall, youthful 45, very blind with thick spectacle lenses and a Roman nose like Lord Zetland's. But poles away from Lord Z.'s exclusive, viceregal, patrician ambience. These two people have sacrificed their money and their health for this house, which is not a hereditary possession.

Wednesday, 22nd November

On arrival at Paddington station I watched a porter drive an electric trolley over the edge of the platform on to the railway line. The machine having tilted over, pinned him against one line. Yet he went on smoking, never moved and never called out. Instantly soldiers and other porters jumped down, and within three minutes had lifted the trolley off his legs and freed him. Then he collapsed. I went to the restaurant, ordered some tea, and felt sick. Yet I had done nothing to help. I am amazed and deeply impressed by the porter's stoical courage, and the quick, concerted action of the bystanders.

Ian McCallum dined at Brooks's and talked about the new House of Commons to be built by Gilbert Scott. He had with him the White Paper and plans, and thinks the neo-Neogothic designs fairly competent. He doubts whether the *Architectural Review* will attack it.

Miss P. told me that last night at 11 a rocket fell in Battersea. The noise was the loudest and most terrible she had ever heard. It fell one and a half miles away, yet several window panes in our house were broken, and the ceiling in my large room is cracked worse than before, and sagging rather perilously.

Friday, 24th November

Had a postcard this morning from Father Francis Moncrieff, written from Hambleton, saying that old Mrs. Astley Cooper died last Sunday after three weeks' illness. Mrs. Cooper was very good to me when I was in disgrace with my family ten years ago, and gave me my missal. She was a remarkable old woman with a first-class brain, a man's attitude to life and its problems. She hated pettinesses, and had no patience with small irritations or small points of view. Accordingly few women liked her. She had a sad life, in losing her favourite children and quarrelling violently with the others and her relations. But she had a magnificently embracing sense of humour, was a realist and a cynic, and could never be taken in or deceived. She discovered Noël

Coward as a boy, was an intimate friend of Malcolm Sargent and of Scott Moncrieff, whom she helped translate Proust's novels at Hambleton and who dedicated the series to her in the moving poem published in *Swann's Way*. She was a convert, who loved and revered the Church, respecting it for its intellectual, rational and ruthless approach to life. Although she frequently rebelled, she always returned to it. People were frightened by her direct manner, her immediate circumvention of all conventional and social façades. I have had many a meal with her, she sitting, groaning and shaking with mirth at some foolish person's expense, a massive, shapeless lump of a woman, over the most delicious English food. Fred, the tall, respectful, stately, P. G. Wodehouse butler, was always in the background. Rarely can two people have had a more profound affection and admiration for one another. Unfortunately Mrs. Cooper became more and more self-adulatory in a sly way, and her constant, roundabout fishing for praise exasperated me. I had not seen her for some three or four years. I shall always respect and love her, for she contributed a lot to my life. There was absolutely no nonsense about her. Her trouble was that she was a woman with a brain, born into English upper-class county circles.

James telephoned just before midnight that tomorrow evening he is at last to sleep with his first woman. Everything has been arranged. He dreads it and is terrified, and will telephone first thing on Sunday morning to let me know how it proceeded. Asked me to think of him and pray for him tomorrow evening.

Saturday, 25th November

Went to tea with Logan who told me the same stories over again, but one new — to me — saga about the wickedness of Lady Ottoline Morrell, who succeeded in breaking up happy relationships, and tried to separate Ethel Sands and Nan Hudson. Lady O. was constantly throwing herself upon men. Logan asked me if I liked foul-mouthed men who otherwise led blameless lives. I said, No, I preferred clean-mouthed people who gave physical expression to their lusts. He seemed shocked. Why? For two hours he criticized everyone, asking me if I did not agree. Since half the people criticized were unknown to me, I was unable to agree. This disappointed him. When I suggested that a mutual acquaintance was malicious, and another a pompous prig, he flatly contradicted me. Tom Mitford at Brooks's said he would like to be taken to tea with Logan, 'for I am a keen etymologist'.

At the Ritz bar Guy Burgess called to me. I dined with him and Charles Fletcher-Cooke at the Gargoyle. Drank too much beer and gin mixed, and talked a great deal about politics and sex, disagreeing with Guy over both. He does and says the most dangerous and indiscreet things. However we laughed a lot. Mary Churchill who was there, joined us. I do not know her. She is prettier than her sister Diana and looks like her mother. She talked all the time about her father whom she adores unreservedly. I walked home from the Gargoyle in the moonlight. It took an hour. In bed at 2.

Sunday, 26th November

James telephoned this morning, and said tersely, 'I am still alive. It was quite easy, but was not riotous.'

I fear that in this diary I disclose the nastier, the more frivolous side of myself. I sincerely believe and fervently hope that I am not as nasty as I may appear. It is difficult to be entirely honest about oneself, because one does not necessarily know oneself. One thinks one knows. The consequence of being as honest as I try to be, must surely be that readers of these lines would pronounce me worse than many of my contemporaries who do not keep frank records of themselves. Frank? Not entirely, because I withhold things.

Monday, 27th November

Michael Peto lunched at Brooks's. Lord Braybrooke was to have done so, but when he learnt that Mark Turner could not come, he decided not to. Mike and I agreed that an impasse has been reached over Audley End. On returning to the office on foot just in front of Victoria Station I was, with the minimum of warning, stricken with a blackout. A passing cab drove me home.

Tuesday, 28th November

Kathleen Kennet, Eddy and Nancy lunched with me. Nancy had long wanted to meet her. I began by saying to K., 'Nancy is simply mad about Captain Scott.' 'So am I,' she replied. Nancy told me she had discovered how they peed – into a tin inside their bags. K. said Captain Scott hated any unkindness to animals. It was torture to him when they suffered on his account. Nancy says she wants to go to the Pole after the war.

Wednesday, 29th November

Lunched at Eaton Terrace, Anne's little house. We picnicked off soup and lobster salad, the last brought in a brown paper parcel by John Sutro. Sachie Sitwell there. When he laughs his face breaks into a thousand tiny fragments, and reassembles. I have never seen anything more endearing.

Mrs. Ionides came to the office, and agreed to leave Riverside House to the N.T. in addition to the Octagon and the Orleans House grounds. Now we shall not be hard up for funds to maintain the Octagon.

Eardley and I walked from the office this evening to Sibyl's. Talked to Elizabeth Bowen and John Lehmann about our morbid dislike of revisiting houses we had lived in during our adulthood, as opposed to childhood. Knickerbocker, the American journalist, came in later, and told us how he drove into Paris at the head of the American army in a jeep. The welcome was something he can never forget. Sibyl left before her guests with Stephen Tennant, who to my eye does not look particularly young. He has long fair hair, and the mannerisms of an Edwardian hostess. T. S. Eliot came in and went out again before I knew who he was—a dark, sharp-featured man, with hair brushed smoothly down each side of his head.

Thursday, 30th November

Hubert Smith and I attended a conference at the Middlesex County Council offices with representatives of that Council and of Heston, to discuss Osterley. Much to our surprise both Councils appeared ready to make up the annual deficit, even offering to increase rather than decrease the deficit figure.

Called for Anne Rosse at Bridget's flat and walked to the Dorchester. Dined with Emerald. Two stars present were very witty, but so spiky, pulling everyone to pieces, that I hated them both and the whole evening. I was dumb and unable to contribute a word. One of the stars said, 'Sibyl Colefax is getting too big for her boots,' to which the other replied, 'You mean she is getting too big for her hump.'

Friday, 1st December

Joan Moore lunched with me at Wilton's. She brought a huge sack which the waiters filled with oyster-shells for her hens. It was so heavy that we had to wait for a taxi to pull up at the door.

It was with much reluctance that I dined with Emerald again tonight, but I had promised to do so earlier in the week. I had a hot bath and set forth in the worst form, taking three books for her to read. Met Peter Quennell downstairs in the Dorchester. We drank whisky and soda together and went up. As so often happens when one least expects it, the dinner was hugely enjoyable. There were the two Chaplins, Alice Harding and Peter. Anthony Chaplin told us what it felt like in the rear of a bomber with a gun. He said the cold was quite appalling. You were numb all the time, and sick. But the spirit of camaraderie and loyalty among the crew was such that it could only be described as pure love. He said that in 1940 many of our planes were destroyed by bombs dropped from above by our own planes.

We talked of George Moore. Emerald showed us a letter from him to her, beginning 'Dearest Maud', comparing her to Christ and Sophocles, and acclaiming her genius. She was very modest about it. Then she brought from her bedroom a large cardboard box, shook it and said, 'These are all letters to me from George Moore. I cannot tell you what they are about.' Peter tried to persuade her to let him go through them with her, but she was reluctant, not wanting them published. Then she talked of Paris before 1914 and the affectation of Robert de Montesquiou—who Peter said was the prototype of Charlus—and how he loved to be pressed to recite his own poems, leaning against a marble pedestalled bust in an absurd posture. While she was telling this story I realized wherein her genius lay, for she has a prodigious memory, and a wonderful gift of narrative, spiced with a frivolity and humour which are unique, and totally irresistible. It was an enjoyable evening because conversation was not a denigration of contemporary socialites whom I did not know, but about the recent historic past.

Saturday, 2nd December

Just caught the 11.50 for Cambridge by jumping into the train as it was moving along the platform. Stood all the way which gave me sciatica. Met Michael and Frances Peto on arrival and went to a play in Cambridge about the Brontës which I enjoyed very much. Drove to Longstowe Hall and stayed the night with the Fyffes in their girls' school. It was fun dancing polkas, lancers, Highland flings with the girls, all of whom looked pretty and some bewitching in their long dresses, swirling around the great hall. I liked Fyffe, a very shrewd, matter of fact, Scotch architect. When the girls had gone to bed we discussed Audley End; but I fear the project will come to nought.

Sunday, 3rd December

I left soon after breakfast. The train connections extremely bad so that
138

I did not get to Euston till late in the afternoon. Impossible to cross Piccadilly because of the Home Guard procession to the Palace. All day I read and finished Rosamond Lehmann's novel, *The Ballad and the Source*, which Logan P.-S. thinks the best novel since Henry James. I daresay he is right, and I am immensely impressed. My only criticisms are that the story is told in dialogue, and I do not think it altogether convincing that a child of 10 to 14 should be the channel through which a terrible drama is unfolded. Nevertheless, what a story!

Tuesday, 5th December

Magdalen FitzAlan Howard lunched at the Queen's restaurant, poor old thing. She is so gentle, and so pitiable. Why? Because she is a middle-aged spinster? I don't think so. But because of her slightly faded, lost air of one stranded by cruel time, and cruel love. Anyway she enjoys a harmless little gossip, and like all fervent Catholics is interested in the marital predicaments of other Catholics.

I went to a late tea at Emerald's to meet Madame Cárcano, the Argentine Ambassadress, again. She wants advice upon the enlargement of her country villa in the Argentine. A little difficult for me to give satisfaction in this matter. But she is an agreeable lady. Lady Kemsley came, and talked about Dropmore and the lamentable deterioration of the house owing to its requisition by the army. She said it was a fine house, now utterly ruined. I promised to get in touch with the Ministry of Works about it. It was difficult to concentrate on what Mme Cárcano was saying while Emerald in loud whispers was explaining to Lady Kemsley who I was. Lady (Claud) Russell came in. Her beautiful name is Anastasia, and she is a Greek. Emerald addressed her in her inconsequential way, 'We were just saying that Greece must become a British colony in order that all this shooting may stop.'

Wednesday, 6th December

Grandy Jersey lunched, and brought me a musquash fur lining in a brown paper parcel, which he said had belonged to his grandfather and he feared was too old to be of any use. Nonetheless I am grateful and delighted. I took it to John Walls who plucked at it, and the tips of the fur came away in their fingers. They are sending it to their experts to see if they can stop it moulting.

Lunched with John Philipps at the St. James's Club. He told me that when I first met him at the beginning of the war he was odious — which I had sensed for myself — and drunken. Now he was reformed, and was only happy at home in Pembrokeshire. This candour I find endearing.

I left Diane Abdy's flat with Joan Moore. We agreed that cocktail parties were absolutely unrewarding and soul-destroying, and wondered why we ever went to them. She asked me, 'Will you ever go to another?' I sighed and said, 'I fear I shall.' I walked to Albany to meet Lord Wilton at Johnny Philipps's. He is about 23, tall, fair, handsome, and very shy. He is passionately interested in architecture and wants to buy a large country house, but cannot find one large enough. I intend to find one for him.

Emerald described how she dined last night at a large party of earnest women who asked her questions like these: 'Lady Cunard, what do you think about the state of morality among south-eastern Europeans?' Answer, 'Not enough immorality.' 'What do you think then about the lack of education in the industrial north?' Answer, 'Too much of it. There should be less,' and so on.

Matheson being taken suddenly ill, I had to go through the Executive Committee agenda with Lord Zetland in the office. He was remarkably friendly, and to my amazement some item amused him, and he began giggling. Then pulled himself together with a jerk. But it was too late. He had betrayed the fact that he was a human being. I shall no longer be in awe of him.

I am so pleased I decided not to go away for the weekend. Instead I have worked hard at home, and been very happy. Alvilde lunched out with me, after which I went straight home again. John Fowler telephoned and persuaded me to leave off work and dine with him. The moment I put down the receiver I regretted it. When I got there he was so friendly and amusing that I was glad I went. He brought up dinner on two trays which we ate in front of the fire. Told me horrifying stories of acquaintances being blown to fragments in the streets and in their houses because they would not have Anderson shelters.

John Walls report that the fur Grandy has given me is ginette, a kind that always moults a little; but that after beating and combing this one, which once had moth, it ought to be all right. The texture is so silky and opulent that I have decided to have an overcoat built to fit it.

Went to Harold at K.B.W. at 6.30. He told me he thought Clayton-Hutton was a little mad, bad and dangerous to know, but was undoubtedly a poetic genius. He has not heard anything of him since. Harold thinks he might well commit suicide [he did].

Tuesday, 12th December

Bought for four guineas a so-called Constable oil sketch which I saw in a shop window in Warwick Street. Went to the Wildenstein gallery to see the exhibition there. Robin Darwin asked me what I was carrying. He gave the sketch one look and roared with oafish laughter, saying that not by one in a million chances could it be a Constable, and asked how much I paid for it. I was so shaken that I lied, and said 10/–. After I had seen the high quality of the Constables exhibited I realized what a fool I had made of myself.

Met Jamesey in Sloane Square for a drink. He very affectionate and sad about departing, and leaving me and others, so that I do believe he cares for me a little. But I do resent his egocentric and tyrannical ways.

After dining with Bertie Abdy we went to the Bearsteds' suite in the Dorchester and drank brandy, which is death to me. B. Abdy has very definite views. He repeated that he lived for art, pleasure and himself. Not enough, thought I. I advocated the exhibition of surplus works of art, now stored in museum basements, in tube stations where thousands could admire them while waiting for the trains. He was very shocked, which I think foolish. He hates and despises even the best quality English eighteenth-century furniture. I was shocked.

Wednesday, 13th December

At 5 o'clock I took Tom Mitford to tea with Logan. I think Tom, whose manners can be abrupt, was bored, and certainly Logan was rather boring, for he would read from his own books and from the *Dictionary of National Biography* about all the Mitfords that had ever been. But he is a dear old man, and when he got up, all bent, and fumbled in his shelves I rather loved him. When Tom and I left it was pitch dark, the fog having thickened. It was almost impossible to see a thing. By tapping with my stick against the kerb, he clinging to my left arm, we reached the King's Road. After a fond farewell, and Tom's farewells are so fond they always touch me, we separated. Slowly and cautiously I followed in the wake of motor lights and walkers' torches, presuming that I was on my way to the Chelsea Hospital road. After half an hour, not knowing where I was, and almost desperate I bumped violently into someone. I apologized. The victim apologized. It was Tom. Peels of laughter ensued. We clove to one another, and agreed not to separate again. We staggered to his flat, and abandoned our different projects for that evening. Instead we ate scrambled eggs and drank red wine. Once I am indoors I love pea-soupers, the cosiness, the isolation, the calm broken by distant squeals of taxis and thuds of wary footfalls, the tapping of sticks against area railings, and the blessed expansion of confidence between two friends.

Saturday, 16th December

Stopped to look at the ruins of Donnington Castle which Macgregor tells me are fourteenth century. All that remains is a central gatehouse with two round turrets of red brick and flint. I continued to Roche Old Court, one mile off the Andover–Salisbury road, close to the Pheasant Inn. The little manor house, fourteen rooms in all, is of red brick with stone dressings. Chettle says the date is *circa* 1620 because the brick is in English bond. In front of it are an old brick wall and several old farmbuildings, including a tithe barn of timber post construction, *circa* 1400. The house inside has much early plain wainscoting, and stairs of William and Mary period. The owner, Major Trevor Cox, M.P., was at Eton with me. Was at Hill's house. Says he remembers me. I vaguely remember him. Eton is an unfailing bond between those who were educated there, and an irritation to those who were not. He is not going bald like me, but grey about the whiskers.

I arrived at the Vyne at 5.30. Mrs. Chute, grey-haired, once doubtless a pretty woman, now like a superannuated school-girl, received me. As schoolgirls pick shyly at their pinafores, so she picked at her skirt. We had tea in the Henry VIII linenfold panelled parlour. He, Charles Chute, a brother of Jackie Chute, came in later. He is tall and better looking than his brother, and lacks any charm whatever. Highly educated, a scholar at Eton, winner of several firsts, he is pedagogic although not a schoolmaster. Rather abrupt, contradictory and snubbing. I did not care for either—much. He hates Horace Walpole, and

142

has little use for his own forebear, John Chute, Horace's friend. Thinks them both, and me too I have little doubt, 'scugs'.

Sunday, 17th December

During the night it poured with rain. Water dripped through my bedroom ceiling, so I put my sponge bowl to catch the drips. Before breakfast, at 8.45 precisely, a sort of school bell rang, and we all trooped into the chapel for prayers, that is to say, the Chutes, I, the headmaster and mistresses of the school billeted here—the boys are now on holiday—the matron, followed by five servant girls in uniform. Mr. Chute read the prayers, and the schoolmaster alone read the responses in so loud and aggressive a voice that I guessed he hated him. A sort of sparring match ensued. However it was all over in ten minutes. I liked it, but it is the first time I have ever attended Protestant prayers in a country house. The schoolmaster, rather sulky and surly, and the mistresses, singularly dreary, attend every meal. The mistresses exhale a forced, bumbling bonhomie. There is one perky little Irish woman, at whose lamentable jests it is customary to roar. I joined in the chorus out of politeness.

The Vyne is a very wonderful house. Yet I was a trifle disappointed. The rooms are awfully dark. The John Chute staircase, though a tour-de-force, is too narrow to be magnificent. The early Renaissance panelling is of great historical importance, yet ugly. The Webb fireplaces look out of place, and the Webb portico is top-heavy. It does not belong to the façade, upon which it has been stuck like a postage stamp upon a piece of string. Mr. Chute conducted me through practically every room. The Chapel is superb, with traces of early Renaissance in the friezes of the stall canopies, stained glass and coloured tiles.

When I left, worn down by the Chutes, I decided I hated country houses and never wished to see another. I drove at 4.15 to Bramley Church and looked at the fine Banks monument there, which is almost as good as the superb Chaloner Chute one at the Vyne. Yes, I think the Chutes were Parliamentarians which accounts for their puritanism today. Then to Stratfield Saye. Found Gerry and his very handsome son and daughter-in-law (to whom I was introduced, titles and all mentioned by Gerry) cutting branches and clearing the shrubbery at the conservatory side of the house. A vast improvement has already been made. I can think of no house needing improvements that has fallen into better hands. We had tea in the dining-room, a beautiful room with a ceiling taken from Wood's book on Palmyra. From the window the landscape with water is just like the Vyne's. Gerry has

143

already begun to clear away the fussy beds beyond the terrace. The Douros left and I settled down to talk to Gerry about Tuesday's agenda and the Vyne, when the Douros returned. Their car would not start, nor would it start when I pushed it round and round the sweep with mine. All that happened was that my bumper got jammed in theirs and could only be extricated by a jack. All I received for my pains was a scolding from Gerry for being maladroit. After this interruption it was time for me to leave. Gerry did not press me to dine.

Monday, 18th December

Lunched with Derek Hill at the Reform. Filthy food—smelts, well named, and rice pudding. The rogue in porcelain, somebody has called him. He is certainly attractive, but was rather distrait and inattentive today. I daresay I bore him. He spoke with much affection of Jamesey and sorrow over his impending departure. I attended a very interesting conference at the C.P.R.E. office concerning the list of historic buildings which the Ministry of Planning is to compile under the new Act. I thought we were a good representative collection of people, Keeling in the chair, Abercrombie next to me, John Macgregor of the S.P.A.B., and James Mann from the Wallace, etc.

Worked late in the office and from there walked to Brooks's. Got drinking with John Walter.

Tuesday, 19th December

At Brooks's Lord Braybrooke lunched with me; also Esher and Mark Turner. We talked about Audley End, without reaching any conclusion, other than that the Fyffes' school was 'out'. In the afternoon a meeting of the Country Houses Committee. Very small attendance. Gerry did not come, but Harold Nicolson came for the first time. The Committee agreed to my proposal that the Trust should ask the Government for funds for country houses, not inhabited by the families of their donors.

John Preston came to see me. He is greatly improved, and I found him sympathetic. He told me he was present at a recent press conference in France which was addressed by Eisenhower. The General inspired tremendous confidence and convinced the troops that by hook or by crook he would not allow the field to stagnate during the winter months. John thereby deduces that the recent break-through by von Runstedt may not be altogether unwelcome.

Tony Gandarillos drove me away from Sibyl's Ordinary, via the

St. James's Club where he drank two whiskies and soda before facing the fog. At the best of times he is an alarming driver, but tonight he was terrifying. We were constantly on the pavement. I laughed so much that I thought I should have died. He is like a teddy bear. He told me he had twice been married. Also that at dinner at Emerald's some weeks ago Peter Rodd insisted upon talking to her about Nancy Cunard, her daughter, which all Emerald's friends recognize to be a forbidden subject. Nancy [Rodd] miserably embarrassed, but could not stop him. Emerald finally said, 'Mr. Rodd, Nancy does not like me. It is a very painful subject.' The consequence is that Emerald does not speak very kindly about poor Nancy Rodd, who is utterly blameless.

Wednesday, 20th December

Met Goodhart-Rendel at the Travellers to talk about Hatchlands, and lunched with him. He has glassy, fish-like eyes, rather protuberant, which dart around. They give him a sinister appearance. Anyone who did not know what a clever and learned man he is, might consider him unbalanced.

I dined with James in the fog. There were orange flares today at Hyde Park Corner. The fog confines one within a small world. Beyond the enveloping Dickensian gloom is the vast, illimitable unknown. James was in his best mood. We drank rum and dined at the Gargoyle. We visited pubs down the Strand. I do not enjoy these visitations, because I find it difficult to swallow half a pint of beer, and I never know what to say to strangers. J. told me that yesterday Clarissa had been with Mrs. Churchill, who was practically in tears over the news. Dame Una thinks the war will be prolonged another three years. I cannot bring myself to recognize such a thing.

Tuesday, 21st December

The shortest day. Eardley and I went to Morden Hall by tube. The house is nothing, a comfortable Victorian mansion. It is the park and grounds in this horrid suburban area that count. There are some 120 acres. It will be useful to the local people, and I think on the whole the N.T. are right to hold it, although its aesthetic value is slight.

Harold dined with me at Brooks's. He was very upset because Ben has been knocked down by a lorry in Italy and is in hospital with concussion. An officer friend of Ben's in England had been informed by letter, and reported the accident to Harold. I told Harold that if it were serious he would have been informed by cable, and he should not worry. After dinner he took me to Pratts which is next door. He is going to second me, and Tom propose me for membership. The subscription is only £5 a year. One can get food there till midnight, a distinct advantage. Tonight Bill Astor, A. P. Herbert and others were assembled, and Harold delivered himself of a lecture against American criticism of British imperialism, and nothing would stop him. There were two Americans present, but he would not let them get a word in edgeways. I was a little embarrassed.

Friday, 22nd December

I gave Miss P. all the furniture in her bedroom as a Christmas present. Her delight and gratitude were touching. Eardley and I gave luncheon to Sir Geoffrey Hippisley Cox at the Basque Restaurant. We discussed the scheme for making Montacute into a furnished museum, or rather country house. He is very enthusiastic, and will be chairman of a small sub-committee. He is intelligent, with the right ideas, not a highbrow, and not—for once—a peer. I drove straight to Hampstead, to Fenton House, which belongs to Lady Binning, an elderly, delicate, hot-housey lady. Fenton House was built in 1693 of beautiful red brick and has wrought-iron gates of the period. It is large for London, and has a large walled garden. Much of the pine wainscoting has been stripped by Lady Binning. She intends to leave her excellent furniture, and wishes the house to be a museum, but I feel it ought to be put to some use. Her porcelain collection is first-rate and at present bequeathed to the V & A, but she is prepared to alter her will.

She gave me tea, and we liked each other, I fancy. At the end of tea she disclosed that she was anti-democratic, very pro-German and pro-Nazi. She denied that the Germans had committed atrocities, and declared that the Jews were the root of all evil. Oh dear! She ought to meet Tom.

John Preston came to say good-bye to me at Brooks's. He leaves for the States tomorrow. Friends come and go, for short, for long periods, and one takes it as a matter of course. Only I remain stuck, which, to use an Irishism, is unsettling.

Saturday, 23rd December

Motored Tom to Swinbrook and lunched in Lady Redesdale's cottage. Bobo was there. She has become rather plain and fat, and says she weighs 13½ stone. Her mind is that of a sophisticated child, and she is still very amusing in that Mitford manner, which is not everyone's taste, but is certainly mine. She talked a little about the Führer, as though she still admired him, and was very disapproving of the zest with which the British press records the bombing of German cities. Being with her made me sad, for I love this family, and I see no future for Bobo but a gradually dissolving fantasy existence.

I continued to Gloucester, picking up on the way a drunk and dissatisfied tramp. Along the wilder road above Cheltenham I felt a little frightened of him. I turned him out in Gloucester and gave him half a crown. Called on the Dean and inspected the Old Raven Tavern, a miserable, dilapidated, half-timbered building, once the home of the Hoare family, some of whom migrated thence to the U.S.A. in the Mayflower. The N.T. has prematurely consented to accept this inn, but I query the propriety of doing so. I attended a 4 o'clock service in the Cathedral and the distribution of children's presents from a Christmas tree at the west end, a moving ceremony. Then had tea with the Dean and Mrs. Costley-White, who have left the Deanery for a smaller, Georgian house in the Close.

Wednesday, 27th December

All this Christmastide my father has been perfectly charming, and companionable. I believe that by taking the initiative and showing a sympathy for his not inconsiderable difficulties, which I ought to have done years ago, I may at last have broken down his suspicion and reserve. At least I hope so.

I left Wickhamford after breakfast and reached Swinbrook at 10.30. Lady Redesdale gave us sherry and cake. Bobo made Tom laugh a great deal. He is perfectly sweet and patient with her. Indeed with those of whom he is fond his manner is irresistible. He said good-bye to his mother, who was brave and good about his departure, which he told me might be for three years. An extremely frosty morning, the air glacial, and all living things arrested. The sun came out once and made the trees, swathed in hoar frost, glitter like fairy godmothers in the pantomime. At Oxford I stopped to look at some seventeenth-century lacquer furniture which Mrs. Price offers us, together with some early needlework hangings. We lunched off bread and butter and cake, en route. Tom such a good companion. He is my oldest friend, whom I first met in 1919, and have loved from that moment onwards.

Friday, 29th December

Peter Watson lunched at Brooks's. He said Cyril Connolly's book was too subjective to be first-rate, although Cyril considers it quite objective. It is the brilliant production of a disappointed, uncreative critic, approaching 40, who is frightfully ugly.

Sunday, 31st December

Lunched with Keith Miller-Jones and Tom. Tom never addressed one word to Keith who thought him morose and rude. Tom kept repeating, as though to himself, but I suppose they were addressed to me, Hermione Baddeley's not very funny jokes in the pantomime we went to yesterday afternoon. Nevertheless he wanted to pay for the three of us, saying that he must get rid of his money for on active service there is absolutely no way of spending it. But we would not allow this. Keith was resolute, which is not surprising.

At 7.30 according to plan I went to Lady Moray's house where Tom was. He was anxious for me to meet her; and I am glad I have met her. She is well dressed, very pretty, with a creamy complexion and golden ringlets of hair through which she runs her fingers. She has the slightly croaky and caressing voice of the cosmopolitan American woman. She evidently brings the best out of Tom. He accompanied me downstairs, and I said good-bye to him on the doorstep of Hans Place.

Dined at the Chaplins'. Lady Kenmare, James and Derek Hill there. Anthony talked marvellous uproarious nonsense for two hours about a bogus Constable he had bought, purporting to be of Willy Lott's, Tilly Losch's cottage he called it. James and I left at 11.20. We walked in the moonlight. At Hyde Park Corner we heard a crash, followed by the roar of a rocket that made our hearts beat. Then we laughed. Just before midnight I left him at Sloane Square station and continued homewards. Crowds were singing in the square like zanies. There were sounds of merriment from lighted windows. They seemed forced to me. There were no church bells, and for the first time I did not feel left out, nostalgic or particularly sad. Merely indifferent to it all.

1945

The year has opened in a melancholy way. Tom has gone to Burma and James to Washington. The V2 rockets have begun again to some tune. One fell on Tuesday morning with a terrific explosion and roar on the eastern wing of Wren's Chelsea Hospital, completely wrecking it and breaking windows for miles around. In the afternoon I walked down St. Leonard's Terrace and asked after Logan. He was in bed, but he and the servants were unhurt. All his windows on both sides of the house were smashed, doors wrenched off, both outer and inner; and partitions and ceilings down. Much of his furniture was destroyed. Yesterday rockets fell like autumn leaves, and between dinner and midnight there were six near our house. Miss P. and I were terrified. I put every china ornament away in cupboards. The V2 has become far more alarming than the VI, quite contrary to what I thought at first, because it gives no warning sound. One finds oneself waiting for it, and jumps out of one's skin at the slightest bang or unexpected noise like a car backfire or even a door slam.

Jamesey sailed yesterday. On Wednesday we drank whisky at the Allies Club and with much affection pledged a renewal of friendship and confidences. We agreed that during last year there had been a coolness.

Last Saturday Major Benton Fletcher died suddenly at no. 3 Cheyne Walk. He was found fully clothed on his bed on Sunday morning. I was called. He was evidently in process of cooking something in a saucepan on an electric ring. The saucepan had burnt into an un-recognizable tangle of metal, but did not set the room on fire. Benton Fletcher was lying hunched up, as if frozen stiff. Indeed I believe he may have died of the cold, for he would not spend a penny on heating. The neighbour said to me it would be only decent for us to lay him flat. I did not like the grisly prospect. We tried. It was impossible to bend the limbs and straighten him. All the while there were those glazed and staring eyes. I felt sick, and said to myself, 'Give me V2s every minute rather than a repetition of this experience.'

At first it was thought there might have to be an inquest. As there was absolutely nobody to take matters in hand I had to arrange about the post mortem, the funeral, and caretaking of the house. I went through all his papers. He had hardly any personal belongings and only very few clothes. He lived entirely alone, with no one even to clean for him, in great dirt and squalor. This sort of death *is* a bourgeois business. I only hope I die in splendour. I want my body to be burned immediately on a pyre, not at Golders Green, preferably at Wickhamford, close to the church, and my ashes to be scattered there. Then an enormous marble monument, two, three storeys in height, to be erected in the nave above our pew, with a lengthy epitaph in complicated Latin, so that the stranger reading it will not make head or tail of whom it commemorates, or what it means. It *must* be beautiful.

Saturday, 6th January

The rockets keep on falling, chiefly round the river, which I am told is their guide. There is little doubt, so the Chelsea people maintain, that *they* are getting *their* eye in. But *they* have no eye, and surely no mind either, being launched hundreds of miles away. Certainly they are increasing. They make my windows rattle in a horrible sort of concussion, which is disturbing. No anti-aircraft device can stop, or arrest them. Therefore, if the war continues through this year I do not see how, considering their number and wide range, they can fail to get most of us in the end. They are perpetual swords of Damocles over the head.

At 7.30 Lieutenant George Dix U.S.A. Navy came for a drink. Nice. At 10 o'clock John Sutro took me to a film drinking party. It was hellish; thick smoke, stifling heat and everyone talking at cross purposes at top speed. Noël Coward there, red in the face, assertive, middle-aged and middle-class. I left at 11.

Sunday, 7th January

I picked up John Wilton and drove him to Audley End. I like his quiet intelligence and his taste in things and people, which concurs with mine. Lord Braybrooke met us at Audley End which was perishingly cold. We had a sandwich luncheon in the lodge over a fire which was not hot enough. The troops are out of the house which has barely suffered from them, and is quite clean. John liked it very much, but in Lord B.'s presence was shy and never once spoke of what was in his mind. I felt that Lord B. was nonplussed. However, on the way home J.W. opened up and suggested buying the house, endowing it and living in it. It would be too wonderful to be true. He stayed to dinner and talked till 11 when I went firewatching.

At 11.30 Matheson and I drove to Brompton Cemetery to pay our last respects to Major Benton Fletcher's remains. Deep snow lying, and intense cold. I wore a thick pair of snow boots over my shoes, and thus clad braved the snow and slush. But feet so unnaturally gigantic that I kept tripping up over my toes, and once dangerously near the grave's edge. At the chapel no one but ourselves, a nephew by marriage, and Roger Quilter the composer, his only friend, who appeared grief-stricken. We watched the old man, who had had so many acquaintances, lowered lonely into his grave. We promptly turned and left him to his own devices. Oh, the cruelty of it all. The nephew told me that before 1914 Benton Fletcher's name was to be seen at the end of every list of dinner parties, and balls, in *The Times*. He quarrelled with nearly everyone but me, and died unloved, neglected, and mourned by Mr. Quilter.

A girl came to see me in the office this afternoon ostensibly to talk about Manoeline architecture, and to seek my advice on a thesis she is writing at the Polytechnic. She walked into the room, dressed to kill, draped in gold chains and bangles, her fingers covered with flashy rings, smoking from a long, gold cigarette holder (a thing I have not seen before), and was wearing rimless pince-nez. She knew nothing about the Manoeline, or even the subject she is writing about, which apparently is not architecture at all. None of these vacuities would have mattered, had it not been for the pince-nez. It was with difficulty that I got rid of her.

The cold persists. It is appalling, and I have run out of anthracite. I only have two bucketfuls of coal left. I ordered 10 cwt. of anthracite, my first order since March of last year, in November. It has not been delivered yet. I was to have gone to Kiplin in Yorkshire today. Thank goodness the visit was put off by Miss [Bridget] Talbot who has a chill.

John Philipps lunched. He says he is mad on farming his own land and studies the cow sheets night and morning. The war has made him as interested in cows as he used to be in William Kent. We went and bought beautiful leather waistcoats in Turnbull & Asser's.

Had tea at Emerald's, after the office shut. Mr. Partridge was brought in. E. tried, I like to think, to put him at his ease, but her thin manner overlaid an inclination to show him the social differences. She introduced him to us all in turn: 'Princess Kallimachi, who lives at the Ritz; Lady Kemsley, whose husband owns all the newspapers: Mr. Peter Hesketh, who owns a whole town: and Mr. L.-M., head of the National Trust, who looks after all the public houses.'

Saturday, 13th February

Yesterday I resolved not to be disagreeable and cross, or rude, or to show pique, envy, and malice. The day went fairly well, for I was at home most of it, though I was not too pleasant to poor Miss P., who has a cold, and *will* sniff. But this morning in the office I was distinctly unpleasant to Matheson in complaining that the agents never came into the office on Saturdays.

Lunched at the Argentine Embassy in Belgrave Square. The Ambassador is charming and cultivated, and Madame Cárcano no less so. Peter Quennell was there and Jakey Astor, who has just married Chikita Cárcano. I had been asked to help them find a house, but they were so vague as to what kind and date of house they wanted, and where it was to be, not seeming to know whether it was to be large or small, in Scotland or in England, that I gave up.

The Education Officer of the Cambridgeshire County Council called this morning about Audley End, and is convening a meeting of representatives of other East Anglian county councils, which he wants me to attend. His interest seems unfeigned. This may spur John Wilton to make up his mind. He dined at Brooks's. He is complaisant and will agree to eat what one suggests, drink what one suggests, and do what one suggests. Yet I feel there is a will of iron underneath, which if one struck it would send out sparks and dent the offending instrument. His is one of the most curious minds I have come across. It resembles the Princesse de Polignac's—questioning, cautious, non-committal, tentative, then—crash! out comes a devastating bomb, but muffled, for he seldom raises his voice; nor did she. Nothing escapes him, and his memory is alarming. He is acutely observant like Cecil Beaton. Every blemish of others is recorded on that photographic retina. If he could write he would be a great novelist in the George Sand manner. Or is he just a Disraelian young duke, Byronically moody and damned? He seems determined to take Audley End, and has steeped himself in the history of the Nevilles. We drank at Brooks's till midnight, then went to Cheyne Walk in spite of my warnings that there was no fire, the anthracite not having arrived, and only a handful of coal dust left. We lit the coal dust with difficulty and drank tea. At 2 there was a siren and four flying bombs shook my windows. At 3 John Wilton left in a hired car.

Slept till 10 and breakfasted at 11. Nancy lunched at the Ritz. She was distressed by Simon Elwes's sudden illness. He returned on Friday after three years in India. Spent Saturday playing very happily with his children. At dinner felt sick and went to bed. At 2 his wife rang up Nancy to say he had had a stroke and was dying. This morning not expected to live. Peter astonished Nancy by being quite indifferent. He said he had never admired his character and that his wife, Peter's sister, would be provided for. Peter is a horror.

A wonderful concert in the Albert Hall, B.B.C. orchestra, Boult conducting. The Rachmaninoff concerto with Moiseiwitch at the piano. Brahms symphony inspiriting. Lady Kenmare was in Emerald's box, wearing a little hat of strawberry feathers, as it were entwined in her grey hair. She looked too beautiful for words.

Michael Rosse came back this evening on leave from Holland. At 6 I went to Bridget's flat. Anne was in a great state and fluster, awaiting him. Soon Michael telephoned that he was on the way, so the assembled party mostly dispersed, I among them. At midnight Anne and Michael rang me up to say I should have stayed, but I thought I had done the discreet thing. I dined at Brooks's because it was too cold to stay at home without fuel of any sort.

Thursday, 18th January

Grandy Jersey lunched with me. He wishes to hold up the Osterley negotiations until the County Council have consented to purchase the land belonging to his trustees. But this they have said they will not do. However, he has met Pepler at the Ministry through me, and will follow his advice. He took me to Müntzer in Albemarle Street, a decorating firm he has bought and is now running. He wishes, he says, to make money. It seems to me a sure way of losing it. I like Grandy. He is inscrutable, but well-intentioned.

Friday, 19th January

Heywood Hill lunched with me. He is so shy that, because I was not in the club precisely at 12.50 and because he is a corporal in uniform, rather than wait he went away. Eddy, whom I met in a bus lunched with us too, for Heywood returned later. Heywood is rather like John Wilton in that he appears to lack self-confidence, and is exceedingly gentle in manner, but has underneath a will of iron. He and I went to the Wildenstein Gallery to see Derek Hill's pictures.

Saturday, 20th January

It is so appallingly cold—snowing again and freezing—that I cannot, without anthracite, face my room in Cheyne Walk. Went to Brooks's and there worked before the fire, interrupted at times by Sir Warren Fisher's chat about the superiority of Brooks's to all other clubs. At 3.45 I set out to walk in the snow. In Westminster Abbey I found Robert Adam's grave slab in the south transept. It is simple and worn by the feet which have trampled over it these 150 years. There is no other memorial or monument to him, whereas there are tablets to Wyatt and Taylor, who are less distinguished architects. I looked at many monuments. How dirty they are. How wonderful though. They are history. The Abbey enshrines England's history. It is a volume of a thousand pages. England's most precious sanctum. How cumbersome Charles James Fox's oversize monument is, and how baroque are some of Gibbs's to unknown persons. Roubiliac's to the Duke of Argyll is the noblest, with the most panache of them all.

I had a drink with John Philipps. He showed me Beatrix Potter's drawing of 'Johnnie the town mouse' and said, 'That's me to the life. I am just like that. I saw a woman in the street the other day, just like that too. So I went up to her and said, "You are a mouse. You ought to have married me." ' Whenever I see one of these delicious drawings I find it hard to reconcile the Mrs. Heelis I met with the Beatrix Potter who conceived and produced them. For Mrs. Heelis was an unbending, masculine, stalwart woman, with an acute business sense. She was rather tart with her dim husband and adored her sheep, not for sentimental Beatrix Potter reasons but for hard cash Heelis ones. She drove bargains with farmers at sales and the National Trust over her benefactions.

Sunday, 21st January

At the Albert Hall concert I roughed out some notes for the letter John Wilton is to send to me at the National Trust. At tea in Brooks's he took pen and paper, and made me dictate word for word his letter to me, which he copied down. From nothing did he dissent. This almost embarrassed me as though, I told him, I were a Jewish moneylender making him sign away his birthright.

Madame Massigli is very beguiling with her Roman nose and profile. She dresses beautifully, with true French chic. The Ambassador is tall and jet black. It always amuses me how ambassadors at dinner parties will agree in heartfelt tones with our views on the world situation; then can go home and straightway declare war upon us. The Massiglis motored me in their luxurious car as far as Sloane Street. We parted with expressions of the most fervent mutual esteem, and promises to meet continually. Shall I ever see them again? I walked home.

Wednesday, 24th January

A terrible day. Arctic cold. I caught the 9.40 a.m. from King's Cross, reaching Darlington at 4. Changed for Scorton, arriving at 4.45. Already getting dark, and a leaden, snow-filled sky of the most ominous description, the silence promising the blackest frost. There was no car to meet me at the station, somewhat to my surprise. Consequently I walked two miles from the station to the village, carrying my bags. My hands were numb with cold. On reaching a garage and thawing them before a fire, they hurt so badly I feared they were frostbitten. A taxi drove me to Kiplin Hall, put me down and drove away. There was no Miss Talbot who had asked me to stay. I trudged round the empty house, in which not a glimmer of light was to be seen, and could not get inside. What I did see in the twilight was enough to convince me that this house was not acceptable. The centre part, the brickwork and the eccentric towers, almost French Renaissance in plan, were interesting. But there was too much nineteenth-century alteration and addition.

I chased round the village enquiring for Miss Talbot. Finally a friend of hers told me she had telegraphed that she was not coming down from London after all. I was furious, and returned to Darlington. Since I could get no room in any hotel, I decided to catch the 7.50 p.m. back to London. In the train there was no heating, and I reached King's Cross at 3.35 a.m. frozen to the very marrow. There were no taxis at that hour, and there was no alternative to walking with my bags to the far end of Cheyne Walk. Got home, in my wet and clammy clothes at 5.30. As I tried to force a comb through my hair, which was stiff with hoar frost, I cursed that wretched Miss Talbot.

Friday, 26th January

I believe this to be the coldest spell England has experienced for fifty years. Everything is frozen stiff. People are suffering tortures from cold, without enough fuel. Last night at home, squatting under layers of coats and rugs I could not get warm enough to work, so went to bed in my clothes.

Today I went to a late tea with Emerald. The Dorchester was beautifully heated, yet Emerald was throwing wads of newspaper into an empty grate, setting matches to them and murmuring that London was as deprived as Paris, and we were heroes. She may say this with some justice by next winter.

Saturday, 27th January

Walked to the Adelphi to see what, if anything, remained of Adam's work there. Nothing to speak of. Just the butt-ends of some buildings with the familiar wide pilaster bands of terracotta, disporting huge honeysuckle emblems. What a monstrous abomination of a building the new Adelphi block is. Utterly and absolutely without merit. While I was at Charing Cross there was a terrific V2 explosion. It sounded right in my ear. I learned afterwards that many people in widely scattered parts of London thought the same thing.

Dined at the Étoile. Cyril Connolly sat at the next table. He said he came back from Paris two hours ago; that in Paris you felt the French were living, whereas in London you knew the English were dead. Poor English!

Sunday, 28th January

The appalling cold and frost persisting, I live and work, when not in the office, in Brooks's, only returning to Cheyne Walk to sleep. I dined excellently with Colin Agnew, a dear little, tiny man, who lives for pictures and nothing else, except his friends, of whom he has many.

Monday, 29th January

Never read the diaries or impressions of men who have written in the fear of death, for their records cannot be honest.

158

The thaw having set in, our pipes burst, and we are without water, if we disregard the condensation pouring from the walls. For the past fortnight the pipes have been frozen and out of action. Which predicament is the worse? At any rate we are warmer now, thank God.

Wednesday, 31st January

Dr. Wittkower of the Warburg Institute lunched at Brooks's. He is so hesitant, and so burbling in that irritating German accent that I can barely listen to what he says. Yet he is a great scholar. Within that huge head one senses, almost sees, cavern after cavern crammed with documents in German, French, Italian and English, and rolled parchments covered in the dust and must of ages. He told me a lot about the Institute and his own book about Lord Burlington. He offers any amount of help, and will put numerous books of reference at my disposal at Denham, where the Institute staff is living during the war. A kind and generous man, ready to impart information from his great store. This is by no means always the case with scholars. In return, I have helped him a little by introducing him to Lord Spencer and persuading that difficult nobleman to put the Althorp papers at his disposal.

At 2.30 to Batsford's where, with Mr. Harry Batsford and Charles Fry I made a final selection of illustrations. Mr. B. is the dirtiest, yet the sweetest old person I ever saw. He smokes, and coughs, and shakes incessantly, while the cigarette ash spills down his front, and not only ash. Saliva also. His eccentricities are Dickensian. He adores cats, and fills his coat pockets with the heads, tails and entrails of fish. As he stumbles down the pavements he distributes these remnants to the congregating cats. The scene is like the Pied Piper of Hamlin. The smell of his clothes is overpowering. Charles is devoted to him.

Saturday, 3rd February

This morning in the office I typed out a memorandum I composed in the train yesterday with much care and thought, suggesting that the museum aspect — for lack of a better phrase — of the Trust's work should be recognized to be as important as the agents', solicitors' and accountants' departments now are; suggesting that, instead of Country Houses Secretary, a foolish title, there should be a chief curator or some such officer, responsible to a new Committee of Taste. I feel very strongly on the subject, and pretty confident that Esher, who is my consistent ally, will agree.

I joined Rory's party for a farce, called *Three's a Family*, American nonsense about babies, nappies and a stooge aunt. Quite funny. English comedians make the mistake of laughing at their own and each other's jokes, to show the dense audience when they ought to be amused. It is like putting too many apostrophes after facetious sentences in a letter. We dined at Rory's house.

Monday, 5th February

Trained to Chippenham and motored to Lacock where I joined Eardley and Mr. Gordon Hake, the architect. He has long white hair and wears a cape and sombrero. A polite man, with, I think, good taste and ideas. On the way back I got into conversation with a radiant young Air Force officer on the platform at Chippenham. He was a dentist, and told me that you never pulled a tooth out; you pushed it down on either side, and it popped out. I was too late for Sibyl's Ordinary.

Tuesday, 6th February

Went to see Harold after 6. He was very upset by the death of his great friend, Robert Bernays, M.P., in an aeroplane crash. He said there had been another aeroplane crash in which the Prime Minister's staff en route to the meeting of the Big Three, were involved. They cannot release the news yet. Harold told me that Ben is better but still in hospital in Italy. His spine is affected by his motor accident and he is encased up to the chin in plaster of Paris. His beard causes him much discomfort.

Wednesday, 7th February

At a meeting of the Montacute Committee Bertie Abdy stunned the members by denouncing the purposes for which we were met. He said, 'We can't possibly let the public inside a house with valuable works of art. They smell.' With much tact the chairman, Sir Geoffrey Cox, disregarded this observation, as though it had not been made, and proceeded with the next item on the agenda.

Pauly Sudley dined with me. He is very odd indeed. He said his whole life was tormented by guilt over not liking what he ought to like. I said, 'But there should be no such thing as "ought" in your case.' Then he said he could not travel by train, or cross the Channel, two complexes he was unable to overcome.

Had a late tea with Logan, who was less rambling and more lucid. Yet some of his remarks were quite irrational. He said all the aristocracy took bribes and commissions in selling their possessions to each other; that one of the national museum directors had bought some illuminated manuscripts from a bishop's wife, ostensibly for his museum, and sold them elsewhere at great profit to himself. He could prove it, he stoutly maintained.

Friday, 9th February

By train to Bramber to look at the Castle, which the Trust is urged to buy. All that remains is a high piece of Norman gatehouse, and some flint ramparts. I took a bus to Brighton and looked at Single Speech Hamilton's house by Adam on the Steyne. It has an apsidal library with vaulted ceiling, and a rather pretty little octagonal boudoir behind a square, coved hall.

I dined with the Moores. Bewitching Mrs. Fellowes arranged that I should take her to Coleshill next Saturday week, which will doubtless involve us in troubles all round. The Argentine Ambassador said that none of us knows in the least what the Russians intend to do—ever; that when de Gaulle went to conclude the Franco-Russian treaty, and everything was tied up and settled for signature, Stalin suddenly announced, pen in hand, 'You must of course agree to recognize the Lublin government, or I shall not sign.' De Gaulle objected that such a condition had never been part of the bargain. Thereupon they parted, and the treaty was not signed. Twenty-four hours later Stalin asked for de Gaulle, and signed then and there. No reference to Lublin was even made by him. Alan Lennox-Boyd was saying last night that the Allies don't know the strength of the Russian Air Force, or if they even have any civil planes in existence. They know nothing about Russia at all. What amazes me is how the Allies can ever have imagined they would be treated like civilized persons by these bloody barbarians. How I wish to God we were fighting against them, and not with them.

Sunday, 11th February

I dined last night and lunched again today with Desmond Shawe-Taylor and Eddy Sackville-West at Brooks's. The latter wishes to be buried in the Sackville vault at Withyham, amongst the velvet palls and silver coroneted coffins of his eighteenth-century ancestors. He went there the other day — 'just for fun' — with his father. His uncle lies there on a trestle.

I was taken last night to a *louche* club. What we saw going on was disturbing in general and disgusting in particular. There is something horribly genteel about brothels and their equivalents. Male and female harlots talk politely about the weather, and their talk, for they have no conversation, is laced with prurient innuendoes and punctuated with adolescent giggles. Why the hell don't they get down to business straight away, and hold out their hands for the notes? Instead they perch like suburban housewives on the edge of their stools, prolonging the ghastly farce as though to make believe they are respectable dowagers on gilt chairs in a Mayfair ballroom. I walked home alone, sickened and unsatisfied.

Monday, 12th February

Meeting day. Lord Esher told me how much he agreed with my memo about the aesthetic aspect of the Trust's work, and did not agree with the Secretary's proposal that my department should be subordinate to the agents'.

Tuesday, 13th February

Joan Moore lunched with me. She read me extracts of a letter from Jamesey. We both agreed he was one of the very best letter-writers — I said the best of our age. She is devoted to him, yet far too clever to be taken in by his wicked little blandishments.

To a lecture at the R.I.B.A. given by Goodhart-Rendel on Lutyens. Very good indeed, in spite of his speaking too fast, and lisping. He convinced his audience that Lutyens was an architect of the highest calibre, *vide* his Viceroy's House at Delhi, and designs for Liverpool Cathedral, with its medley of piers in the nave and huge space under the dome. Anstey said that Lutyens would take his place among the immortal dome builders, Michelangelo and Wren. Gerry Wellington proposed a neat vote of thanks in a very charming, ducal manner. Eddie Marsh accompanied me back to Brooks's and afterwards to the Dorchester for Sibyl's Ordinary. At my table were five men, all members of Brooks's. I sat next to Olga Lynn and Lord Gage. Enjoyable dinner. Olga Lynn told me she suffered from diabetes and took an injection every morning at 8; that two generous friends in this room gave her large sums of money every Christmas, and there was no feeling of obligation. We agreed that the very rich never derived the same joys as the rather poor, like ourselves. Lord Gage talked of school-masters and their inhumanity. Lady Aberconway said the Parisian poor were fishing for starving cats from tenement blocks with a line, and a hook at the end attached to a bit of fish. They hoisted up the cats and ate them.

Wednesday, 14th February

I set my alarum for 7 o'clock, and the inevitable consequence was that I slept very badly, waiting for the damned thing to go off. Lord Braybrooke met me at Saffron Walden station, his humble little Ford car sitting under the grand 1840 portico, erected for the benefit of his forebears' carriage and pair. With rude spluttering sounds as of an amplified sewing-machine, the Ford lurched from the portico under the supercilious gaze of one ancient porter, lolling against the wall. We drove to Audley End. After a talk, Sisson joined us. We walked and motored round the boundary which Lord B. proposes selling to J. Wilton. I said I thought the land across the road, including the Adam round temple, ought to be included. We had a picnic luncheon in the lodge. Sisson, the steward and I went over the house. This time so much of it struck me as of poor quality: the gloomy rooms in the North wing; all the 1825 'Jacobean' state-rooms in the South wing, including the 1785 state bedrooms by Rebecca.

I was home soon after 6. At 7 the doorbell rang, and there was my father who had called unannounced in a taxi. We welcomed him and Miss P. gave us dinner in the kitchen. He told me how my grandfather, on inheriting Crompton Hall, sent every single piece of eighteenth-century furniture to Druce's to be refashioned, as well as the priceless oak beds. All of them were ruined by Druce. The oak four-posters, which had been in the Crompton family for generations untouched, were made into buffets, pedestals for aspidistras and ferns, and over-mantels for Ribbesford. My grandfather 'improved' Crompton itself in the most ghastly way. My father was delightful, because totally relaxed. When it was time for him to go no taxi was obtainable. I walked with him to the bus stop, for I don't think he has ever been in a bus in his life. Immediately the bus drew up there was a flash, and the terrific explosion of a rocket.

Friday, 16th February

George Dix is a well-bred, well-mannered, civilized American; and

163

he is direct. He has a craze for papier mâché, having bought several good early trays, an inkstand by Clay, a maker in Covent Garden, and a number of chairs, which I don't find very pretty; also two rare vases, positively ugly. He has a number of Edward Lear water-colour sketches, all dated 1854 with the time of day, viz. '8 a.m.' and faint descriptions, 'Rocks', 'Pale lemon sky' pencilled in. We dined at the Reform Club not too badly, and talked for hours. I walked home, arriving at 3.20 a.m.

Saturday, 17th February

In talking to Garrett Moore I made a hideous gaff by reading to him part of a letter from James in which he wrote that Garrett was the reincarnation of Lord Fawn. When I got home I made two discoveries, one – that Lord Fawn was a foolish, pompous ass, and two – that Jamesey had written that Garrett was the antithesis of Lord Fawn. Now should I, or shouldn't I telephone to explain? Decided that I might make matters worse by doing so. James would be furious with me, because he is devoted to the Moores. Moral – never read to friends parts of a letter about them from a mutual friend. Read either the whole thing or nothing. Nothing is better.

After lunching I went to Lansdowne House. I need make no comment on the mess made of the exterior. The interior is worse. Of poor Adam's work, what has been allowed to remain, is now a travesty. The façade has been pushed back one room's width, so that the glorious entrance hall and the ante-room no longer exist. The bow room is left, but the niches have been ruthlessly cut into disproportionate openings. The room-for-company-before-dinner seems to survive, although I suspect that the apsidal end of the ante-room has been stuck haphazard on to the east end of this room. The two rotundas at the end of Smirke's picture gallery have been hacked about, and galleries introduced. The whole maelstrom is a deplorable instance of thirtyish decadence – total lack of respect for great architecture of the past, and total lack of confidence in that of the present. The result a shamefully hideous mess and muddle.

Sunday, 18th February

The singing in the Oratory this morning moved me to noble aspirations. This is, I suppose, the motive of the Roman liturgy, as it is the essence of the Christian teaching. I took the underground to Richmond, and walked across the desolate green, made less green than
164

it should be by the concrete shelters, to the Old Palace where the Jerseys now live. After luncheon Grandy took me to Syon.

The Duke of Northumberland was away and his nice house-keeper showed us round. The Doric double cube hall is a masterpiece of vigour. The twisted columns of the lower windows upon fat, writhing console scrolls, the brawny ceiling ribs, and above all the curvature of end apses and steps make this monumental room alive. A large chunk of plaster has just fallen from the ceiling. The Vestibule is as lovely as I imagined, with its incredibly vivid colours, yellow, red and blue. Two of the gold figures from the entablature have fallen and smashed to pieces, and there are cracks in the scagliola floor. Every window in the house has been smashed by bombs. The buzz bombs last summer did the worst damage. The famous verde antique columns of this room are swathed in bandages to protect them, and so cannot be seen at all. Next comes the Eating Room, the chimneypieces all boarded up. Apses and screens again here. The Cipriani *chiaroscuros* are thin and feeble; the ceiling early Adam. The Red Drawing Room must be magnificent. The gorgeous rose damask walls are covered in sheets; the pier glasses boxed up. The housekeeper showed us a circular painted rosette of Angelica Kauffmann that has fallen from the ceiling owing to an upstairs bath overflowing. It is painted on parchment. On the underside are the remains of a white paste which stuck it to the ceiling. The rosette looked atrociously executed, when held in the hand. A child could have painted it.

The long Gallery is of course a *tour de force*. If one may criticize, it is too fussy. Adam was very clever in accentuating the gallery's width, which is a mere fourteen feet, by his ceiling design, contrived to appear as though part only of a continuous larger design. In the square closet the glass panels and canvases have been removed for safety. The bird-cage from the round closet has also been put away. Several canvases from the Gallery panels have been blown out. They are of very indifferent workmanship. Patches of damp have appeared on the look-ing-glasses, for there is no central heating at all. But there is electric light. We climbed on to the lead roof where Grandy photographed me under the Percy lion. As far as the eyes can see there are trees, and Kew Gardens across the river. Syon is more parklike than Osterley. We saw the vaulted crypt, now full of pictures from Albury, and Fowler's charming conservatory with glass dome, still intact. It was a beautiful, sunny spring afternoon, and the sun on the lead roof positively radiated warmth—the first warm day since last May.

We returned to Richmond for tea, having looked at the outside of

Asgill House and of Trumpeter's House, which Grandy is about to rent. Virginia is very gentle and appealing. She is extremely short-sighted and has to wear spectacles, which is a pity. She has lovely fair skin, white teeth and a neat figure.

After tea I called, by pre-arrangement upon Aunt Katie, my grandfather's sister, the sole survivor of that large family. My grandfather, born in 1847, was a second son, so Aunt Katie must be about 90. She is very blind and quiet, but distinguished and sedate. She hardly uttered, and derived no pleasure from my visit. She was somewhat out of humour and growled at her companion for knocking against her chair. 'For the last time I must ask you not to do that,' she barked. She did however tell me she was brought up at Clarksfield Lees, and the view across the valley, though magnificent in her day, looked upon distant factory chimneys.

Monday, 19th February

Today I bought a pair of gunmetal and ormolu Regency candlesticks and a pair of Copenhagen fruitstands of the same date, in gold and blue, very pretty – all for £21.

Tuesday, 20th February

Charles Fry and I went to High Wycombe by train. He is not a congenial travelling companion. Like Mr. Harry Batsford, he chainsmokes, splutters and coughs at every breath. He stops for gin or whisky at every step. He loses his temper with waitresses at luncheon and in the tobacconist's shop. He rushed through High Wycombe church, not stopping to admire the Carlini monument. At West Wycombe he rushed round the house. Poor Mrs. Eaton, whom I am very fond of, was rushed off her poor old legs. The house has been shaken by the flying bomb which fell at Hughenden last summer. The sun was shining. How beautiful it was on the colonnade. Charles conceded that the house was the theatrical creation of an amateur with good taste. He would not stay to tea because he wanted to go to George Dix's cocktail party. We returned hurriedly to London. The great draw at this party was the Duchess of Richmond, a very sweet, simple, old lady. She talked affably to Charles and me about West Wycombe, then about tripe, animals' intestines, and haggis. I really think Charles is Satan. He makes me say the most outrageous things, and even makes a dear old duchess talk about brutish indelicacies.

George Dix took me into no. 9 Clifford Street. It was once a great town house, called Clarendon House. It is now divided into tailors' shops. An extraordinary discovery, a huge staircase hall of late seventeenth-century date, a double flight staircase with Ionic columns and thick balusters of acanthus leaves. A ribbed plaster ceiling over all, and pedimented doorcases, like Coleshill in miniature.

I took the train to Richmond and walked to Ham House. Sir Lyonel is now aged 91; young Lyonel is 60. The old man is courteous and charming, rather deaf, but very sprightly and straight. He wears an old-fashioned black cravat. Lady Tollemache looks younger, but they were married in 1881. This time conversation took a more positive turn. As at Osterley, so here we must ask the Government or the London County Council for help. Ham is superb, but far more impracticable than most great houses. Quite impossible as a private residence these days, and not suited to any institutional use. The first floor is all state-rooms; the second all intercommunicating rooms. The attic floor not fit for animals, far less for modern servants, when obtainable. The basement vast, dark and rambling. All the best pictures and furniture are away in the country. I had tea with the family and then walked round the garden with young Lyonel. Rather touching, but oh what an unhappy man. All of them seem hopelessly defeatist, anti-Government, anti-people, and anti-world. More so than me really. Of course their difficulties are formidable, but unlike the French aristocracy the English usually manage to adapt themselves to current trends, and play a leading rôle in the end, if only to survive.

Thursday, 22nd February

I went to see Dame Una, in bed with a slight fever. She looked very ill and pale, her poor face thin and her grey hair springing from cadaverous temples. I am so frightened that she may not live long; for this would devastate Jamesey. She was full of chatter and gossip notwithstanding, and much amused by the naiveté of the American young. Her bedroom was very severe, like a hospital ward. A hard modern bed, with no yield about it.

Friday, 23rd February

Took an early train to Bookham, arriving 9.30. I walked to Polesden which is beginning to look shabby. Mlle. Liron, Mrs. Greville's old maid, was evidently pleased to see me. With her I am a success. She says I am the only friend she has from whom she can ask for things. Professor Richardson's gravestone to Mrs. G. is up. It looks like the top of an old-fashioned servant's trunk, half buried in the grass. It has two ribs protruding from it, resembling those wooden supporting struts which the lids of such trunks used to have.

Sunday, 25th February

I dined at Emerald's. Gladwyn Jebb had been at the Yalta Conference. He said the food, and above all the wine, were superb: that Roosevelt seemed as though he were dying; that Stalin wore a fantastic uniform with a red star on the breast and monstrous epaulettes, and a thick red stripe down his trouser legs. He looked like a bear dressed up. While talking he fidgets, and when particularly emotional, walks round his desk-stand like a bear on a leash. He is very quick in all his retorts, cracks jokes and has charm, which I don't like to hear.

The dinner began badly, and I was preoccupied in trying to remember the Latin collect I learnt by heart this morning. Then Gladwyn Jebb insinuated that Emerald had made a misstatement. Emerald jumped upon him. 'You have got it wrong. Just mind your words.' She said she admired Sir Orme Sargent and pumped Jebb about him. Had he been in love? 'Good gracious, no, never.' 'Oh then, is he a homosexualist?' 'Certainly not. He is nothing of the kind.' Tony Gandarillos drove me home and said that Nancy Cunard had been to say good-bye to him. She was off to Paris. She asked if her mother looked much older. When Tony said No, she said, 'What a pity.' She said Emerald was 69, for she, aged 50, was born when Emerald was 19.

Monday, 26th February

I had tea with Lady Binning in Fenton House. She is perfectly agreeable to our keeping the house as a semi-museum, if we cannot get anyone to live in it. She said emphatically that she could not like Lord Esher, no matter how much I expostulated, because he was a Jew!

Tuesday, 27th February

Went to Emerald at 6. John Lehmann was alone with her. Presently others came in, including the Duff Coopers. Lady Diana was wearing a hat like a Tudor head-dress, square, with a veil of spots. Emerald said to Desmond MacCarthy, 'Do tell Diana how much we admire her hat.' He replied, 'I can't very well, for I have just told her how much I dislike it.' Daisy Fellowes walked in wearing a yellow satin turban, wound round the head into a twist at the top, and a jewel in it. Even she failed to look un-selfconscious. A horrid, uneasy gathering, being chivvied from the edge of one seat to another.

Wednesday, 28th February

In talking to me in the bar of the St. James's club, Charles Fry spat all over me. Like an absolute gentleman I merely laughed. He said, 'Good God!', took out his handkerchief and wiped my face. I passed it off but could have been sick. Coming home, for no reason I fell flat on my face on the Piccadilly pavement, bruised my hip and was shaken. A kind old man who was passing by, said, as he ran to help, 'Dear me, I am sorry,' tripped, and fell flat on his face likewise. I was unable to run towards him, but lay laughing, and crying with the pain, and laughing. He did not laugh.

Thursday, 1st March

I went to Brighton and lunched with Goodhart-Rendel in his flat. In talking to, or rather lecturing one, he paces up and down the room. He is very informative about architecture, rather dogmatic, and yet not very inspiring. He owns all the gardens and foreshore terraces of Sussex Gardens at Kemp Town, built by an architect called Charles Busby for Kemp in the 1830s. It is an ambitious and splendid layout, perhaps unique of its kind, although no individual house is of high account. It would be a new departure for the Trust to hold these lands.

Friday, 2nd March

Went by car to Oxford. Arrived at Lady Margaret Hall with some trepidation. Was ushered upstairs to the flat of the Principal, a plain, elderly, smiling dame, Miss Greir. When she had swathed herself in an old rabbit fur coat, full of moth, we drove off together. A little beyond Chipping Norton we ate our luncheon in the car, and discussed what it was that activated live wires within feeble constitutions. She gave instances of teachers, philosophers and statesmen; I of architects, painters and poets. We arrived at Cornwell, and wandered round the hamlet, lately tarted up—tastefully, let there be no mistake—by Clough Williams-Ellis, if self-consciously. The manor house we could not enter, for we had no permission, and it is an A.T.S. convalescent home. I had omitted to get permission beforehand. It is a pretty house, with a gay Georgian façade, urns (modern) on the parapet. It faces a valley in which are canals and a pool, and beyond, a beech-lined road. The remarkable thing about the façade is the flat string courses, which, on reaching the windows, dip downwards, so as to form sills, and sweep up again. A very ugly yellow-varnished front door. A picturesque Cotswold back to the manor. We made a circuit of the outside, having good views from each quarter. It is expensively maintained. There is much to be said for Clough's theatrical sense in this drab age.

At 3 o'clock we drove to Daylesford, but could not see the house from the road. It, like Adlestrop opposite, contains a huge camp of American troops. We drove to Chastleton which is open to the public. Walked up the drive to the front door where we pealed a great dinner bell. On payment of 1/- each the old butler conducted us round. We were shortly joined by a party of American officers, looking like Thomas Patch cartoons. They smoked as they shuffled round. Only the hall and white painted oak drawing-room were visible. There is nothing very good in the way of furniture. Bishop Juxon's chair is, I think, made up. But Charles I's bible, given to the bishop, and the Jones family portraits are evocative relics of this ancient home. The texture of the stone outside is very beautiful. The famous box topiary work is weird, and rather ugly.

I left Miss Greir at Moreton-in-Marsh station and continued to Bourton House, and had tea with Miss Bligh and her old sister, both very sweet and both wearing red wigs. Together we prepared scones in the kitchen which we ate in the dining-room, the old ladies running to and fro. They refused my request that we should eat in the kitchen. Miss Bligh showed me Major Benton Fletcher's musical instruments, which she has stored. So did Mrs. Murray, who has another consignment at the Rectory. She is the alarming hunting wife of the Archdeacon. She clips her 'g's and hammers her sentences hard as though on an anvil. I got to Wickhamford for supper.

Saturday, 3rd March

Midi and I set out on a fine and frosty morning to Pershore station. We picked up Mr. Harry Batsford and drove to Pirton Church, which has a fifteenth-century tower; and on to Croome. There is now an aerodrome close to the park. I disagree with James and Charles Fry who find Croome a tawdry house. The hall has the familiar Adam

Doric screen, but is otherwise rococo. I noticed two very classical tables with Doric entablatures which I suppose were designed for the room. The Gallery has a Roman coffered ceiling, and some of the wall panels, meant to be in stucco, were never completed and were left in grisaille. The saloon cannot be by Adam. It is rather coarse George II work, as one can tell from the gilt picture frames. The mahogany library book-shelves with honeysuckle finials are superb.

After lunching at the Angel in Pershore we returned to Croome. Mr. Harry took photographs inside the church with an enormous box Brownie, which he propped on a tower of heavy bibles and prayer books taken from the Coventry pew. The postures of the defunct noblemen with coronets perched precariously on their marble heads are rather funny. This Gothic church, so pretty in photographs, is somewhat thin in reality. We walked down to the beautiful orangery, of which the sash frames have all been smashed. The vase and swags of fruit in the tympanum of the pediment are finely carved in high relief.

We drove to Strensham, past the castle folly (surely by Sanderson Miller, for it resembles the Hagley one). At the end of a grass-grown drive we came upon a lonely little church and pretty vicarage, perched on the edge of a steep bank above the Avon. The front door of the vicarage was opened by a witch-like housekeeper. The dilapidation and dirt of the inside were truly frightening. In an inner room Mr. Davenport, the little old vicar, with long wavy white hair, was bent over a water-colour drawing of Oxford, hand-printing a verse which he had composed, to record the scene. He said he had not been to Oxford for 22 years, or left Strensham during that time. He made an extraordinary spectacle, like a Phiz illustration of some Dickensian curiosity shop proprietor in the 1820s. The church is as dilapidated and neglected as the vicarage. But it is remarkable. It contains several monuments to the Russells, of which one, possibly by Scheemakers, is a work of art. The nave barrel ceiling is supported by tie beams, one with a huge central boss of an angel holding an open bible. There are painted panels of saints on the gallery front. The church is dark, eerie and mysterious. Mr. Harry conducted us over Strensham Court, piled high with tea chests. It is an 1840 classical house with portico, now falling to ruin. After a large tea in a pub in Ripple we put Mr. Harry into the train at Ripple station.

I interviewed Lady Margaret Sackville, a charming woman, who wants to become curator of Knole. She is a poet and has only £100 a year to live on. I foresee family embarrassments.

Sunday, 4th March

I drove Mama to Harvington Hall. She brought her two pekingeses, to which she talked dog language incessantly. Inspected four or five pieces of furniture offered to the collection. Thence to Charlecote. My mother is the most extraordinary travelling companion, for she makes friends everywhere. In asking the way at Droitwich of a man sweeping his doorstep, she got from him his life history, how much rent he was paying and how many children he had. Finally he called his wife, and the two of them sat on the step of the car stroking the dogs. At Harvington the caretaker, unsolicited, brought us tea, discussed her ailments, her son's love life and her religious beliefs.

Tuesday, 6th March

The Distillers own no. 20 St. James's Square. It has suffered badly from bombs. An oil bomb fell at the rear, burning out the Adam rooms there. The other rooms have suffered more or less; ceilings down, looking-glasses smashed. The wonderful coved room upstairs is not badly damaged.

Thursday, 8th March

I was motored by an agent from Yeovil to Trent, five miles away, where we ate sandwiches in the pub. In the afternoon we looked at the 1,200-acre estate which Mr. Cook has bought. I think there is little point in the Trust holding it because it is no more remarkable than the surrounding country in these parts. The manor house is very disappointing. It was horribly spoilt about 1912. Charles II's hiding place still survives but little else. The King spent nineteen days here after Worcester. I took the 4 o'clock train from Yeovil and got home at 10.45, very tired.

Friday, 9th March

Eardley and I walked to King's Bench Walk to a party Harold and Vita gave together, a very exceptional occasion. Harold in a gay and frolicsome mood; Vita very beautiful, regal, tall and thin, wearing a wide-brimmed hat over her eyes and smoking from a long cigarette holder. She is never frolicsome.

At Brooks's Lord Spencer told me that Professor Richardson made an excellent speech for him in Northampton, but said that all Americans were vulgar, and gave too long a dissertation on Georgian water closets. He had to keep these embellishments out of the newspaper.

Dinner at Emerald's. She showed me a portrait by Steer of a coster-monger, done in 1880. Mrs. Snow, the American, to whom she showed it, kept repeating 'My dear, what a wonderful likeness.' Emerald made me pick up a heavy marble bust of a Venus, which she stroked while saying to Cecil Beaton and me, 'You know the uniformity of these Greek sculptures is the secret of their beauty. This might be the body of a man. Just take them away [pointing at the breasts]. No, leave them. Some men have breasts like these, so they tell me. Is that true, Cecil? You ought to know. No, now don't laugh,' and so on.

Stephen Spender at Harold's party talked to me about anarchism, and said it did not work; that syndicalism could no more run a nation than a concatenation of parish councils.

Saturday, 10th March

A sunny, balmy day. I walked without an overcoat to lunch with Alice Harding at the Basque Restaurant. The Sachie Sitwells, their son Reresby and George Dix there. Sachie has old-fashioned good manners. Anecdotes fly from his lips like little birds from an open cage.

Dined with Rory and Lady Kenmare. A large party. When the women left the dining-room Beverley Baxter and Lord Margesson, formerly chief Whip and Minister for War, started talking about the recent debate on Yalta. They said it was perhaps a pity the Prime Minister claimed the Polish settlement, which they agreed was the only possible solution, to be a wise and beneficent one. Quite suddenly I became furious, and, red in the face, exclaimed, 'Beneficent, my foot! Expedient doubtless. It is a disgrace and an indictment of Parliament that only twenty-one Members had the courage of their convictions to vote against you. The Poles have every reason to feel betrayed. Our country has openly and brazenly betrayed them.' I was somewhat surprised at myself. Lord Margesson became indignant, and said, 'Look here! We must have your reasons for this allegation, etc. What would you have the Government do?' I said rather truculently, 'The allega-tion is borne out by the deed. What the Government ought to do is something honourable. It's not for me to dictate. I'm not a professional politician,' which was a bit lame. He said more angrily than before that politicians were just as other men. I checked myself saying what I thought of him and most of them. In the course of the argument that ensued I said the Russians were less to be trusted than the Germans, and were far more dangerous. We had got our enemies wrong, since it was peoples not systems that we were evidently fighting against. And I defended the Pope and bishops against the charge of condoning Fascism. I told them that the Pope had to put ideals before countries, and that all Christians ought to put the Church before their own country. Lord M. and the other men present were, I could see, shocked and annoyed. Not an enjoyable evening.

Monday, 12th March

In between the two meetings today I lunched with Esher, who was very outspoken in his objection to the agents' encroachment upon the aesthetes' work. He laughed mischievously and said, 'After all, L.-M., you must remember, they are only plumbers.' At this morning's meeting it was decided to extend the function of the Country Houses Committee, henceforth to be called the Historic Buildings Committee.

Thursday, 15th March

This morning and this evening we had two very close and noisy rocket explosions. There had been several during the night. The damage they are said to do is terrific. Three hundred people were killed by one in the City last week. This evening's one made a prolonged, echoing roar like a roll of thunder.

Friday, 16th March

This morning I walked from Wooton Farm up the lane to Friday Street, where Christopher Gibbs met me, and motored me to Severell's Copse. When unspoilt, Surrey landscape is rich and luxuriant like those tight, condensed water colours by Linnell. After walking through the Copse with the timber control officer, we continued to Leith Hill Place. Dr. Vaughan-Williams was there. He is rather old and muddly, but disarming and very generous. He seems only too anxious to divest himself of all mundane trappings. We walked round the house, making a list of those contents he would like to remain in the house. They consisted mostly of Wedgwood and Darwin prints and minia-tures. Two great black figures on plinths, signed and dated Coade 1797. Lunched with the Gibbs family at Goddards. Good olde English down-to-earthe foode.

Dined at the Argentine Embassy. Jacqueline Killearn, whom I haven't seen since I was 18, told me that her father, Sir Aldo Castellani, is incarcerated in the Quirinal with the Prince of Piedmont, and that all parties have treated him abominably. He is not the least interested
174

in politics, only in his medicine and his friends. She has not seen him for six years. She has not been home to England for six years. Lord Margesson was polite to me in spite of our difference the other evening, and said I was the first person to have explained to him George Lloyd's complex character. There was one row at dinner, when Chips foolishly belittled the K.C.s, saying they were not in society and were bourgeois. At this I spoke up. I said I hardly knew the C.s, but he was undoubtedly one of the most brilliant and distinguished men of our generation. Emerald said to Chips, 'You are as much an upstart as K.C., and so am I. We are both from across the Atlantic. As for you [to Lord Margesson], you know nothing about the arts or the intellect. You are only fit for politics and love. You know nothing of anything else.' Chips then said that Mrs. Corrigan was in the best society, and that anyone in Paris who was not received by her was 'beneath consideration'. Jacqueline and I agreed that talk about 'society' was outside our understanding. To her such talk was unintelligible, and parvenu.

Saturday, 17th March

To the office this morning, with a hangover. How ill drink makes me, and what a bad effect on my temper. To Denham by train. Walked from the station to the Wittkowers' house. A coldish wind but all the blackthorn out. Yesterday there were Lent lilies at Leith Hill Place. Dr. Wittkower was away and I looked through several eighteenth-century tomes. I was given a good vegetarian luncheon in the kitchen, with five odd German Jewess blue-stockings, all down to bedrock (or do I mean rock bottom?), serious and friendly.

Monday, 19th March

I travelled to Yeovil with Bertie Abdy. He holds the most unorthodox views about art. Deprecates every artifact that happens to be English, which makes me want to ask him why he consented to join the Montacute Committee. A horrid day, it poured with rain and Eardley failed to turn up. I thought the Committee most tiresome for, apart from Christopher Hussey, none of them has the faintest idea how the house ought to be arranged.

Thursday, 22nd March

G. M. Trevelyan came to the office early, with the proofs of the

National Trust book. He thinks not enough reference has been made to specific N.T. properties and too much has been said about the various aspects, archaeological, entomological, etc. of the Trust's work. He showed me the first half of his Introduction, and asked what he should say in the last half. I said, please stress the Trust's opposition to museumization, and its wish to preserve the face of England as it was under private ownership.

Friday, 23rd March

I dined with John Fowler. I arrived at 8.30 because he always eats late; even so we did not sit down till 9.45. Geoffrey Houghton-Brown was there and Captain (Billy) Henderson, who arrived at 8 o'clock this evening with the Viceroy from India. He breakfasted this morning in Sicily, having dined last night in Cairo. He said the aeroplane was very comfortable, with good food and beds to lie down on. India was a continent of enchantment – the beauty of the peasant women, all wearing silks and silver bracelets and anklets. He said there are 360 servants in the Palace at Delhi; the building is very ugly, the dome raised on stilts; and many of the rooms face internal wells. The sandstone of the building gets so hot that in summer you cannot bear your hand on it at midnight. The best architecture is Sir Herbert Baker's Secretariat.

Saturday, 24th March

This morning I called for Mrs. Fellowes at the Dorchester and motored her to Faringdon, where we lunched with Berners and Robert Heber-Percy. At 3 we called at Coleshill. The Miss Pleydell-Bouveries took us over the house, but Mrs. F. was not as pleased with it as I had hoped. She did not think it well equipped, for it only has three bathrooms. We went on to the roof. The cupola with its golden ball is swathed in rugs to prevent it being a landmark to German aeroplanes by moonlight. From here the beautiful, stalwart chimneys can be seen to advantage. Mrs. F. had vertigo looking over the parapet. I noticed in the large saloon how finely carved the Chippendale armchairs are. A curious thing I observed in the elevation was that the lines of the cornice are curved and the roof dormers are set, not at right angles to the roof, but slightly splayed outwards. Presumably this arrangement was intended to minimize the severity and marked tightness of the design, and to create 'movement', in the way that the stylobate of the Parthenon was deliberately laid out of the true. We had tea off a large
176

table, covered with a thick old linen cloth. Mrs. F. much liked the elder sister with her twinkling eye. She is like a little hedgehog.

We got to Compton Beauchamp at 5.30, exactly the same moment as Chips Channon and Terence Rattigan.

For so sophisticated a woman, Daisy—this is what Mrs. Fellowes tells me to call her—has simple country tastes. Yet I cannot help seeing her as Reynolds's Mrs. Graham, the society lady masquerading as a housemaid with a broom. She keeps a cow which she likes to milk herself, when she is here. She asked someone the other day if the cow would mind her going to Paris for a long weekend without being milked during her absence.

Compton Beauchamp combines so many qualities that are desirable in a country house. It is completely surrounded by a moat, for romance. It has a pleasant, central square courtyard, for shelter. The approach is by a symmetrical forecourt with two detached flanking stable wings, retaining wall, stone piers and magnificent iron gates, for grandeur. The principal façade is classical Queen Anne of rustic simplicity, for cosiness and dignity. The other façades are medieval and Jacobean, for historic continuity. There is an extremely pretty garden at the back with contemporary raised terraces. A box garden behind that; another magnificent iron gate between piers, cut and set askew to the wall. It is a small paradise in a fold of the downs, with tinkling fountains in the forecourt and courtyard. A dream country house in which I could gladly be incarcerated for the rest of my life, and which I would never be tempted to leave.

Tuesday, 27th March

To St. Leonard's-on-Sea to inspect some furniture which a Mr. Tate wants to leave to the Trust. While I was under a table running my fingers in a professional manner up and down the legs, like a horse-coper examining fetlocks at a sale, I realized how ignorant I was, with no pretentions to judge what is genuine and what fake in furniture. I rely upon instinct, sharpened by years of experience, rather than upon imbibed knowledge from textbooks.

Wednesday, 28th March

This evening I went to Tony Gandarillos's house. After three glasses of whisky and soda I realized in a flash that I must be careful. At the moment of enlightenment Poulenc and a companion arrived. How crazy and ugly French men can be. This enormous man, ungainly as an elephant, strode into the room while talking at the top of his voice, and gesticulating like a fury. With a good deal of the traditional *ou-la-la* he threw himself into an armchair, imprecating and shouting in French, as though I did not exist. Had I not been a little drunk I would have hated this middle-aged Frog, eminent though he be.

Easter Sunday, 1st April

I am staying at Monk Hopton near Bridgnorth for Easter. The house of red brick is not beautiful or interesting. Lady de Vesci, *grande dame*, handsome, slim and upright, works hard at her garden all day. It is too full of conifers for my taste. The surrounding country, lush with deciduous trees, is on the other hand superb. Poor Bridget has injured her eye with a twig.

I was called rather early this morning, and lent a bicycle. Pedalled three miles to Mass at Aldenham Park. The house stands well on an eminence at the end of a long, straight avenue, approached through wrought-iron gates, with a clairvoyée. Expectation of coming upon a worthwhile building dwindles as the bicycle nears the goal. The Georgian house must have been encased in stone and given plate-glass windows in the nineteenth century. By the historian Lord Acton? I did not go inside. A nuns' school occupies it at present. There are red brick stable buildings. The detached chapel, about 1870, is on the terrace. It is a rather nice, classical structure. The chapel was filled with nuns in white hoods. I sat behind them in the small congregation, mostly children, the Actons' presumably, because like all Catholics they have dozens. Ronnie Knox said Mass in that unmistakable Oxford accent. I got back to breakfast at 11.

Monday, 2nd April

Bridget returned to London this evening. Lord and Lady de Vesci and I went for a long walk across fields and through woods to Upton Cresset, now a farmhouse. It is a red brick Elizabethan house, with two vast, twisted chimneystacks, and a detached gatehouse of two round towers. We entered this. It has remains of some elaborate plasterwork in overmantel and ceiling; and a newel staircase.

Wednesday, 4th April

My much anticipated-with-apprehension-but-pleasurable dinner with Daisy Fellowes. There she was, splendid in black lace and a black
178

mantilla over her hair, with violets in it for my benefit, so she said. A limousine took us to the Basque Restaurant in Dover Street. There was no wine, so we had to be contented with two glasses of sherry each, nothing more. The bill came to £4.10.0 with tip, which was monstrous. There was no actual breakdown in conversation, yet there were awkward pauses. I felt mesmerized like a rabbit by a stoat, and frightened to death until, come the pudding, I pulled myself together with 'Fool!' and pinched myself, with 'To hell!' and proceeded to enjoy the rest of the evening mightily. Anyway I am to go to the theatre with her next week.

When I got home I read in the evening paper that poor Ava [Lord Dufferin] had been killed. Ava was with Tom the friend I most admired at my private school, and at Eton, where the three of us edited magazines together. I saw little of him at Oxford, and rarely met him afterwards. He had the best brain of my generation, and was at school a brilliant scholar, winning prizes after doing the minimum amount of work, always at the last moment. As a boy he was an eccentric in that, during intense concentration, he would literally eat his handkerchief and suck ink from the end of a pen without realizing what he was doing. I think he was ruined for life by the late Lord Birkenhead, who at Oxford taught him and others of his group to drink. Consequently he became a sad physical wreck before he was thirty.

Thursday, 5th April

This morning's *Times* has an appreciation of Ava by Frank Pakenham. All day I have thought of him, and lamented that the opportunity never came to bridge the break in our friendship. On the very few occasions when we did meet the affection was still there.

Took the 9 o'clock train to Salisbury. Eardley met me and motored me to Boyton. This is David Herbert's house, which he has inherited from an uncle and wants to sell. We looked at it for Cook. It is a beautiful square Cotswoldy house with pointed gables, about 1610, and projecting porch. Built of stone, covered with a harl in dappled wash. Much Jacobean and William and Mary wainscoting, and one long parlour on the first floor facing east, with ordinary ribbed plaster ceiling. Troops have been in it, but treated it well. There is a mown terraced lawn, and a long vista of curving woodlands and a meadow.

Returning to Salisbury we called at Dinton. The American camp immediately in front of Hyde's House is a real desecration. I have never seen anything so disagreeable—concrete roads, tin huts with smoking chimneys, in short a hideous shanty town in what was a beautiful park. The original concave glass panes of Dinton House glinted in the sunshine.

Sunday, 8th April

And now what I so long foreboded and dreaded has happened. I was at home working all day. At 6.30, when just about to leave for Bridget's to take her out to dinner, Nancy rang me up to say Tom had been killed in Burma. They heard yesterday. He was wounded in the stomach, and died on Good Friday. Whether he was with Ava they don't know. I could barely finish speaking to Nancy, who was very composed. She says her parents are shattered. Beloved, handsome Tom, who should have been married and had hosts of beautiful children; Tom, caviar to the general possibly, but to me the most loyal and affectionate of friends. It is hell. Luckily Bridget was dining with me. She was wonderful, calm and sympathetic, and wretched too. I loved her for it.

Tuesday, 10th April

Asked Nancy to lunch at Gunters to show her the Appreciation, about which I had cold feet lest she might be embarrassed. But she seemed to like it. I was greatly cheered and took it to *The Times*. Nancy was very brave, laughing and making jokes, but said she was still stunned. When Bobo was told she said, 'I do envy Tom having such fascinating arguments with Dr. Johnson now,' and to the vicar's wife, 'How lucky Tom was to die on Good Friday,' which amused Nancy very much and would have amused Tom. Lady Redesdale has come up to London, and to N.'s surprise is braver than any of them, and almost cheerful. There has been a gathering of the sisters. Diana unexpectedly walked into the Mews where they were all assembled, not having seen her father for seven years, he declining to set eyes on her ever since her marriage to Tom [Sir Oswald] Mosley. Nancy said she sailed in unabashed, and at once, like the old Diana, held the stage and became the centre of them all. To their amazement Lord Redesdale greeted her affectionately. Diana had motored up in a Daimler with two policemen in attendance. Lord R. in his old-fashioned way insisted on sending out cups of hot, sweet tea, which he said was what policemen always liked best. Diana whispered in some trepidation that Tom Mosley was waiting in the car, and warned Nancy to keep her father away. But he insisted on taking Diana downstairs when she left in spite of Diana's remonstrances, saying that he would accompany her to the car. Finally she had to explain, 'Farve, the Man Mosley [Lord R. always refers to him as such] is waiting in the motor for me.' Lord Redesdale laughed and let her go. Infinitely poignant I think.

At 6 I called for Daisy Fellowes at the Dorchester. She was in her suite drinking champagne with her husband, who sat in an armchair looking as though in the last stages. Daisy treats him with much solicitude and sweetness. He has had one leg amputated, for he suffers from clotting blood. In her car we fetched Compton Mackenzie. He is out-going, forward-looking, communicative, friendly. We drove to the Chancellor of the Exchequer's house in Lord North Street and picked up Lady Anderson. One policeman on duty outside the house. Drove to the theatre for an Agatha Christie play. Returned to the Dorchester and had a delicious supper with more white wine. Lady Anderson told me she was anxious to form a committee of Gerry Wellington and me to advise on the decoration and furnishing of 11 Downing Street. She is anxious that the house should be dealt with in such a way that succeeding Chancellors of the Exchequer cannot scrap their predecessors' alterations and make their own. The same danger faces no. 10. She said she dreaded to think what hash Ernest Bevin might make if he ever inhabited one or the other.

Compton Mackenzie, rather like a child, produced a birthday book and made us all sign our names against our dates of birth. He has a sharp pointed beard and wears a cape.

Thursday, 12th April

Yesterday I came by train to Haverfordwest. I am staying at Picton Castle. This afternoon Johnnie Philipps motored me across the Priscilly Hills to Llangwair, the Bowens' place. They have let the house to the Salvation Army for the war. It is filled with old women bombed out of the East End. The Bowens picnic in a caravan and a tent, winter and summer. Llangwair is a medium-sized house, the outside rough-cast, the inside wainscoted with William and Mary panels. Situation over a rushing river, facing the hills above Newport. Picturesque. A Welsh stranded gentry set-up. Johnnie was a great help in assessing the merits and demerits, for he knows his country well. We were given tea in the caravan and on the grass, for we could not all get inside the caravan.

Friday, 13th April

We rise very late here; and how one sleeps and yawns. Relaxation does not suit me. Johnnie and I walked over the fields to Slebech, his widowed sister Sheila de Rutzen's house, her daughter Victoria riding her pony beside us. It was a cloudless day. The banks were thick with primroses and the woods with bluebells in bud. From a hillock between the two houses we had distant views over the creek of the river. Slebech is actually on the creek, and more romantically situated than Picton. We went over this delightful house. A fresh unit of troops was trying to clean up the appalling mess left by the last. Since January water has been allowed to seep from burst pipes through the ceilings and down the walls. Most of the stair balusters have disappeared. Mahogany doors have been kicked to pieces. Floor boards are ripped up. All rooms mottled with and stinking of damp. I imagine dry rot has set in everywhere. We walked back above the river through the woods. It became so extremely hot that I took off all but my shirt.

After tea we did a tour of this castle. The thick ribbed thirteenth-century undercroft is archaeologically important. A pity it is so disfigured by a criss-cross of hot-water pipes and wires. The great hall is decent provincial Palladian. The small, low drawing-room is rococo. Some good pre-Adam chimneypieces of marble. The chapel is of Wren date, with rough contemporary pews. The walls have been stencilled with Victorian texts and darkened by two very poor stained-glass windows in memory of an aunt.

Sunday, 15th April

At tonight's dinner party, which I attended at a round table in a resonant room, everyone talked across at one another. It was like trying to speak to someone on the telephone when other peoples' lines have crossed one's own.

Wednesday, 18th April

I went with Bridget and Anne to Ava's memorial service in St. Margaret's, Westminster. Archbishop Lang of Canterbury conducted the service and gave an address. He referred to Basil's unusual gifts and—what I thought was correct but brave—the temptations that had beset and nearly overcome him, but which he had so resolutely resisted. The Last Post was played from behind the aisle, not made less poignant by the roar of traffic during the silent pauses. I thought how sublime this would have sounded in the Abbey, the prolonged notes receding from the larger waste of Gothic piers, and echoing down the distant cloisters.

Dined with Daisy for the Cavendish ball in the Dorchester. I danced mostly with Bridget, and we walked away arm in arm, discoursing. Both of us remarked that the older men become, the more they stick their behinds out when dancing. Why is this?

Wednesday, 25th April

Came home at 7 to find that a bomb had fallen near by and my water tank had in consequence burst. All my best books are saturated, which makes me very unhappy. I spent a melancholy evening mopping up. There was an inch of water in the big room.

Thursday, 26th April

Angst is the strangest, most unpredictable enemy. It assails one for no apparent reason in the most unlikely places. Today in Manchester walking from the station to the Midland Hotel I was so overwhelmed with a sense of my own futility that I was terrified lest someone might speak to me. It was most unlikely that someone would, for I know nobody and nobody knows me down here. But I skulked close to the wall on the side of the street away from the sun so as to be as inconspicuous as possible. I have noticed that April is always the worst month for this kind of nonsense.

Friday, 27th April

A bitter east wind, in fact the Protestant wind, so named by James II when he feared the beastly Orange's armada. I called myself at 7 and caught a train for Mow Cop. Yesterday (apart from the skulking episode) and today have been blissful because I have been totally alone. From Mow Cop station I climbed the steep hill to the ridiculous castle folly which belongs to the N. Trust. It blew so hard at the top that I could scarcely breathe. Having inspected this monument associated with the Primitive Methodists, I descended across the fields to Little Moreton Hall. A truly picturesque scene, with the cows lying—it is going to rain—before the moat. The house looked more grotesque than ever; the gallery is so uneven and undulating that it must topple over into the moat. The chapel end subsides in an acute angle. And yet it stands like the Tower of Pisa. How, I wonder?

183

I love the old-fashioned farmyard atmosphere, the heavy, polished Victorian furniture in the great hall, the brown teapot, the scones and marmalade and eggs for luncheon. Charming farmeresses waiting on me, and gossiping with each other, and me, and for ever polishing. The caretaker, Mrs. Bailey, was away in hospital. She is the daughter of my great friend, Mrs. Dale, the farmer's wife, descended from the Dale 'carpeder' who left his name on the compass windows, having made them 'by the grac of God' in 1559. One of the ladies confided in me that this daughter was temperamental, odd and, she whispered very loudly, a shop-lifter.

On my return I called on Bridget. Mark Ogilvie-Grant was with her. He is just back from a German prison camp after four years' absence and, he assured me, was disappointingly sane and 'un-psychological'. He was released three weeks ago. For the last six months all he was given for breakfast was ersatz coffee, for luncheon three or four small potatoes, and for dinner vegetable soup with, twice a week, some scraps of meat in it. He is thinner.

Monday, 30th April

The account of that brute Mussolini's summary execution and the indignities inflicted upon his corpse by the hands of the partisans does not make edifying reading. But how typical of present-day political morality. No one party, no one nation seems to behave better than another. Doubtless the summary execution was a better way of despatching Mussolini than by a long-drawn-out trial, which would have exasperated the people and have led to a lynching, like Caruso's death. In fact it is obvious that you cannot try civilian captives, who will excuse their past conduct before the law with the plea that they were acting according to the instructions of their superiors, or the constitution of their country. But the fate of Mussolini ought to be a salutary deterrent to aspiring dictators of the future. It won't be of course.

This afternoon Mr. Sedgwick motored me to see his house, South End House, at the end of Montpelier Row, Twickenham, facing the Marble Hill estate. It is a fine 1720 building with projecting closets from ground floor to roof in the Owletts manner. One large room was built on in Strawberry Hill style, with a magnificent chimneypiece like a Westminster Abbey tomb, flanked by Gothic piers and capped by pineapples. The Sedgwicks dislike it and want to take it down. I tried to dissuade them. He and his wife gave me a delicious tea. The house is divided into four flats—lovely they are—Walter de la Mare and

Professor Reilly occupying two. In the garden is a splendid plane tree of enormous girth, contemporary with the house.

Tuesday, 1st May

At 4 o'clock to the Bank of England. Ruby Holland-Martin gave me permission to be shown round by an official. To my surprise there is absolutely nothing left of Sampson, Taylor or Soane's work inside, and outside only Soane's outer wall. And that has been mutilated by Sir Herbert Baker. I was disgusted by the re-erection of the Taylor court room, which Baker tampered with to suit his own devices. Had he demolished the whole building and built anew from the foundations I should have respected him more, but he has compromised by reproducing Taylor vaulting and Soane motifs in the basement. Yet Baker is a distinctive architect and craftsman. His clocks, for example, are truly noble artifacts not to be despised. His lapses into Kraal detail are undignified in classical work.

I worked and dined alone in Brooks's. At 10.30 a member rushed into the morning room announcing that Hitler's death had just come through on the tape. We all ran to read about it. Somehow, I fancy, none of us was very excited. We have waited, and suffered too long. Three years ago we would have been out of our minds with jubilation and excitement — and with prognostications of a happy issue out of all our afflictions.

Wednesday, 2nd May

Had a drink this evening with Lady Berwick at the Ladies Carlton Club. Victor Cunard brought an earnest young Italian from the Embassy. He was fanatically anti-Fascist. He thought Mussolini's death the best way out, but I was glad that he hoped there would be no further reprisals, and that Donna Rachele and her children were being protected by the partisans. He, a northerner, has the greatest contempt for the southern Italians. Lady Berwick spoke brilliantly about the Italian character, which she knows well.

Saturday, 5th May

I really love Blickling and feel happy here. I spent the morning in the Long Gallery, at the large table in the window overlooking the garden. The sun cast square blobs of yellow joy upon the floor, but did not reach the bookshelves. I looked through the old architectural books, while Miss O'Sullivan worked away at her catalogue of the 12,000 volumes. I seriously consider spending part of my holiday here. After luncheon I left for King's Lynn. Stayed the night at the Globe with Penrose, whose company elevates me. He has become an Anglo-Catholic, and is convinced that Christianity alone can save the world. He is an optimist. He is standing as Liberal candidate for Lynn.

Sunday, 6th May

Went to Mass at 10 and was devout, the result of Alec's uplifting society. Sisson came for luncheon and we spent the afternoon in St. George's Hall, which Alec has bought to save. At present it is in a deplorable state, and full of junk. It is supposed to be the largest British guildhall surviving. Alec and Sisson think more of it than I do. True, the shell is intact, and so are most of the roof timbers. Nevertheless only one of the intricate curved tiebeams is intact. The building dates from the late fourteenth century. From the sixteenth to the nineteenth it was used as a theatre. Shakespeare's company is known to have acted in it. Behind it long medieval warehouses trail down to the river. Included in the property is a stone-fronted Queen Anne town house, which to me is more attractive than this rather dreary hall. We wandered round the town which has a doomed, anachronistic, unwanted look. King Street and Queen Street are, I think, the finest old streets anywhere in England.

Monday, 7th May

Grandy Jersey lunched at Brooks's. I have asked his firm to make an estimate of the repairs needed to the stuffs in the state-rooms at Blickling.

Grandy overheard two shopgirls in the street this morning say they did not feel like 'jubilating', and would be happier going to the shop as usual. All day there has been a feeling in the air of expectancy, hysteria and uncertainty. The papers tell us that the Germans have capitulated, yet make no announcement about the ridiculous VE day. Aimlessly I walk to Bridget's flat and have a drink with her and Anne [Rosse], then back to Brooks's. Aeroplanes keep flying low over London, nobody knows why. People say peace negotiations have broken down, and we have declared war on the Russians. Passionately longing for peace though I am, I know in my inmost being that this is what we ought to do. Lanning Roper turned up in naval uniform. He is handsome, and serious.

All this evening people have roamed the streets in an uncertain sort of way, jubilating very half-heartedly. When Roper and I left Brooks's to walk down Bond Street there were not many jubilators in Piccadilly. In fact there was little shouting and gaiety.

Tuesday, 8th May

This is V day at last. I got home at 9.30, had a bath and changed. At midday went to Bridget's flat, and with her and Anne to lunch with John Sutro at Driver's. We were joined by Oliver Messel and a quiet, mystery man of about 50. We ate oysters and lobsters and drank sweet champagne. Then returned to hear Churchill's speech at 3 o'clock. It was merely a short announcement that peace had been declared. We were all rather disappointed, and wondered what was the necessity for telling us what we already knew.

I went to John Sutro's house at 7 and found Bridget there. Had it not been for the mystery man arriving uninvited at 8 o'clock and staying with us, the evening would have been unalloyed fun. The three of us being such old friends were perfectly contented with our own company. Bridget was more beautiful and alluring than ever I remember her. John and I kept remarking upon this to each other over and over again. We drank muscat wine, and listened to the King's speech at 9. It was perfect, well phrased, well delivered in his rich, resonant voice, expressed with true feeling and tinged with an appropriate emotion for the occasion. Bridget and I cooked the dinner, she scrambling eggs, I frying bacon in great quantity. This was all we had, but it was delicious. We drank a bottle of excellent white wine and some very old brandy, sitting till 11.45 at the table. All the while the sad mystery man sat speechless. John played Chopin on the piano. At midnight I insisted on our joining the revels. It was a very warm night. Thousands of searchlights swept the sky. Otherwise there were few illuminations and no street lights at all. Claridges and the Ritz were lit up. We walked down Bond Street passing small groups singing, not boisterously. Piccadilly was however full of swarming people and littered with paper.

We walked arm in arm into the middle of Piccadilly Circus which was brilliantly illuminated by arc lamps. Here the crowds were singing, and yelling and laughing. They were orderly and good humoured. All the English virtues were on the surface. We watched individuals climb the lamp posts, and plant flags on the top amidst tumultuous applause from bystanders. We walked down Piccadilly towards the Ritz. In the Green Park there was a huge bonfire under the trees, and too near one poor tree which caught fire. Bridget made us push through the crowd collected on the pavement to a ring of people round the bonfire. They were very funny, bringing huge posts from nowhere and hurling them on to the fire. Six or seven people were struggling under barricades of wood and whole doorways from air raid shelters which they dragged on to the fire. The fire's reflection upon thousands of faces, packed on the pavement, squatting on the grass and cramming the windows of the Piccadilly houses reminded me for some reason of a Harrison Ainsworth illustration of the crowds witnessing Charles I's execution. One extraordinary figure, a bearded, naval titan, organized an absurd nonsense game, by calling out the Navy and making them tear round the bonfire carrying the Union Jack; then the R.A.F.; then the Army; then the Land Army, represented by three girls only; then the Americans; then the civilians. If we had been a little drunker we would have joined in. As it was Bridget took a flying leap over the pyre in sheer exuberance of spirits. The scene was more Elizabethan than neo-Georgian, a spontaneous peasant game, a dance round the maypole, almost Bruegelian, infinitely bucolic. No one was bullied into joining who didn't want to, and the spectators enjoyed it as much as the participants. I thought, if we could have a V night once a month, and invite the Poles, Germans, even Russians to do what we were doing now, there might never be another war.

We left B at Mount Street. John and I went to his house where I slept the night. This was about 3 a.m.

Wednesday, 9th May

Woke rather bedraggled at 10.30, but pulled myself together enough to prepare a scratch breakfast. John is hopelessly disorganized in the absence of his wife, but the best company in the world on such an occasion. He, Bridget and I had planned to motor to the country, but the back tyre was punctured, and that was that. This VE business is getting me down with fatigue. I was rather pleased to stay at home instead. I went to tea with Dame Una, who read me long and excellent letters from James. Then to Alvilde, and found crowds of people. Paul Sudley told me Tom Goff was complaining that I had diddled him out of Holt Court, his inheritance, by persuading his father, whom I knew to be out of his mind, to give it to the Trust, while he, Tom, was overseas. Raymond Mortimer, whether or not to tease me I don't know, said that Tom Goff had a real grievance, and if he went to law the N.T.'s position would look very ugly. Derek Hill, who misses nothing, took all this in, and repeated it word for word to Eardley later. I feel sensitive about this unjust charge. Lady Cecilie, Tom's mother, was present throughout all our discussions about Holt Court and never said a word or made a sign of dissent.

Dined at Lady Kenmare's to meet the Italian Ambassador and wife. He is delightful, she intense. Emerald said to me, 'You are a very perspicacious man, Jim, oh yes,' when all I had said was that Mr. Churchill was devoted to his brother Jack, now dying in hospital, because he was 'the repository of his confidences'. Emerald recounted her row with Noël Coward last night. He greeted her with, 'Emerald darling!' She replied, 'Why do you call me "darling". I don't know you very well.' Then she said, 'I have never liked you.' And again later, 'You are a very common man.' Tony Gandarills practically had to separate them.

Friday, 11th May

This morning to a meeting at Horne's office with Brian Fairfax-Lucy and his solicitor, where we discussed the transfer of Charlecote to the Trust. Brian wishes us to pay for maintenance as from the date of acceptance, which was last month. He is such a generous person that I hope the Trust won't haggle. He also wants us to buy the First Folio and the gold cup given by Charles II to his ancestor.

An enjoyable dinner at Emerald's tonight. Lord Margesson is quick-witted and teases Emerald deliciously. He is a good talker when he gets on to beastly politics, as Emerald remarked, and has a beautiful timbre to his soft voice, which he never raises even when roused; on the contrary he lowers it. I suppose the House of Commons teaches a man to control his emotions. Emerald was tonight quicker with her repartee than I ever remember. I was amazed by her brilliant, incisive mind. Conversation flitted from nonsense to seriousness. Lord Gage said, 'Once in Berlin a painted young creature said to me, "Darling, don't be county now." Imagine such a thing, to me, who literally am the county of Sussex.' Emerald said the Minister for Food invited her to sit on his knee. Lord Margesson spoke well about the Bolshevik situation. He said Churchill was terribly depressed by their stubborn non-cooperation, and the blackout they have lowered over their side of the German front. They will allow no one to penetrate it, and no one to enter Vienna. It is thought they are putting all Germans to the sword, with the exception of those thousands they are deporting as slaves to Russia. This a most terrible and sickening thing. Clarissa [Churchill] said one must not mind. But I do. All agreed that we are powerless with the Bolsheviks. It remains to be seen whether they march further west, or remain content with what they have already got; whether they are motivated by imperialism, or are merely taking steps to forestall Great Britain one day turning a democratized Germany upon them.

A notice to quit this house (no. 104 Cheyne Walk) has already reached me. June 11th is the day I must leave. What is to happen to poor Miss P.?

I stay the weekend with the Somerset de Chairs at Chilham. The approach to the Castle is through two lodges built by Sir Herbert Baker traditionally and decently. A narrow lime avenue to the entrance. Sir Herbert did a great deal to the house for the late Sir Edmund Davis, wisely and modestly I think. Nearly every window mullion had to be renewed; also the glazing. Much grey panelling has been inserted and faked up. The best interior feature is the arcaded staircase of 1616. In two bedrooms are chimneypieces of beautiful Bethesden marble. Two bedrooms have original plaster ceilings. Otherwise there is little left. Somerset is quite certain Inigo Jones was the architect because the watermark on the early plan corresponds with the watermark on some other paper used by Inigo, a German paper.

After luncheon we walked across the fields to Godmersham. The situation of this house, though only two miles from Chilham, is quite different. Whereas Chilham with its wonderful descending brick terraces is situated on a hill overlooking a valley and the Downs, Godmersham, which is early Georgian with flanking wings, lies in a broad and unconfined basin. From the house, which springs out of the green park meadowland, the sides of the basin gently rise from all sides. From every window are visible quietly curving lines and contours. The Trittons have spent thousands on altering and improving. She is the widow and heiress of Sir Bernard Baron, who was fabulously rich. The consequence is the house is a little too perfect. The furniture is superb. Good pictures are few; some Devises and Zoffanys. The garden side was entirely rebuilt by Walter Sarrell. The Orangery is by Felix Harbord. I question whether it is entirely successful. The early Georgian entrance hall is untouched, a magnificent Burlingtonian specimen, with heavy enrichments, apses with shell soffits, and plaques
190

in high relief. Mr. Tritton attributes the house to Colin Campbell, but on what authority I don't know. He took us round with great pride.

Tuesday, 15th May

I was told by someone who accompanied them that the two Princesses insisted on walking round the town incognito, on VE night. They walked at such tremendous speed that their companions had the greatest difficulty in keeping pace. The public never recognized them until, on returning to Buckingham Palace, they started shouting for the King and Queen.

Wednesday, 16th May

Philip James, Art Director of C.E.M.A., lunched. He wants to take a National Trust house, close to some provincial town, as an art centre. I said I heartily approved the idea, but had been disillusioned by the number of similar suggestions, all of which had come to nothing. At 6 o'clock I met Geoffrey Houghton-Brown at 17 Alexander Place, off Thurloe Square. He has offered me the first floor and one spare room upstairs. It is good of him. I like the idea.

At Sibyl's Ordinary tonight I sat next to Lady Birkenhead, Freddy's mother. She adored Ava who, she said, constantly stayed with her. She used to find her best books floating in the bath after he left, and the floor a swamp. Freddy and Randolph Churchill shared a room in Czechoslovakia, and Randolph was quite intolerable. Freddy threw a book at Randolph, who got out of bed, and a fight ensued. Once at a party Randolph gave Lady Birkenhead a violent blow, aimed at Lord Castlerosse. I left with Harold for Pratt's where we drank a glass of port. The Duke of Devonshire joined us. His funny old-fashioned starched collar had come detached from the front stud and twisted round his neck in a very extraordinary manner. I did not know him well enough to tell him, and Harold was so busy talking he never noticed.

Thursday, 17th May

I have avoided the office yesterday and today, for the move from 7 Buckingham Palace Gardens to 42 Queen Anne's Gate is proceeding. The new house is smaller than the old and in a state of near ruin, for it is close to the Guards Chapel which was destroyed by a flying bomb last year. At 10 I went to Peterborough, standing in the corridor, with a first-class ticket. From there took a train to Oundle, arriving at 1 o'clock. Was met and driven to Cotterstock by Lady Ethel Wickham, who is delightful and absolutely on the ball. She has quite made up her mind to leave the property to the Trust in memory of her husband. We talked and smoked all afternoon, having despatched our business during luncheon.

Tuesday, 22nd May

Clough Williams-Ellis called at the office at 4.30 to discuss his book on the N.T. and stayed till 7.15. He is an man of fantasy, with long whiskers, and today was wearing a deep blue shirt and stock. He is cranky, hearty, arty and disarming.

John Wilton, who had telephoned at breakfast time to announce his return from Paris, dined at Brooks's. He was very communicative and stayed till midnight, when I walked home. We telephoned Lord Braybrooke and arranged for John to visit Audley End on Thursday. He wanted me to accompany him but I declined to do this. He seems quite determined to proceed with the purchase.

He told me that he went to Belsen camp during the hot weather. The stench was so overpowering that he and others were physically sick. Then they became accustomed to it. The atrocities committed there were worse than the press disclosed. He saw several corpses with deep cuts across the small of the back. Starving fellow-prisoners had done this in the attempt to extract human liver and kidney to assuage their hunger. Other corpses had their private parts torn off. He himself saw a wooden shield, the sort on which we mount a fox's mask, with a man's chest impaled upon it, the nipples and hair intact. He saw a torture chamber with stone bench, troughs and channels for the blood to run into. He looked at the Beast of Belsen behind his cage. He was later shot. He said that our troops watched him and the German S.S. guards under arrest in dead calm and with horror-struck dignity. But some American and British troops did walk a few S.S. men out of the wards and shoot them.

Wednesday, 23rd May

Matheson and I talked to Pepler of the Ministry of Planning. He asked me to prepare a list of not more than fifty of the greatest country houses which, if offered, we should ask the Government for funds to maintain.

Having failed to get on to the 4.15 from Paddington owing to the crowds, I caught the 6.30 for Chippenham. Paul Methuen, in battledress and a beret, drove me to Corsham. Just returned from Belgium, and always absent minded, he started driving on the right side of the road to our peril. I stayed the night in his brother's house in the village, because their agent, Captain Turner, was staying in the Court. He is also agent for the Cirencester estate, and we discussed this in relation to the N.T. The Methuens live in Nash's Gothic library where they have all their meals. A military hospital occupies the rest of the house. Paul gave me to read his reports on historic monuments in Calvados. They are very good and beautifully illustrated by him.

I watched the hospital orderlies banging the furniture of the state-rooms, with the backs of their brooms. Mercifully the settees are put away.

Paul is strictly vegetarian, because he dislikes the idea of flesh. In consequence his complexion is fresh, clean and youthful. He is a good man, though opinionated; and so floating in the clouds that it is hard to pull him down to face facts. She is dignified and sweet in manner. She is however sharp, and does not suffer fools gladly. They are a liberal-minded couple, and very devoted.

At 6.30 we drove to Great Chalfield Manor to see the Flemish tapestries, which after all Major Fuller bought in Uxbridge. They are now hanging in the great hall where they look well enough.

After dinner we talked about laying spirits. Paul and Norah believe implicitly in them, and commune with spirits 'over the other side'.

Friday, 25th May

Daisy Fellowes has just returned from Paris, her hair cut and curled, which is far more attractive than when recently scooped up from the back, with a tumble of matted fringe over the forehead. She says you can get anything done in Paris through bribery. De Gaulle is very unpopular, for he concerns himself only with France's prestige in the eyes of Europe, and does nothing to improve the milk-round or stop the cynical corruption of rich and poor alike. She says the Prime Minister has made a mistake in driving the Socialists to insist upon a general election, not because they think a coalition Government should terminate, but because they are fed up with his autocratic ways in matters not exclusively concerned with the war.

Saturday, 26th May

I caught a midday train to Derby, where it was very cold again. Found a taxi and drove to Kedleston. Down the long drive there suddenly bursts upon the vision the great house, best seen from the Adam bridge. It is very grand, very large and symmetrical from this side, the north. The two pavilions are plastered and coloured ruddy brown. The centre block is of severe, dark Derbyshire stone. Lord Curzon, with his just sense of the magnificent, erected the screen of Adamesque railings, the great gates and overthrows to form the fore-court, now overgrown with grass. At the entrance to these gates is a series of army huts with a little suburban garden in front of each. Again, all over the park are unsightly poles and wires, something to do with radio location. The two north pavilions, designed by Brettingham and built by Paine, are in themselves quite large houses, at least large enough to command a respectable park for themselves. The south side is disappointing, for poor Adam has again been roughly treated here. His two additional pavilions were never carried out. His beautiful centre block and dome, so full of movement and grace, is not given a fair chance, with the tiresome poplars in front of the east pavilion, and the west hidden by scrubby little trees. Also the parish church should not have been left where it is, enveloped by the house like a rat by a boa constrictor. It does not enhance the group like, say, the church at Dyrham, which, the most perfect example I know of "sharawadgi", is a beautiful Gothic foil to the classical house, indeed dominating without oppressing the group, and lovely in being of the same radiant Bath stone.

Lord Scarsdale's mother greeted me at the door of the east pavilion where the family live. The Army are occupying the west pavilion. The centre block is unoccupied, and under dust sheets. Whereas Lord Curzon thought he was pigging it with only thirty indoor servants, today they have one woman for three hours each morning. The mother is living here with a granddaughter, Mrs. Willson, a young Grenadier officer's lethargic wife, and her baby; also Mrs. Willson's sister, Julie, aged 16, very bright and well informed. On my arrival they conducted me round the outside of the house, and after tea round the inside. In the church is a monument which Adam designed for a Curzon, with background pyramid. It is dull and uninspired. Lord Curzon's own monument to himself and his first wife is splendid. His marble effigy was put in place during his lifetime.

Structurally the house is fairly sound, but superficially tattered — the dust sheets don't look as though put on by a trained housemaid — and minor dilapidations are evident. The bluejohn inlay of the Music Room chimneypiece is flaking off. I think only Syon can be compared to Kedleston for splendour. The monolith alabaster columns of the hall are of a startling green which no photograph even faintly indicates.

The marble floor is springy, and I wonder if it is very safe. The acoustics are appalling. One thing worries me about this wonderful room. On entry you are confronted with a three-foot narthex before the hall proper begins with a screen of columns. The hall ends in engaged columns. I can't see why Robert Adam had to do this. There may be good reason for a narthex in a church or public assembly room, but not in a private house. But then Dr. Johnson criticized this room for looking like a town hall. Again the oval screen compartment of the Boudoir is, I think, a mistake. In the Saloon I have nothing to criticize. Americans have unscrewed and stolen the centre of the door handles for souvenirs, the brutes.

Sunday, 27th May

All morning I toured the house by myself, taking notes as I went. The Dining-room alcove end is spoilt by the large doorhead impinging upon the wall. The Library contains a number of good architectural and topographical books. The bedrooms are pretty with coved ceilings. The Orangery is suffering badly from damp. The Bath House is falling to ruin. So is the Boat House. But then what can these unfortunate people do? Theirs is a tragic predicament. I notice that the portico has lost swags and wreathes. When the sun comes out the sharp shadows give the south front the movement Adam intended. This visit has made me sad. I am convinced that this wonderful house is a doomed anachronism.

Monday, 28th May

A very full day. Interview with the Principal of Trinity College of Music. He is taken with the idea of the Benton Fletcher Cheyne Walk house becoming a centre of early keyboard music study. I lunched at Wilton's with John Wilton and Sisson, who liked each other and discussed the Audley End project. Took John to Drowns, where Christopher Norris demonstrated how the Polesden pictures should be cleaned. Interviewed Mrs. Gates about her inventory of the Ellen Terry Museum contents. Had tea with Hinchingbrooke, and examined his small panel of tapestry for Montacute.

Tuesday, 29th May

Forsyth and I trained to Shrewsbury. We reached Attingham in time for luncheon and spent the whole day going over the house, examining and criticizing the County Council's proposed alterations to suit their college. Attingham is far more Regency than Adam, and shows the influence of Holland. All its proportions—portico, pilasters, rooms—are exaggeratedly attenuated. I would not have them otherwise.

Forsyth is doubtless a most worthy man. But he is a frightful bore. His Victorian manners give one the jitters, whereas good manners ought to put one at ease. He will never go through a doorway before another man of whatever age. He hesitates, bows, retreats, apologizes and looks bashful. In a person of over 70 and his distinction this is absurd. He is terrified too of committing himself to an opinion, even when one looks to him for it. Yet he is untrustworthy as regards carrying out instructions. I hate obsequiousness. I could shake him.

Wednesday, 30th May

Lady Berwick motored me to the station this morning. She stood on the platform talking, and when I begged her not to catch cold, said it was such a pleasure just to talk to somebody. Poor woman, she has not much companionship with Lord B. I got to Evesham in the afternoon, took a bus to Badsey, and walked across the fields to Wickhamford.

Thursday, 31st May

Motored to Charlecote, picking up Clifford Smith at Leamington Spa station. Brian [Fairfax-Lucy] was his smiling and helpful self, but the agent an obstructive ass. Clifford's hesitant enthusiasms were constantly unleashed at the wrong moment, and so delayed progress in the outdoor consultations. I had to chivvy him indoors where he properly belongs. Today we examined the Brewery, with its vats and implements, all of which can be revived; and the harness room with rows of brightly kept bridles and bits, and the coachhouses stuffed with Victorian buggies, spiders and barouches. I urged the family to save and leave these things, for they will make a fascinating exhibit to future generations who will not have known the world in which they played a prominent everyday part.

Clifford and I discovered in the gatehouse, the stables and disused servants' hall, several ancient pieces of furniture, notably the hall table of great length, another Elizabethan table and a Queen Anne walnut veneered table, which must have been thrown out during the last century. We are going to have them brought back. The house was too drastically altered in the 1850s. The strange thing is that Mrs.

196

George Lucy, who perpetrated the abominations, was the one member of the family who most loved Charlecote and revered its Shakespearian associations. Yet she over-restored the house out of all recognition, and introduced furniture and fabrics, like napkins, which she pretended Shakespeare and Queen Elizabeth saw and used. The ability of righteous people to deceive themselves always amazes me.

The Gatehouse, forecourt garden and stables form an extremely picturesque group. The park, with deer and sheep, the Avon below the library window, the flat meadows on the far bank, the long lime avenue, make Charlecote a dream of slumbering beauty.

Friday, 1st June

The lengths to which I have gone, the depths which I have plumbed, the concessions which I have (once most reluctantly) granted to acquire properties for the National Trust, will not all be known by that august and ungrateful body. It might be shocked by the extreme zeal of its servant, if it did. Yet I like to think that the interest of the property, or building, rather than the Trust has been my objective. I have to guard against the collector's acquisitiveness. It isn't always to the advantage of a property to be swallowed by our capacious, if benevolent maw. These pious reflections came to me in the bath this morning.

Early after luncheon Midi motored me to Hagley in her new (old) car, I providing coupons for three gallons. From the outside, Hagley is just like Croome, only its *piano nobile* is raised higher so that the basement floor provides decent sized rooms, of which one, a sort of passage way, is a grotto of shells and spars. Lady Cobham is very fat and spread, but has dignity. Lord C. was at Eton with my father, and is handsome, austere and unsmiling. He has an involved mind which works slowly, methodically, and seemingly backwards. He has profound knowledge of Hagley, and is very proud of it, rightly. He took Midi and me round the house till we were nearly dropping with fatigue. In the Vandyke Room are some good pictures, particularly one of Lord Carlisle, and the famous Quentin Matsys of the misers. Three-quarters of the house was burnt out in 1925, but reconstituted by Lord Cobham with exemplary discretion. He even employed Italian *stuccatori* faithfully to copy from photographs the intricate designs of walls and ceilings, of which the former partially survived. Thus the big military trophy swags in the Saloon are, apart from a few lost pieces, the originals tidied up. The chimneypieces, all being of stone, were spared. Only Lord Cobham can tell what is old, and what

197

new. Yet when he pointed out the new stucco it did look to me a little thinner than the original. Notwithstanding the renewal, the Saloon walls are about as fine as any I have seen. The tapestries and most of the pictures were saved. The Gallery was not destroyed, and the carving of picture frames, chimneypiece and furniture is attributed to Chippendale. Oddly enough it is in the natural wood, never having been gilded or painted. Lord C's uncles played cricket in this splendid room, and in consequence the furniture and delicate woodwork suffered greatly. He said that his grandfather, although a scholar, allowed this. The Chippendale torchères and candelabra, which are in the most delicate Chinese, or rocaille style, are sadly knocked about. The same uncles were allowed to play a jumping game of their own invention on the rare volumes in the library.

At tea time a daughter came into the library from the farm, wearing trousers, her hair touselled and spattered with dung. Lord Cobham told us that an American officer, on being shown the Vandyke *Descent from the Cross*, pointed to the figure of Our Lord and asked, 'Who was that guy that looked sick?'

I got to Paddington at midnight, and walked to Chelsea, carrying my two bags and walking-stick.

Saturday, 2nd June

The new office is chaotic still, the house falling to bits, and no windows.

Charles Fry dined with me to discuss the National Trust book. He arrived very drunk indeed. He was maudlin, self-pitying and self-concerned. It is quite impossible to associate with him in this condition. What bores drunks are!

Monday, 4th June

I bought Evelyn Waugh's new novel today. The reviews say it is as good as can be. I lunched with Leigh Ashton who said that his Museum would co-operate with us in maintaining and cataloguing the contents of our houses. This is a splendid thing. He said Charles Fry was obstreperously drunk in the St. James's Club all yesterday, even after my experience with him the night before. I had an interview with the National Council of Social Services at 2.30. They are now eager to establish the committee for mutual help, they thus receiving accommodation in, and we a use for, some of our houses.

At 17 Alexander Place I bribed the sailor painting there to do several things for me, including fixing up bookshelves. I gave him £1 in a gauche way. I hope he and his wife are honest. She is going to look after my two rooms.

Went to Billericay to lunch with a Mrs. Cater. The house no good at all. Just the end of a Tudor Essex farmhouse, the other part being modern. She, poor woman, showed me her pictures, which were of no account. I told her as politely as I could that the Trust could not accept. Before I had set foot in the front door I knew the place was no good.

Wednesday, 6th June

Met R. in the bus and lunched with her in Cheyne Walk. She affects to be mightily concerned about the election. She still hankers after a *ménage à deux*, but can't find the second person. 'Don't we all?' I said rather brutally, lest there might be grounds for any misunderstanding.

I hired a car and took some of my more precious things to Alexander Place. Then to Claridges to meet Lady Muriel Barclay-Harvey, who wants to lend her family portraits to Montacute while she rebuilds her own house, Uffington near Stamford. Anne dined with me. Her advice tonight was, 'Laugh, and the world laughs with you; weep, and you sleep alone.'

Thursday, 7th June

Today Miss P. and I did not go to the office, for we moved from no. 104. The van came in the morning early, and the men were helpful and kind, but terribly rough. I had a moment of sadness while peeing in the *cabinet* for the last time, but have few serious regrets at leaving this dilapidated little hovel. Only the river and my splendid Whistlerian view I regret. No. 17 is wonderfully clean, but the bath is not fixed up and there is no telephone yet. It was lonely here tonight without Miss P. or a telephone.

At 6 I went to see Lord Newton, who talked of Lyme again. My impression is that with adroitness and tact he can be helped to do what he and we want, and that he looks upon me as an ally, who sympathizes with his predicaments.

Went to Brooks's at 7.30 a.m., and had a bath and breakfast. Then took the train from Blackfriars station to Eynsford, spending the morning with Mr. Major, a dear old boy who wishes to leave four acres and a colony of wooden shacks, called *Robsacks*, in which he lives. The place has good views of Lullingstone Castle and a valley the other side of the ridge on which it is perched, but nothing else to recommend it. After dinner with Desmond at Brooks's I put my books more or less in order on the ramshackle bookcase which Geoffrey has lent me. Previously I had a drink with Anne, whom I love as much as any of my friends. I count her among my first five women friends. At least I think there are as many.

Saturday, 9th June

In the train to Swindon I brought my diary up to date. A woman sitting opposite me was bewildered by seeing someone covering sheets of paper in shorthand. I suppose people seldom write in shorthand unless they are dictated to.

Wednesday, 13th June

After a meeting in the office Brian Fairfax-Lucy lunched with me at Brooks's and I found myself speaking too frankly about his odious father. When I excused myself, he agreed with what I said, and elaborated to some tune. He said that all Sir Henry's children were terrified of him, and the lives of all of them had been ruined by him. The inhibitions of some of them were due to his treatment. After luncheon [Professor] Richardson introduced me to Lord Crawford, who was absolutely charming. One must beware of charmers.

I went round Chandos House this evening. It is vast inside but by no means interesting, save the staircase, another Adam achievement within a narrow compass. Mrs. Hawker invited me to meet her son Lord Scarsdale at Claridges. I accepted only because I understood he wanted to discuss Kedleston in relation to the National Trust. He kept us waiting three-quarters of an hour, and when he came never mentioned the subject.

Thursday, 14th June

To Gunby for the night. The Field-Marshal extremely pleased to see me. The old man has become rather more ponderous and slow. He has bought several more portraits of Massingberds.

This morning I walked with him round the estate, visiting employees, paying their wages and collecting savings funds from them. This estate is extraordinarily feudal, and has an air of wellbeing and content. The cottages are all very spick and span and the inmates on the best of terms with the Field-Marshal. He has a habit of stopping and turning to me whenever he has something to say, which delays progress, and makes walking with him in the winter extremely cold. He is very concerned about the election. I have never since a child seen such huge and succulent strawberries as the Gunby ones. We ate them with honey, far better than sugar, and cream. Although the war is over there is no alcohol in this house.

This morning the telephone man came to Alexander Place to say he would install my telephone on Monday. My bureau is to arrive that day. My bookshelves and curtain rods are to be put up next week. So things are moving. The bath however is still unattached to the pipes. The house painter and I picnic together. I leave the house each morning at 7.30 to bathe and shave at Brooks's, where I virtually live. Sometimes I breakfast with Professor Richardson, sometimes with Walter Ogilvie.

In Heywood's shop I met Diana Mosley and Evelyn Waugh with Nancy. I kissed Diana who said the last time we met was when I stayed the night at Wootton Lodge, and we both wept when Edward VIII made his abdication broadcast. I remember it well, and Diana speaking in eggy-peggy to Tom Mosley over the telephone so as not to be overheard. Diana looks as radiant as ever. She was the most divine adolescent I have ever beheld. Divine is the word, for she was a goddess, more immaculate, more perfect, more celestial than Botticelli's seaborne Venus. We all lunched at Gunter's and Harold Acton joined us. It was the first occasion on which he and Evelyn had seen Diana since her marriage to Tom. Her two Guinness boys from Eton also joined us: Jonathan, a little cross and supercilious, Desmond good-looking like his father. He, aged 13, said to me about his father, 'I wish Bryan would not go on having more children, for the money won't go round at this rate.' Diana said she had ordered a taxi-cab; she supposed it would come. 'The driver, I think and hope, is a fifth columnist.' She *is* funny. Evelyn said his book is already sold out—14,000 copies.

Kathleen Kennet, who took me to the theatre, said Peter Scott's new book on battle boats has 24,000 copies printed. The play, *The Skin of our Teeth* was hell. We could not be bothered to understand what it was all about. I had tea with the Kennets at Leinster Corner. K. and I are the best of friends again. Indeed I love her dearly.

I dined with Simon Harcourt-Smith, who said that in my Adam book I ought to discuss Adam's relationship with Chippendale, his importance compared with Gabriel and contemporary foreign architects, and the Roman-Greek controversy. At 10 I left Brooks's for home and ran into a friend in Piccadilly. 'Where are you hurrying?' I asked. 'To the Music Box,' he said, 'come too.' There Sandy Baird, whom I have not spoken to since Eton days, introduced himself to me, and me to a *louche* little sailor. The sailor called me Jimmie, and while Sandy was getting us drinks, said 'Give me your address.' 'Ask Sandy for it,' I replied. He hissed in a whisper, 'God, no, I can't ask him.' So much for fidelity, I thought. He also said to me 'I don't want money; only friendship.' I was flattered, but would not accompany them to another club. I hate these places. They disinter one's dead adolescence, and point to the pathetic loneliness of middle age.

Sunday, 17th June

In Warwick Street church I looked about me, because Evelyn had said the Belgian priest there proposes to dismantle the walls encrusted with silver hearts and thank-offerings and erect a new chapel along the north aisle.

Monday, 18th June

National Trust meeting day. The new secretary, Mallaby, appointed. I walked to Brooks's with Esher, and we lunched together. I suggested that all future minor staff candidates ought to be vetted by the committee before appointment, and not left to the Secretary's sole choice.

Had a drink with Mary and Auberon Herbert, who is now a captain in the Polish Army. He told harrowing tales of Russian atrocities committed upon the Poles. He saw thirty Polish women raped by a regiment of Bolsheviks who had 'liberated' a town in which he was. The soldiers ripped open the women's clothes with their bayonets, and four other soldiers held down a limb each. He says the Poles consider the Russians a far worse menace than the Germans. Then I dined with

Pauly Sudley, who spoke not one single word throughout the meal—not one word. I left at 9 o'clock.

Mama made me drive her to Broadway to see the Sidneys' Flemish primitives and Tudor family portraits which, I gathered, they had just discovered in their Northumberland house, Cowpen Hall. Colonel Sidney is one of my father's favourite cronies and one of the stupidest men in all England, which is saying something. Among the portraits was a small one of Sir Philip Sidney with reddish hair. When I extolled Sidney's literary merits, the Colonel gave an impatient wave of the hand, saying, 'Yes, yes, a fine soldier, a fine soldier.' 'A humane as well as heroic man,' I ventured. 'A fine soldier, fine soldier,' he repeated.

I drove alone to Charlecote and lunched with the Fairfax-Lucys, meeting Brian's wife, Alice, for the first time. Attractive, quizzical and intelligent. Not John Buchan's daughter for nothing. They were very forbearing in letting Clifford Smith and me go round the rooms and make a selection of things from the list she had prepared the previous day.

On my way back to London I motored up the drive of Compton Verney. The beautiful park is a mature specimen of Capability Brown's work. Alas, all the balustrading of the lovely Adam bridge has been knocked down by the soldiers. When I got home at 11 my opposite neighbour called, which I thought a distinct bore. He made me have a drink in his house. The ground floor has been baronialized and given a vast cocktail bar.

Went by train to Horsmonden. Was met by Mr. Courthope and driven to Sprivers. He lives here with his sister. It is a red-brick house, built in 1756, small, pretty and unspoilt. An enormous bushy wistaria completely envelops the Georgian front, greatly to its detriment. The garden is waist-high in grass and weeds, and the gravel drive indistinguishable from the lawns. Altogether rather a mess. The house has a central hall with rococo cartouches on the walls, enclosing heraldic escutcheons of the Courthope family who built it. Otherwise, apart from the chestnut doorcases, two staircases of very rustic Chinese Chippendale design, and some rococo chimneypieces, there is nothing much inside for the public to enjoy. I got back at 7 and John Wyndham dined with me. He is Lord Leconfield's nephew and eventual heir. He is anxious for his uncle to hand over Petworth now. We decided to stress upon the feudal, reactionary Lord L. that (1) during his lifetime he will not be disturbed in any particular, (2) he may be better off financially, (3) he may retain the contents (for the best will be exempted on J.W.'s succession) and (4) by transferring now he will establish the only assurance that his successors can live at Petworth. John Wyndham is dark, bespectacled, like a wise young owl; not demonstrative, but cynical and extremely bright. He seemed quite, but not very pleased with the outcome of our meeting.

Saturday, 23rd June

With all my luggage, pens, papers, notes and books I reached Blickling by 8.

Sunday, 24th June

I am blissfully happy this afternoon. I write this at my table on the raised platform at the south-east end of the Gallery, as I had for so long pictured myself doing, surrounded by 12,000 calf-bound books, looking on to the beautiful but unkempt, unmown garden. There is still quite a lot of colour in the formal beds now rank in long grass. Ivory's temple at the far end of the vista is in a straight line with me. Here I intend to work for a fortnight, and pray to God that no distractions will prevent me. But my character is weak, and I bow before temptation. I sleep and breakfast in Miss O'Sullivan's flat in the wing; I take all other meals at the inn, where the landlady Mrs. O'Donoghue is my friend. It is a warm sunny day. The air smells of roses and pinks. The tranquillity accentuates the extreme remoteness of Blickling, this beautiful house which I love.

Monday, 25th June

And here is temptation literally at the door, and again at the end of the telephone. At midday Wyndham Ketton-Cremer called on me as I was working in the library. He plans to come over next Tuesday week (another temptation) and take me to Wolterton. After he left I was told that Lord Wilton was on the line. By the time I reached the telephone, he had gone. After work I walked to Aylsham, hired a bicycle and rode to Oxnead. Looked at the old church where the latest Paston memorial is to Dame Katharine Paston, dated 1636, with a very fine bust of that lady, wearing choker pearls round an open neck like Henrietta Maria. It is a work of art. I wonder who the sculptor was.* I wandered in front of the house, of which only one wing is now left. It has three large chimney stacks and stone mullioned windows. At right angles to it is a long barn-like building, all of brick. In the grounds are remains of substructions and terraces, punctuated by widely spreading Irish yews. There are fragments of gadrooned stone urns resembling some of those now at Blickling, whither Lord Buckinghamshire removed them in the eighteenth century. There is an isolated brick screen with three open colonnades of Jacobean date in the field by the canal. It has two apses in the end openings, and buttresses behind them, as though once they held statues. What it means I could not ascertain. Standing at the front gate I learned from a roadman that Mr. Mosley lived there; and then I remembered Aunt Dorothy saying that Johnnie Mosley had bought a house in these parts. Oxnead has the air of a deserted, neglected home of an extinct family.

John Wilton put through a personal call from the Savoy at 9 p.m. He seemed anxious to see me, so I suggested his coming for the week-end, and he has accepted. Temptation always wins every encounter.

Tuesday, 26th June

A telegram from Müntzers the decorators, announcing their arrival at midday. Damn! This is not temptation, it is worse–duty. Miss O'Sullivan is much put out because she had prepared to do her week's baking today. Also a cinema company is due to film a scene here, the day of their arrival depending upon the weather. Mercifully it is raining. Müntzer's men arrived, but not Grandy Jersey. I gave them luncheon and brought them to the Hall. They made several useful suggestions and will submit a written report to me. They said the tapestries must be repaired and cleaned; and the panelling in the dining-room vinegared urgently. I suggested their tinting the snow-white ceiling in the Peter the Great room.

In spite of Müntzer's men (they left at 3.45) today's work was rather successful. At 9.15 I went for a glorious bicycle ride round the estate by Itteringham.

Wednesday, 27th June

This morning the R.A.F. sergeant gave me the key of the garden door in the north-east turret, so that I need not go all through the back

* It was Nicholas Stone.

regions of the house to reach the library. Instead I can slip unobserved through the garden. The Gainsborough film people were taking shots this afternoon, whenever it stopped raining. All morning it poured. I wrote the entire day, save after tea when I bicycled to Cawston. The hammerbeam angel roof of the church is superb. Along a frieze, over the clerestory, are angel masks with wings spread from their cheeks. They look like great bats. This roof apparently dates from 1380.

Rode past Reepham to Salle church, the finest of the lot. It is of later date than Cawston, about 1450, is symmetrical with projecting wings and angle turrets at the west end; corresponding north and south porches and transepts. The symmetry is exact and almost classical. The interior is very spacious and the clear windows with square panes are so vast that I wonder the walls sustain the roof. God is light, they seem to declare. The rood screen, not as fine as Cawston's, has original white priming on the woodwork. Three-decker pulpit, the sounding board Jacobean. The front cover, a skeleton without flesh, but still immensely impressive, is very slim and tall, shaped like an elongated candle-extinguisher, suspended from an original crane. An Ivory mural tablet to Miss Evans, dated 1798.

Thursday, 28th June

Conducted the film producer round the state rooms. To my surprise he was well informed. He said, 'You must not remove the nineteenth-century library shelves, for they have a period interest and show how the house has grown over the centuries.' He might have been me speaking. Birkbeck, the agent, appeared in the afternoon and motored me round parts of the estate. He showed me his nursery of young oaks and Douglases; also his new plantation opposite Hercules Wood, with which he is exceedingly pleased. We talked with Salmon the carpenter and Atto the woodman. Walked to the mausoleum and Lady's Cottage, thatched and almost drowned in an ocean of bracken. The troops have broken into this romantic little building and knocked it about too.

Friday, 29th June

I wonder if cart horses are as satisfied as I am after a full day's work. After a cup of tea I bicycled northwards for a change. Visited Ittering-ham church, just on the estate. Nothing of interest, bar some retreating perspective panelling, probably brought from a private house. On to Little Barningham church. Thought there was nothing here when, on leaving, my eye caught a small wooden effigy of Death, perched upon a pew-end, sickle in one hand, hour-glass in the other. Beyond the pew door were the following lines, dated 1640:

> 'All you that shall pass this place by
> Remember that you soon must dye.
> Even as you are, so once was I.
> As I am now, you soon shall be.
> Prepare therefore to follow me.'

Instead, I continued to Barningham Park, and without being stopped, bicycled down the drive through rows of Nissen huts. A dull evening; the place and park flat and dreary. Had a good look at the outside of the house. It is tall and top-heavy, of Tudor red brick, with central projecting porch and slim, octagonal angles; great chimneystacks and pedimented windows; crow-stepped gables, typically Norfolk. The wide window-panes and overbalanced dormers give this house a Victorian air. I peered through a window to the right of the porch and saw a big Jacobean stone fireplace. The ruined church beyond contains monuments to the Mott family. Came home by Calthorpe. Church here aisleless, wide, empty and barrel vaulted, with holes in the roof. The font cover is gaudily painted, and so is other woodwork. The emptiness and colour remind me of a French parish church. Too exhausted to visit Ingworth church on the way back to supper.

Saturday, 30th June

Humphry Repton's tombstone on the south wall outside Aylsham church has the following, appropriate quotation under his epitaph:

> 'Not like Egyptian tyrants consecrate
> Unmixed with others shall my dust remain,
> But moldring, blending, melting into earth
> Mine shall give form and colour to the rose,
> And while its vivid colours chear mankind
> Its perfumed odours shall ascend to heaven.'

'Form and colour to the rose.' The sentence is borne out by a long, leggy briar, with one tiny bud, clambering up the wall from roots among that distinguished dust.

I worked the entire day until 6.45 and am well away with the Roman-Greek controversy. Walked to the station at Aylsham and met John Wilton. From the moment I greeted him at the station it has poured with rain. He is staying at the inn, where we dined. We walked round the lake, talking.

Today a whole holiday from work. Unfortunately a beastly day and raining constantly. John back from Europe says the British troops hate the French, and like the Germans. The American troops do the same. Nothing the politicians may say prevents it. We walked after luncheon to the mausoleum. While we were there it flashed lightning, and we feared the great iron doors might be struck, so hid in one of the empty embrasures. The thunder was deafening as it rolled and echoed round the reverberating dome of the mausoleum. We agreed that nothing could be more dramatic or eerie. The Buckinghamshire coffins remained motionless on their shelves.

Worked all day till dinner, John sitting around the state rooms reading and apparently content. Stuart telephoned this evening from London. He is back from the continent. I can see further temptation looming.

Wyndham Ketton-Cremer spent the morning with me in the library, which, he says, contains the finest collection of seventeenth-century tracts he has come across. We lunched at the inn, and he agreed to take John on our tour. We called at Heydon first. The large house is let by the Bulwers to Lady Playfair, an old woman. It is a pretty house, centre part 1580, with Reptonish additions in the same style. Mrs. Bulwer is a widow, charming, living in a dower house. She showed us her collection of teapots, hundreds of them, all English, mostly porcelain, some pottery, and a few very eccentric. Her house is overcrowded with treasures. There is a Queen Anne dolls' house, inherited by her husband from a direct ancestor. The outside is dull, but the contents are fascinating, particularly a chandelier enclosed in a glass bubble for protection, ivory forks and knives in a shagreen case, the servants and the owner and his wife with their names inscribed. Among other extra dolls' house treasures were a pair of velvet shoes which belonged to Charles I.

Then to Wolterton. Lady Walpole showed us round and gave us tea. The house of beautiful, coursed brickwork. A heraldic achievement in the pediment finely carved. One wing has been added which is a pity. The porch on the north front is unfortunate, and should go. The *piano nobile* is raised high, and the rooms on the ground, or basement floor, are quite habitable and cosy for the cold winters they get in Norfolk. The state rooms are splendid, though at present in a mess, for until lately Lady Walpole had officers billeted on her throughout the war, Lord Walpole still being in the army. Ripley may have been a second-rate architect, but the quality of his craftsmanship is far from shoddy. The carving of the doors is on the other hand coarse. Chimney-pieces of a variety of marbles. Wolterton could be made a wonderful place in spite of the flat terrain. The troops are still in Nissen huts along the drive under the trees.

The wrought-iron stair balusters have a wide handrail of inlaid amboyna. Stairwell worth examining at the top, being beautifully lit. All the subsidiary landings solidly vaulted. Lady Walpole provided a good nursery tea on the ground floor. Her little boy was rude and spoilt. John and I walked back to Blickling from the house. I showed him the staircase with carved hunting scenes on the ends of the risers in Itteringham farmhouse. The farmer complained about the Trust not painting his front door.

Wednesday, 4th July

John left at midday. I worked in the Gallery all morning, afternoon and evening, finishing a chapter.

Thursday, 5th July

Polling day, but not for me. I simply cannot make up my mind how to vote. My dislike of socialism is almost equalled by my dislike of what Mr. Churchill stands for. Ever since the war in Europe has ended I have ruminated upon the outcome. What has it brought us? Perhaps the answer is that it has brought us nothing positively good, but has saved us from something infinitely bad. But to that answer I would retort that it has brought us something else infinitely bad, if not worse, namely Russian occupation of eastern Europe. Moreover this damnable occupation of Christian countries which form part of our civilization, will spread like a disease, and we, being too tired and feeble to resist, will complacently defer, in our typically phlegmatic British way, resisting this disease until it is too late. No, politically speaking, I am miserable. Nevertheless, my joy at the ghastly fighting having stopped, is great. This relief makes me so complacent that if asked tomorrow whether I would be prepared to resume fighting Communists instead of Nazis, I would hesitate—I hope not for long. But a short respite is needed. It must only be a respite.

At 2 o'clock met Birkbeck and the painter at Aylsham Old Hall. The army have de-requisitioned it, and given us £450 for dilapidations, out of which we are allowed to spend £100 if the work is undertaken before August 1st. After that date only £10 p.a. is allowed, which means that no one can possibly inhabit large houses after troops have been billeted in them for six years. It would be quite acceptable if the army, on clearing out, were allowed to reinstate what they had spoilt. As it stands the regulation is unfair and absurd. The Old Hall is a delightful house of about 1700; red brick, with large rooms of William and Mary wainscoting. There is a contemporary overmantel picture of the house itself and the barn beside it, almost as they are now. A pity the roof is of slate. One day we must put back the Norfolk pantiles. I bicycled over to Rippon and dined with the Birkbecks.

Friday, 6th July

A glorious day of full sun. I worked and walked in my shirt sleeves. The R.A.F. were bathing in the lake and lying in the sun. After dinner I bicycled to Erpingham where the N.T. owns a small detached parcel of the Blickling estate. I looked through the windows of Ingworth church, shut at this hour, and noticed a rood screen that seemed to be Jacobean. On the way back a delicious evening smell of amber hay. Bats flitting across the pale lemon sky.

Last night I had a dream about Tom. He was reading and sucking his pipe in the morning-room in Brooks's. I rushed up to him and he threw his arms round me. I said, 'Tom, they told me you were dead, and here I see and know that you are alive.' He laughed and said most convincingly, 'Yes, it was all a mistake.' Then I woke up.

Saturday, 7th July

I bicycled to Aylsham, surrendered my machine at the shop I hired it from, and walked to the station. Train punctual, and there on the platform was Stuart, smiling with pleasure. He was in his sergeant's uniform, unchanged in figure and face, though a little red like a porcupine without quills – the suns of Normandy. We went straight to the inn where he had an enormous meal at 3.30 of eggs and tea. It was as though there had been no break in our relations. Indeed there had been none. We went to the house and looked at the state rooms, then walked round the lake, and reclined under the trees in an Elizabethan fashion, chins hand-cupped. He had a bath in the bathroom next to the Chinese bedroom before we dined. The Sissons having arrived to stay at the inn for a fortnight, ate with us. I don't think either party liked the other much. Incompatibility of interests; lack of common acquaintances; and that instantaneous, suspicious antipathy of strangers. I am always naively surprised when my friends do not immediately click. After dinner Stuart and I left the Sissons and strolled round the lake, pausing at the remote end to take in the view of the house. Across the placid water it looked like a palace in a dream, insubstantial, and as the darkness crept between us, it melted like a palace in a dream. Returned to the inn where we smoked and talked. It was past midnight when I left. The front door being barred and bolted, and no key anywhere visible, I let myself out of a window into a bed of nasturtiums and ran home. Luckily Miss O'Sullivan does not lock her front door.

Sunday, 8th July

We left after luncheon for London. In Alexander Place the bath is installed, but no hot water connected. The house still occupied by the painter, and in a filthy mess.

Monday, 9th July

This morning a meeting at the Middlesex Guildhall with the Middlesex County Council, the Heston Council, and Grandy Jersey. They agreed to purchase Grandy's trustees' additional land. The meeting was a success. Had my hair cut at Trumper's, and in the evening went to Richmond to stay the night at Grandy's. After dinner he invited the Mayor of Richmond and six other worthies to meet me and discuss Ham House. This too a success, for they finally agreed they would recommend contribution of the whole endowment sum we need for that house. After dinner I said to Grandy gaily, 'And where is Virginia? I suppose she has gone out to avoid the mayoral meeting.' Grandy said very solemnly, 'No. We have separated.' All I could say was I was sorry. There are moments in life when all words are superfluous.

Tuesday, 10th July

Luncheon at the White Tower. Ben Nicolson, John Russell and an American called Louis Auchincloss, who spoke so softly that I could not hear one word he said, and was obliged to turn away. Ben said that at Windsor the other day the King was looking at his pictures with him. John Piper was present. The King closely scrutinized Piper's pictures of the Castle, turned to him and remarked, 'You seem to have very bad luck with your weather, Mr. Piper.'

At 3 a meeting with Farrer, Lord Leconfield's solicitor, and Balfour, the Petworth estate's solicitor. They both informed me that Lord Leconfield, with the blood of the 'proud' Duke of Somerset in his veins, was the most arrogant man in England. They warned me when I met him, not to mention Lady Leconfield's name. At 5 I had tea with Lord and Lady Newton. They are in a great fluster about Lyme and their furniture. I agreed to ask Margaret Jourdain to help them with the furniture, although I don't in the least know what exactly they want her to do. Nor do they, it seems. Not an examination, not a valuation, for these have already been done. However Margaret, to whom I have spoken, has agreed to go if they ask her.

Wednesday, 11th July

Dora Prescott, that incorrigible woman, telephoned. I asked her how she liked Paris. She answered, 'It was wonderful. I ate and drank the most marvellous food every day. With people starving in the streets, it gave me such a cosy feeling, a sort of *après moi le deluge* feeling.' Really, how dare she say such a thing, even if she feels it. I hope the deluge quickly immerses her.

Thursday, 12th July

At Slatter's exhibition of Dutch seventeenth-century pictures there are two N.T. pictures, lent by us, the Pieter de Hooch of those beastly, whimsy children with golf clubs, and a Cornelis de Mann which, now cleaned, looks fine. Went to see some furniture offered by old Mrs. Maclachlan. No earthly good. Was to have dined with George Dix, but met Alvilde in the street, and she asked us both to dine with her. Just ourselves.

Saturday, 14th July

This morning I met Margaret Jourdain at the V & A library, to which she introduced me. Lunched at Boodle's with Alastair Forbes. The devil gets into me when I am with M.P.s or political aspirants, and I find myself saying outrageous things which I do not always mean. Thus such people consider me wicked, mad or stupid, possibly all three. Possibly they don't think anything about me at all.

In the train I read the life of Matthew Boulton and James's indifferent little book on the Houses of Parliament. Very poor illustrations and it costs 15/-. Gerry Wellington met me at Mortimer station and motored me to Stratfield Saye for a late tea. The Eshers and Eddie Marsh are staying. The Eshers are very sweet to each other. They tease each other. Gerry is growing a paunch. Eddie is growing old. Gerry is extremely fussy. Eddie broke a miniature and had to own up. Gerry said it didn't matter in a tone of voice which indicated how desperately he thought it did. In handing round the Great Duke's 'George', he said to me who was sitting next to Eddie, 'Don't let Eddie hold it. He breaks works of art.' Before we went to bed he gave Eddie a whisky and soda, exhorting him not to exceed his ration of one bottle for a week's visit.

Sunday, 15th July

Gerry let me drive myself in his car down the Wellingtonia avenue to Heckfield Park for Mass. I like privately owned chapels, and the women trailing in straight from the bedroom, while they adjust their mantillas. When I returned the others had finished breakfast, Gerry having had his alone before they were down, as is his custom.

The Eshers are great ones for sitting around and chatting. They sat in the drawing-room after luncheon and talked non-stop till dinner time. They began upon Jane Austen—Gerry and Eddie strong partisans—whereas Lady E. and I upheld Trollope. Then politics and Russia. Esher is pro-Russia, for he believes they hold the germ of an idea. Some germ. Although most contradictory in his opinions, he is a fundamental Liberal, but no National Liberal. He disagrees with all Gerry's views, even on houses, for he believes Charlecote to be very important on account of the Shakespeare associations. Gerry most emphatically does not. After dinner I left, Gerry motoring me to Mortimer. The train late, arriving Paddington 12.20. I walked in the rain to Alexander Place. Found that house upside down. My room is having the floor boards darkened, and the bed is an island in the middle, with nothing else near it. I slept in this huddle.

Monday, 16th July

I left at 7.30 for breakfast with Eardley. He in his good-natured way is having me to stay in his flat. The office is likewise in a state of chaos, for the workmen are now hammering in the agents' rooms.

Eardley and I travelled by train to Bangor to stay with Michael

Duff at Vaynol. I have a window overlooking the lake and Snowdon, a sublime view—meadows, water, woods, mountains and—why is it? —so much sky. Only Juliet, Michael's mother, is staying.

This morning Michael motored us through Llanberis, up the pass to the little hotel at the far end, whence tourists begin their climb of Snowdon, which from here we could not see, for it was round the corner. Snowdon belongs to Michael, who wishes to protect it and the whole Llanberis Pass by covenants. He told me he owns 60,000 acres in Wales. We returned by Caernarvon Castle. Walked into the central court which leaves me cold. Only the picturesque exterior moves me.

After luncheon to see Michael's quarries, huge terraces cut into the mountain-side, looking like a John Martin landscape—Belshazzer's Feast. I motored to Plas Newydd on Anglesey. Found Lord and Lady Anglesey at the bottom of the stairs, sitting on the floor sorting objects for a local fête sale. And wonderful things they were too, which they were pricing at only a few shillings. Lady Anglesey with very white hair, slight and well made, and well dressed in a tartan skirt, smelling of upper-class scent and cigarettes. She has a little wizened face like a marmoset's, and is extremely attractive. Pretty looks compared to Lady Diana's beautiful looks. Lord Anglesey is very handsome, with much affability and charm. I explained to him what the National Trust was. I suspected that his enquiries were not very serious.

Plas Newydd was built about 1780, then altered by James Wyatt. Lord Anglesey has again done a good deal of altering, and adding a large wing where Wyatt's unconsecrated chapel stood. There is still a Gothic saloon left like the Birr one, and the staircase is classical with shallow apses and columns, somehow unmistakably Wyatt. There are many family portraits and relics of the 1st Marquess, 'One leg', Lady Anglesey calls him. There is an extremely long room with a huge canvas facing the windows, of a pastiche scene by Rex Whistler, who was a close family friend. The best thing about Plas Newydd is the situation, which is unsurpassed—the straits below, the Snowdon range, the tubular bridge and the monument to the first Marquess. The Angleseys plan to pull down half the house which will be an improvement. They complain that there is no one on the island to talk to.

After cursing the caretaker at Polesden for neglecting his duties, and
214

taking away two silver teapots bequeathed to Sir John Bailey, I arrived at Petworth at 3.30. I stopped at the street entrance, walked through a long, gloomy passage, crossed a drive, passed under a *porte cochère* into a hall, and was ushered into Lord Leconfield's presence. He gave me a hurried handshake without a smile, and told the housekeeper to show me round the inside. This she did, bewailing the damage caused to ceilings and walls by Saturday's storm. She and one housemaid look after this vast palace. All the state rooms being shut up and the furniture under dustsheets, I had difficulty, with most of the shutters fastened, in seeing. I liked the housekeeper. She keeps the house spotless and polished. Then I was handed back to Lord Leconfield.

My first impression was of a pompous old ass, with a blue face and fish eyes. He seemed deliberately to misunderstand what the National Trust was all about. He was highly suspicious. He looked up and said, 'Understand, this visit commits me to nothing. I much doubt whether the National Trust can help me.' He complained, understandably enough, of surtax, and would not grasp the fact that the Trust was exempt from taxation. He implied that we would turn him out of the house the moment we took over. He walked me very slowly round the park. He told me that neither his father nor grandfather would allow the name of his great-grandfather, Lord Egremont, to be mentioned, although his grandfather was the son (illegitimate) of that excellent patron of artists. He said that the Victorian architect Salvin, when summoned by his father, stood on the mound in the park, and pointing to the house said, 'My Lord, there is only one thing to be done. Pull the whole house down and re-build it.' His father replied, 'You had better see the inside first.'

At 5.45 Lord Leconfield, tired out, led me to the street door where he dismissed me. Pointing to a tea house with an enormous notice CLOSED hanging in the window, he said, 'You will get a very good tea in there. Put it down to me. Goodbye.' Had I not been forewarned I would have concluded that my visit was a distinct failure.

Friday, 20th July

Dined with Margaret Jourdain and Ivy Compton-Burnett, both delighted to be back in London. Ivy rather repetitive, but funny as usual in her abrupt, clipped manner. She talked of the days before motor cars. She told how it was common practice for a barefooted man to run from a country station two or three miles behind one's carriage in the hope of being allowed to take the luggage upstairs, and so to receive a 6d. tip, if lucky. Usually he wasn't lucky, for the servants of the house where one was staying would shoo the man away, which meant a plod back to the station, unrewarded. Can this have been true in her lifetime?

Sunday, 22nd July

Mass at Warwick Street. I found myself sitting next to Evelyn Waugh and did not speak to him. Had no luncheon, but put my rooms in order, hanging pictures till tea, which I had with Dame Una. Bishop Mathew, who was present, talked to me about Wardour Castle. He had advised Dame Una not to join the Montacute Committee, because it would be a waste of her time. This made me cross. The Bishop laughs like a schoolgirl in a shrill falsetto. I saw him off, waddling with his breviary under his arm. The Dame says he is sure to be a cardinal, one of the new thirty. I hope so. He is just back from Abyssinia and has a high regard for the Lion of Judah's culture. No one else in that country can even talk sense, only gibberish. The nobility are very feudal, but like savages; the ordinary people like wild animals.

Wednesday, 25th July

This afternoon to the Law Courts, and for two hours I listened to the Coughton Court case in Chambers. Four barristers, one a woman, in their attractive curled wigs, each with two little grey pigtails. I wish all men could wear wigs as in the eighteenth century. Our counsel, King, was very dictatorial to Horne and me, and I did not like him. Sir Robert Throckmorton attended for half an hour. I was not at all bored, although the Judge, Vaisey, dealt with the most intricate technical points. I greatly admired his authority in dealing with counsels, his consummate mastery of the case, and his dry humour. He was delightful, and reminded me of Roger Fulford.

Thursday, 26th July

Up early and breakfasted at the Paddington Hotel before catching the 9.10 to Leamington. Arrived Charlecote at 11.30 in pouring rain. Found Clifford Smith and Mrs. Fairfax-Lucy in something of a state. No progress has been made since our last visit. No one will come to remove the billiard table and the other furniture we want to get rid of. She is a sweet woman. Cliffy says there is nothing wrong about her, and everything she says is right. She likes him very much, but begged me the next time I came down not to bring him, for we shall get on quicker without him.

I laughed so much with Alice Fairfax-Lucy while we were staggering under the weight of a bust of a Lucy, in fear that we would drop it, that I almost did myself a mischief, damned nearly. Clifford made two very old retainers carry a pair of marble busts from the great hall into the library, and then back again to their original places. The groans of the retainers were heart-rending.

Friday, 27th July

Clifford rang up to say the silver cup he found at Charlecote and brought to the V & A is exceedingly rare. Its date is 1524 and it is the fourth earliest wine cup in existence, the Danny cup being the earliest.

Saturday, 28th July

I set out to stay with Ted Lister at Westwood, but on approaching Paddington at 9 found a queue stretching from the Bayswater Road, almost from the Park. Taxis were being directed by mounted policemen to the end of the queue. I gave up, and didn't make any further attempt.

Tuesday, 31st July

Matheson left the office today, and we are in chaos.

I had luncheon with Eddy who goes this week to live with Eardley and Desmond Shawe-Taylor at Long Crichel in Dorset. I had a drink this evening with Jock Murray in Albemarle Street. Peter Quennell was present and, speaking of Brendan Bracken, said, 'I always distrust men with pubic hair on their heads.'

Thursday, 2nd August

Motored to Faringdon and lunched at the hotel. Read through my National Trust book which is now out. It looks rather thin and cheap. Called upon Mr. Furley, aged 90, at Kencot Manor, a very simple type of farmhouse, of little importance. I can't think why we hold it. He is a dear old man. He complained of his age and said questioningly, 'I shall never be able to do my carpentering again' in such a tone that I suspected he hoped I would contradict him, but I thought it better not to. Although so old, he walked me all over the house and round the

217

garden; then gave me tea. He is a retired Winchester master. We discussed politics and Stafford Cripps, his neighbour and one time school pupil. He thinks him a man of the strictest integrity, who is carried away by fervour to make regrettable utterances. I left him soon after tea and drove to Lechlade, where I telephoned to Mama, then sat in the churchyard in the declining sun and read.

Stayed this night at Cirencester Park with Lady Apsley, who is an active-minded woman, of common sense. She has just been defeated in the election, but spoke with no bitterness of the socialists, having implicit confidence in the future; why, I don't quite understand. She told me that a friend of hers had returned this week from Rome, having had an audience of the Pope. The Pope said the result of our election would be misunderstood throughout Europe; the continent would assume that England had gone red. The sequel would be revolutions in Denmark, France, Italy, Spain and Greece. This would be one disastrous outcome of the election.

Lady Apsley sits in a chair in which she pushes herself from one room to another, for she is paralysed from the waist downwards, her poor legs stiffly splayed outwards. I found myself wanting to stare at them. Her father-in-law and husband both died within a year of each other, and her son has had to pay two lots of death duties. She wishes to covenant with the N.T. or else make them sole trustees, and thus get off death duties on the park, which is open to the public all the year round. The inside and outside of the house have been spoilt, but the outside not irreparably, because the plate-glass windows could be replaced with sashes, and the creeper removed; so could the Victorian flower beds. The inside could be improved, although it can never have been a very good one. Several family portraits, Romneys and Lawrences, and two Knellers in *grisaille* given by Pope to the 1st Earl Bathurst.

Friday, 3rd August

This morning the agent, Captain Turner, motored me round the property. The whole estate covers 14,000 acres, the park about 4,000. There is an avenue five miles long and a central junction, called Ten Ride Point, a most impressive feature. Several temples, one hexagonal, and Pope's Seat, some mid-eighteenth-century follies, cardboard castellated lodges, and so forth. Though the layout dating from the 1st Earl's time is on an astonishing scale, there are few natural contours, and the park is flat. There is a tall column with an effigy of Queen Anne on the summit in a direct line from the house. Otherwise the rides are made axial with the church, presumably because the tower is so high that it can be seen from a greater distance than the house.

I motored Geoffrey Houghton-Brown to Felix Hall where I deposited him. An extremely hot, burning day, the car emitting strong fumes of oil and dense smoke. On the way we visited Thorndon, near Brentwood. To my great surprise the house remains, the centre block having been gutted by fire in the 1880s, but the walls perfect. The bricks, beautifully jointed, stone dressings and tabernacle framed windows still in excellent repair. The two pavilions not so good. A golf club is housed in one, to which they have made unsightly additions. The other has soldiers in it, and looks bad. The site is an eminence with rural views towards Brentwood and other directions. The two-mile avenue to Brentwood has now gone. What amazed us was the lime trees planted immediately beneath the north front of the main block, just as though the owners had something to be ashamed of. I believe the Petre family sold the place before the war, and the club intend to demolish it as soon as they can. Only an hour or so earlier Geoffrey and I remarked that the screen of trees round St. Clement Danes was just where no trees were needed. Good architecture needs no shrouding.

I arrived for the weekend at Shermans, Dedham, to stay with the Sissons.

Sunday, 5th August

This morning I sat in the back garden roasting myself in the sun and reading Fiske Kimball's Rococo book. Being a civilized man Sisson knows how to leave one alone of a morning—a splendid but little understood virtue in a host. Perhaps I make it too apparent that I like to be left alone. In the afternoon storm-clouds gathered. Sisson and I walked to Flatford Mill, where we watched the milling crowds bathing, running, jumping and enjoying themselves.

Tuesday, 7th August

Doreen Baynes having telephoned, I went to see her at Brown's Hotel at 6, our first meeting since 1939. She has not altered much, and still looks very frail. We both professed inordinate pleasure and deep affection. Nevertheless I sensed that our protestations were a tiny bit forced, simply owing to the time lag. Affection has to be nourished on constant communication, either direct or indirect, by meeting or correspondence – the latter the better I opine.

Wednesday, 8th August

John Wilton telephoned that his trustees refuse categorically to sanction his buying Audley End. I am very disappointed but not the least surprised by this. Helen Dashwood lunched with me at the Bagatelle, wearing a vast magenta felt hat with pheasant's plume, bought in Paris. I met John Wilton at the Connaught, proud and splendid. Disappointed though I am, I cannot be angry with him.

All day I have been made to feel despairing, careless and numb by the atom bomb. Nothing has a purpose any more, with these awful clouds of desolation hovering over us. I am shocked, shocked, shocked by our use of this appalling bomb, a tiny instrument the size of a golf ball, dropped on the Japanese and devastating four square miles. It is horrifying, and utterly damnable.

Thursday, 9th August

At last I have found an electrician. He came to the house at 9 this morning. He was so delightful, fatherly and reassuring that I could have embraced him. Such kindness as he showed is more than one dares expect.

A very full attendance at my Historic Buildings Committee. Michael Rosse was present for the first time. Too much flippancy and exclusiveness today. Esher asked me to lunch with him at Brooks's. We discussed various matters, including this. No agents will work for the Trust unless salaries are raised. Raise them is the answer. Money is always there when needed.

Friday, 10th August

Oh the onslaught of age! I met Lord Redesdale in Heywood's shop. Nancy said, 'You know Farve,' and there, leaning on a stick was a bent figure with a shrunken, twisted face, wearing round, thick spectacles, looking like a piano tuner. Last time I saw him he was upstanding and one of the best-looking men of his generation. I suppose Tom's death has helped hasten this terrible declension. I melted with compassion.

I had to lunch with Charles Fry my publisher at the Park Lane Hotel. He was late, having just got up after some orgy *à trois* with whips, etc. He is terribly depraved and related every detail, not ques-

220

tioning whether I wished to listen. In the middle of the narration I simply said, 'Stop! Stop!' At the same table an officer was eating, and imbibing every word. I thought he gave me a crooked look for having spoilt his fun.

My delight in Churchill's defeat, disapproval of the Socialists' victory, detestation of the atom bomb and disgust with the Allies' treatment of Germany are about equal. Muddle.

Saturday, 11th August

This afternoon I endeavoured to select furniture with old Mrs. Murray Smith in 40 Queen Anne's Gate; but she is in her second childhood, and we made no progress at all. She is bent almost double, her poor old head torn down to her chest. Her house is in an indescribable mess and looks as if it has not been cleaned since she came to live here fifty years ago. It is dreadful that no one looks after this pathetic old lady.

Monday, 13th August

This afternoon with Christopher Gibbs to inspect the Cedar House at Cobham. It has a pretty, irregular Georgian front of red brick, good railings and gate piers bearing stone pineapples. The view, over the road, and into the low-lying meadow is bucolic. The faked up medieval hall, with bogus long window and gallery is horrid. Some oak quatrefoils in the roof spandrels may be original.

Wednesday, 15th August

Miss Ballachey telephoned at 9 to say the war was over, and today and tomorrow were public holidays. I am strangely unmoved by this announcement. The world is left a victim of chaos, great uncertainty and heinous turpitude. Apparently the news was given on the midnight bulletin which I, having no wireless set, did not hear. I did hear at 2 a.m. distant sounds of hilarity. This morning no buses are running, and everything is very tiresome, including the drizzle. I breakfasted at Brooks's since the milkman left me no milk and the charwoman no bread yesterday. Nevertheless I went to the office and drafted letters. Worked all afternoon.

I dined at the Ordinary and didn't enjoy it a bit, although several friends were present, including the Nicolson boys. Nigel was looking wonderfully healthy and handsome. He astonished me and embarrassed Ben by saying loudly, as we sat on a sofa together, 'I do wish men would make up their faces.' I can think of several who might improve themselves in this way, although Nigel has no need to do it. He made wry references to James's behaviour as though he were surprised and pained by it. I left with Desmond Shawe-Taylor, and we walked against a stream of people coming away from Buckingham Palace. We stood for three-quarters of an hour on the Victoria Monument gazing expectantly at the crimson and gold hangings over the balcony. Floodlit the façade looked splendid, but the minute royal standard was out of scale. Desmond could not bear waiting, being an impatient man, but I was determined to wait. Besides I easily get into a sort of cabbage condition and can't be bothered to uproot myself. The crowd showed some excitement, calling, 'We want the King,' 'We want the Queen,' but not uproariously. At last, just after midnight, the French window opened a crack, then wider, and out came the King and Queen. They were tiny. I could barely distinguish her little figure swathed in a fur, and something sparkling in her hair. The gold buttons of his Admiral's uniform glistened. Both waved in a slightly self-conscious fashion and stood for three minutes. Then they retreated. The crowd waved with great applause, and all walked quietly home.

I was mightily flattered by Cyril telling me this evening that my *Horizon* article was one of the best, whatever that precisely means.

Thursday, 16th August

In combing through chapter 2 of *Adam* I realize how badly it is written. It reads choppily and disjointedly. It is heavy, dull and unrelieved by picturesque and humorous allusions. Jamesey would enliven what he wrote so as to make his prose flow and curve, caracole and purl.

I lunched at the Argentine Ambassadress's. Sir Ronald Storrs had Lady Abingdon on one side and me on the other. She had an enormous straw hat with black ribbon round the crown, sloping off one side of her head. This side was next to him. The effect was that of a Picasso portrait of a lady with face tilted awry. The consequence was that he could neither catch a glimpse of her face nor a word she spoke, and so turned to me. I was delighted. He agreed that the Tories in the last Government had badly let us down by condoning all the iniquities of the Bolsheviks in Eastern Europe. For instance, they (Bolsheviks, not Tories) crucified three Lithuanian bishops on hot iron. This was deliberately kept out of the British press. But, he said, Bevin was standing up to Stalin. He opened proceedings at Potsdam by saying, as he thrust his hands into his braces, 'Mr. Stalin, I am a Yorkshireman, and I tells you straight, I don't sign no documents what I doesn't understand, do you see?' The Russians are disappointed with the change of government because they fear the Labour leaders will be more out-spoken than were Churchill and Eden, who were over-anxious not to offend susceptibilities in view of their known pre-war antagonism to the Soviet.

Saturday, 18th August

I asked John Fowler to meet Margaret Jourdain for luncheon at the Normandie, and so fulfilled for him a long cherished desire. We went back to her flat and drank coffee with her and Ivy. John was amazed by the bareness and austerity of their flat, the uniform stark apple-green decoration and the floor linoleum against which their few nice Georgian pieces of furniture look islanded and insignificant. He returned and drank tea with me here.

This evening I changed into a dinner jacket, the first time since the war, and dined with Aubrey Moody on King's Guard at St. James's Palace. Enjoyed it immensely. We ate well, off an expensive snow-white tablecloth and with brightly polished silver. Delicious wines. I sat next a young subaltern who had broken, like me, a vertebra of his spine but, unlike me, from landing on a parachute. Hector Bolitho also a guest. He talks in riddles. He has a round, quizzical face and the manner of a schoolmaster. Nice man, and no highbrow.

Monday, 20th August

Lunched with Hector Bolitho at the Connaught Hotel, till 3.15. He told me that he was born a New Zealander, and first came to London aged 21. He discovered for himself the allure of old buildings, and art generally. The first thing he looked at was the Charles I statue at Charing Cross. This opened his eyes. Hitherto he had never come upon a work of art of any sort.

Then to Batsford's. Charles Fry wants the National Trust to apply for more paper for Batsford to print another 10,000 copies of my N.T. book, which is selling over and beyond their expectations. The 7,500 copies they printed have gone already in under a week.

Tuesday, 21st August

Went by train to Ampthill. Got a taxi, picked up Professor Richardson at Avenue House, he hobbling uneasily with a broken ankle, and drove to Ampthill House. We lunched with Sir Anthony Wingfield, a delightful, intelligent old man in his 90th year. He is very active, only a little deaf and blind. During luncheon we discussed executions, of Monmouth and Mary Queen of Scots. The Professor is the most enlivening companion, bubbling with anecdotes and jokes. Sir Anthony showed me a watch given to his great-uncle at Harrow in 1806 and a letter from Byron. The letter was addressed, 'Dearest John' and stressed that their friendship was based on no 'ordinary affection'. He has silver spoons and forks which belonged to the Prince Regent at the Pavilion, heavily embossed with mask heads and trophies. Sir Anthony's butler, called Cooper, wrote a few years ago a book on his service with the aristocracy which Sir A. has lent me. We walked to look at his house in the street which he wishes to leave to the N.T. It is a fine 1740 house of harsh brick with stone dressings and a project-ing porch, but much knocked about by troops. I accompanied the Professor to Avenue House, built by Holland. It is chock-a-block with treasures. The Professor looks like a Rowlandson figure among so much Georgian elegance.

Thursday, 23rd August

Dined and drank far too much with Michael Rosse on King's Guard. I walked, how I don't know, back with Oliver [Messel] peering into antique shops in the Brompton Road. We went all round his new house in Pelham Crescent, next door to Alexander Place. It is huge, being two houses knocked into one, and was pitch dark because no lights were working. We could only feel our way around by dint of a muslin moon. Consequently my gush was slightly tempered by the invisibility. Found myself swaying, and once had to clutch the back of Oliver's neck.

Friday, 24th August

Jasper Holdsworth lunched with me (having invited himself) at the Café Royal, which was so depressing that it put me in a filthy mood. Jasper never helps one out, and is a sort of nature's vampire. He takes but does not give, and his schemes, professedly to one's, and I will admit, to his own advantage, seldom materialize. It was getting late. His car, he assured me, would arrive in a minute and would motor me back to the office. Of course it never came, and I had to walk.

Saturday, 25th August

This has been a very long day. I woke at 5.45, and at 6.45 the car ordered by Michael Rosse called for me. It picked him up in Mount Street and drove us to Euston for the 8.15 to Holyhead. Travelled in comfort and ease. I read several books during the journey, Michael much amused because I read standing in queues on the boat. I always do this, for what is the point of letting the minutes roll by in vacancy?

At Holyhead Anne's two Armstrong-Jones children joined us. After a smooth crossing we reached Kingstown at 7.30. I was at once struck by the old-fashioned air of everything: horse-cabs at the quay, cobbled streets with delicious horse-droppings on them. Met by a taxi cab come all the way from Birr, costing £8. Letter of greeting from Anne to Michael. Vodka for Michael and me in the car. We drove straight to Birr. Even through the closed windows of the car I caught the sweet smell of peat in the air. Curious scenes, ragged children on horses drawing old carts along country lanes. Our driver sounded his horn loudly through Birr, that piercing, pretty foreign horn. The gates of the castle shot open as if by magic. A group of people were clustered outside the gate. We swept up the drive. All the castle windows were alight, and there on the sweep was a large crowd of employees and tenants gathered to welcome Michael back from the war. Anne, the two Parsons boys, and Mr. Garvie the agent on the steps. Behind them Leavy the butler, the footman, housekeeper, and six or seven maids. A fire blazing in the library and everywhere immense vases of flowers. We heard Michael make a short speech from the steps, followed by cheers and 'For he's a jolly good fellow', a song which always makes me go hot and cold, mostly hot. The crowd then trooped off to a beano and drinks, while we sat down to a huge champagne supper at 11 o'clock.

Sunday, 26th August

I rose late this morning, just in time for Mass in the town 'with the natives'. The church very full and crowded, and somehow horribly sectarian and un-Roman; but clean and polished. Indeed there is an air of well-being and contentment in Ireland, and almost of prosperity after England. The house-fronts in the town are painted and the inhabitants well clothed, whereas before the war I remember them as squalid and poverty-stricken. This shows how English standards and conditions must have deteriorated during the war years. The streets in Birr are swept. There is as little traffic as before the war. The smell of horse-dung everywhere is very refreshing after the petrol fumes.

Bridget came from Abbey Leix yesterday, and today Lord X. He is an agreeable, plump, intelligent Irishman, a Catholic from Galway. He says the priests are so bigoted and politically minded that he fears there will be a strong reaction from Catholicism in Ireland within the next generation. Most of the priests are peasants' sons, with no true vocation. They become priests because it gives them social status. He blames Maynooth College. A generation ago the neophytes went to Rome. Now they are totally nationalistic and provincial in outlook. The Cardinal is positively chauvinistic. Lord X. blames the Vatican for not taking the Irish hierarchy in hand. The people are kept in great ignorance as in Spain.

We went for a walk this afternoon with the children, in the bog, leaping from tuft to tuft. The wide, flat expanse of bog with purple heather growing upon it, and the purple hills, always just in sight, very nostalgic. I find the climate extremely relaxing. I eat a lot, am sleepy, and wake up feeling doped. The food is rich after England, and the cooking full of butter and cream.

Thursday, 30th August

We motored up the mountain, got out and walked over the heather in the sun. The heather smells acrid. It is curious how quite high up you come upon soggy patches of bog where the turf has been sliced away. Oh yes, the climate of Ireland is far too relaxing. There is something dead about the country and the people. It is like living on a luxuriant moon. I dislike the way individuals remain for hours on end standing and staring into space. We passed this morning one woman sitting on a stile, with the face of a zany, staring, not at the view, but at her toes. When we returned this evening, she was still there in exactly the same idiotic posture, and still staring at her toes. This gives me the creeps.

Friday, 31st August

Michael and I motored thirty miles to Abbey Leix to fetch his mother, Lady de Vesci. I was last here at Easter 1936 staying with Desmond Parsons. I had forgotten the extraordinary beauty of the park and trees. The vivid fresh green of Ireland in August after the aridity of England is startling. The house was built about 1780 and is Adam-like. A beautiful hall with columned screen, delicate frieze, and the whitest statuary marble chimneypiece. Two drawing-rooms both with thin

226

decorated ceilings, and one with deep sky-blue Morris wallpaper which, though wrong, is very attractive with the gold mirrors and frames. The library has pink scagliola columns, green walls, mud-coloured bookcases and Siena doorways, all dating from about 1850 and very charming: facing full south. The exterior has been too Victorianized, balustrades added, window-surrounds altered, and some plate glass inserted.

At Roscrea, on our return to Birr, a large brown dog walked under the car which drove right over its body. Lady de Vesci made the driver pull up. She said he ought just to apologize. He got out and we all sat still. I saw the poor dog kicking in the road, but by the time the driver reached it, it was dead and being dragged to the verge. I felt rather sick. This is the first time such a thing has happened to me, though I expected this driver would kill a dog sooner or later. In Ireland the dogs are not well trained to avoid motor cars, as they seem to be in England. Michael and his mother were quite unmoved, and so it seemed were the owners of the dog. What a contrast to my mother's behaviour. If she had been present she would have created the most embarrassing scene, tearing out the driver's hair in rage, hugging the corpse and emptying her purse into the lap of the owner.

Saturday, 1st September

Before leaving Birr for Dublin I spent the afternoon with Anne alone, the others having gone for a walk in the woods. She conducted me round the castle, showing me all the portraits and little things belonging to Parsons ancestors that mean so much to her. She is a proud chateleine and looks after her possessions with tender care. I have the greatest admiration for her efficiency, her vitality, her keen wit and good nature. She always has the ready answer.

The train to Dublin was packed with folk going up to the Games. There is only one train each weekday, and none on Sundays. At Dublin I spent three-quarters of an hour in an appalling jam trying to extricate my bag, which unfortunately the chauffeur had put in the van because he thought I should not get a seat and would have no room for it in the corridor. A typical Irish scene of muddle and con-fusion. Before we got to the train it left the platform, to our dismay. Eventually it returned, whereupon porters and passengers screamed and scrambled over each other, the passengers complaining vociferously at the inadequacy of the system which, they maintained, could only be experienced in Ireland. Had a foreigner agreed with them, they would doubtless have set upon him. In Dublin I was pushed into a four-wheeler with two other passengers, and we bowled over the cobbles to the Hibernian Hotel. Here I found Geoffrey Houghton-Brown and we dined after 10. No difficulty getting a meal at this hour and plenty of waiters.

Sunday, 2nd September

Walked this morning to the Municipal Museum. Quite a good collection of modern pictures: Lavery, Jack Yeats, and the Hugh Lane collection—corresponding to our Tate Gallery. All the churches so crowded we could hardly enter one. The devotion of the men and women is not so much exemplary as alarming, for the Irish are not a spiritual people.

You see no platinum blondes, no tarts in Dublin streets. There is absolutely no evidence of vice on the surface. Yet the squalor of the slums is formidable. We walked into several doorways in Henrietta Street. Splendid mid-Georgian grand houses, now tenements in neglect, dirt and disrepair. But what a wonderful town. Streets of flat façaded houses, dull maybe, but of long unbroken elevation and layout. The atmosphere created by the four-wheelers, the side-cars, the smell of ammonia from horses and the stale straw from mews is of the 1890s. The bouquets of ferns and geraniums tied round lamp-posts conjure up 'art nouveau' poster designs. We looked at the Custom House, the Four Courts, the Castle, Trinity College and several churches. We bought sweets and ate them in the street. The view across the river, which reminded me of the Arno, of the magnificent elevation of the Four Courts is spoilt by mean little trees.

Tuesday, 4th September

Back in London. At 4, Anthony Martineau and I had a painful meeting about Ham House at the Richmond town hall with the town councillors and the Tollemache family: old Sir Lyonel aged 93 and his son. The town clerk and councillors were gushing and deferential; the Tollemaches proud and patronizing. When the Tollemaches left we stayed behind and the town councillors became outspoken in their derision and dislike. I was horribly and uncomfortably aware of the hostility between the two classes.

This evening I had a glass of sherry, South African and rather hot, with Doreen Baynes, once again in her drawing-room in 18 Ovington Square, with the alcove, the peach satin sofa, the satinwood Sheraton furniture on spindly legs, the fragile Chelsea shepherdesses, and the

228

very same wax magnolias not even dusted since 1939. It was a more satisfactory meeting than our last in Brown's Hotel. We both poured out confidential chat. She told me she goes through such agonies over reviews of her books that she often retires to bed for a week, with blinds drawn, silently weeping. We agreed that we were both over-sensitive, infantine, only fairly intelligent and not intellectual; that Dame Una and Eddy were too intellectual for us, and made us gauche, awkward and rather idiotic; and that far from having too much vanity we had too much humility.

Thursday, 6th September

This morning Anthony Martineau and I attended another local authority meeting, this time with the Middlesex County Council and the Heston Council in the Guildhall. Grandy Jersey was not present; but if he had been, there would have been no Lady Catherine de Burgh attitude, such as was evinced the other day. Anthony said I handled them perfectly. This was not quite true, but I certainly tried to treat them as sensible human creatures, without scolding, without high-hatting, and I pulled their legs and my own.

Sunday, 9th September

Hinch talked to me in Brooks's about Hinchingbrooke, which he wants to convert into a Cromwellian museum, he living in a part only, after pulling down an ugly Victorian wing. He says we must expect no reduction in taxation from this Government, but probably allowances will be increased for the benefit of the small salary earner. That's me, hurrah!

I spoke to Dame Una on the telephone. I find that families who are too closely knit incline to indulge in self-adulation. Her Dickens book is having poor reviews, which she attributes to the ignorance of the reviewers. She complains that they have all failed to detect her new discoveries about her subject. I hazard the guess that she biographizes better than she analyses. Nevertheless the Dame says she will go into a third edition by Christmas and her publishers would like to print 100,000 copies. All this was delivered in a clipped, slightly self-satisfied, superior tone, which does not endear her to some people. But she has long ago endeared herself to me, and will not be de-endeared.

Monday, 10th September

Dined with Mark Ogilvie-Grant this evening. Princess Aspasia of

Greece called for me at 7.15. She drove a large, black, glossy car, bringing with her Lady Patsy Ward, whom I like because she is so outspoken. Princess Aspasia is tall and dark, and what is called very well preserved. She is easy and gay and seems intelligent. She was morganatically married to the King of Greece who died of a monkey bite, I believe, and her daughter is the present Queen of Yugoslavia. After dinner conversation got on to rabies—this was none of my initiating—and the fatal bites of mad dogs and other animals. We talked of anarchism, communism and fascism. She said she made no distinction between them. When King Peter, her son-in-law, went to see Bevin the other day, the latter admitted that he disliked the communists, and Tito, who, he declared, had gone back on his word. Balkan royalties must be optimists, otherwise they would cease to work for a return to their miserable thrones. Anyway there is nothing else in the world they can, or are allowed to do.

Tuesday, 11th September

Took the 1.10 train to Cheshire, and was driven from Chelford to stay two nights at Tabley Hall with the Leicester-Warrens, a charming couple, he a little older than my father and married the same year. Both very simple and sweet; she full of prejudices and conventions; he rather less so, but I guess has had a stroke. Their son and heir is the rabbit-faced, chinless boy, who was at Eton with me. He was mercilessly teased, poor thing, which was beastly. Although I was not one of the bullies, being more of a bullyee, I look back upon his torments with sadness, for he was, and I understand still is, as good as gold. I must say I remember no bullying at Eton among the older boys, only among the 12- and 13-year-olds.

Tabley is of similar size and disposition to Kedleston, consisting of a centre block and two projecting pavilions to the north. There is the sweeping perron on the south side; and, to make the resemblance closer, the Charles II chapel from the island has been re-erected and connected to the north-west pavilion. But it is far coarser and heavier, this Carr house, than the Adam one. The exterior is really uninspiring, and from the distance lumpish, although the material is a pleasant hard, red brick, nicely jointed. The place has the same crumbling look as Kedleston; and is equally doomed. The neglected rooms have the same bloom of mould over them. They contain an unkempt jumble of furniture, not properly dust-sheeted, through lack of servants. The interesting thing about Tabley is that although it was begun in 1762 it is absolutely pre-Adam in detail. Walls and ceilings are very black

230

because it is only fifteen miles from Manchester, and close to Knutsford, still a pretty town. The park is flat and dull. The Old Hall cannot be seen from the house because of the undergrowth on the island. It is also unapproachable because the bridge to it is unsafe. The Brunner-Mond mining for salt brine has caused the Old Hall's collapse. So all its furniture has been removed and the fine Jacobean chimneypiece taken down and re-inserted in the connecting corridor to the chapel.

The picture gallery of about 1805 is not in itself handsome, but it has several interesting pictures, all badly in need of cleaning: some by Turner, whom the 1st Lord de Tabley patronized, one of Tabley from across the lake: a series of Devises of Tabley, so faint it is difficult to distinguish the views. The two Romneys of Emma have been sold, but there are paintings by Ward, Cotes, Northcote, all protégés of Lord de Tabley. I did not notice much good furniture, apart from some Chippendale serpentine chests and bedroom stuff, some Regency chairs, a settee from Romney's house in Hampstead. The stairs have a gentle ascent and the brackets are beautifully carved by Shillito. There are good George III chimneypieces and three excellent rococo overmantel glasses. The stable block is plain. There are too many bushes – rhododendrons and shaggy spruce trees – close to the house. The poor Leicester-Warrens don't in the least know what to do with the place, and are too old to adapt themselves to a new form of life in it. A younger generation might find it quite feasible to live in one of the wings, or to let the two wings and ground floor of the centre block for an institution, reserving the *piano nobile* either for use (which I would do) or for show. The *piano nobile* is full of interesting things to see. If Tabley is not on the whole a very refined building, it is nevertheless a great house.

The Leicester-Warrens have a butler and some four indoor servants of sorts. Yet all the wallpapers are torn, the walls damp, and the woodwork in need of paint. What should they do?

Thursday, 13th September

Arrived in London after luncheon. Saw the Coke solicitor who talked of Holkham, and at 6 met Mr. Bradley-Birt, a laughably snobbish, pretentious old gent, who talked about Birtsmorton Court.

Friday, 14th September

National Trust meeting day. Lord Crawford took the chair at the Executive Committee for the first time. He did it well in an easy and engaging manner. He is shy in conversation, yet is a man of stout determination, I would guess. Harold Nicolson and Chorley were elected to the Finance Committee, and Leigh Ashton to the Historic Buildings Committee. I lunched with Esher who told me about his tour. He said Charlecote must be let as a hostel, and only the gatehouse be shown to the public.

Dined at Brooks's with Ben Nicolson, and then taxied to King's Cross where I took the night train to Edinburgh, sitting up in a 1st class, non-smoking compartment.

Saturday, 15th September

Arrived 8.30. Breakfasted and established myself in the Railway Hotel. Had a full and successful day. First I visited Adam's Register House and was shown round by a dour Scot, the curator of the public records. Was rather disappointed with this building. Then to the National Library and looked at two manuscript letters of R. Adam. Then to St. Giles's Cathedral, which did not please me greatly. Adam's University however I thought very fine indeed, in particular the street elevation and Playfair's inner court. After luncheon I climbed Calton Hill, which is Edinburgh's acropolis, with its temple of Lysicrates, etc., and crossing the road, looked at Adam's tomb for David Hume. The city is splendid from this site. A strong, warm wind was chopping the distant sea below the Forth Bridge. Arthur's Seat a prominent feature from here. In the afternoon I walked an unconscionable amount, admiring the architecture of the New Town, George Street, Adam's Charlotte Square. Was duly edified by Steel's memorial to the Prince Consort, with sentimental groups at the corners of aristocrats, bureaucrats, peasants and artisans, paying ridiculous homage to him. The iron railings and lamp standards in this square survive intact. There are some truly majestic Squares and Crescents with palatial houses, like those in Moray Place, on a grander scale than Dublin's, Bath's or Brighton's. Edinburgh is a very black city due, I suppose, to the railway line, which really should not be allowed to run in the great valley. After looking at numerous Adam houses I caught an evening train to Berwick.

From Berwick I was driven to Beale foreshore, where I changed into a ramshackle, rusty old car which drove me in the dark across the sands to Holy Island, quite three miles away. Although the tide was out we splashed through water on parts of the causeway, for the sands are never thoroughly dry. Sometimes when the tide is out a horse and cart have to be used, and when the tide is up, a motor boat. There are two lines of posts to guide vehicles, for off the track the sands are treacherous. A weird, open, grey expanse of mudflat with millions of worm-casts, flights of duck over one's head, and pencilled hills in the distance. The car mounts the bank of the island shore, and bumbles along a tolerable road through the little village of Lindisfarne. Beyond the village is Lindisfarne Castle, perched high on an abrupt rock. The car bumps over the grass and stops. Mr. de Stein and a friend were there to greet me. We walked up a cobbled path to the portcullis, and then further steps. A family of islanders looks after the Castle, and serves de Stein whenever he comes here. Jack, known as the uncrowned king, a splendid old man of 77, strong and healthy, with twinkling blue eyes, his wife the cook, their daughter the maid, their son and his wife, and the grandchildren — all live in the castle.

De Stein is a peppery, fussy, schoolmasterish little man, with whom I should hate to have a row. He has not got a good manner. After dinner we had a long talk about mysticism. He recommended a book by William James on the subject. The friend staying is about my age, fair-haired, stocky, an expert botanist who has worked in East Africa, attached in some way to Kew Gardens, and now in the army. Rather nice. I liked him. I can't quite make de Stein out. He is prudish and disapproving, yet he puts his arm round one's waist and makes rapid, sly remarks which I think it best to leave unheeded.

Sunday, 16th September

After breakfast we went sailing in a cockleshell, moored just below the Castle. De Stein began by being rather dictatorial, shouting directions at the islanders, who I sensed knew their business better than he did, and nagging at us. Now I loathe all boats, large and small. I thought the best plan was for me to make a joke of my lack of expertise. It succeeded. He soon laughed when I was caught up in those damned ropes, and getting in everyone's way. The sail began badly for there was a dead calm. Suddenly the wind rose, and we had to reef in a great hurry. There was a good deal of luffing, and getting one's head bashed by the boom, or whatever the piece of swivelling wood is called. We fairly scudded through the water, the keel dashing itself against the advancing waves, almost to breaking point. The warm sun made the oilskin smell deliciously of fish and seaweed. Up and down we tacked alongside St. Cuthbert's little island, looking at wild duck and geese. If it hadn't been for the anxiety of being lassoed by those ropes and dragged under the keel, if it hadn't been for that slight accompaniment of nausea, and if it hadn't been for the fear of making an unutterable

233

fool of myself, I might have enjoyed this expedition. It was a great relief to be on dry land again.

Before luncheon we walked round the Castle. All the furniture was bought from Edward Hudson, and so is good of its sort, the bulk of the sort being oak. De Stein has given the contents to the Trust with the Castle. It is a charming little castle, all stone steps and passageways with low vaulted ceilings. The interior is totally Lutyens. The walls are so thick that winter and summer a fire of logs washed up from wrecks, flotsam and jetsam, has to be kept burning. There is no electric light, but dozens of candles are kept alight even by day. In the afternoon we motored to Bamburgh Castle, and in the rain walked round, but not inside it. It is very large and very much restored. The eleventh-century keep is square like Rochester Castle's. We went into Grace Darling's museum, which is rather touching, containing old hats, jugs and bric-à-brac which she used. She was only in her twenties when she died of consumption. On our return to the shore the car broke down, so we took off our shoes and stockings and walked across the sands between the posts marking the old monks' route, along which the Catholic pilgrims still process behind the priests and bishops, chanting a way to the Priory. Lovely, almost erotic feel of worm-casts under the bare, curling toes.

After dinner de Stein, who is a financier, talked politics. He is pleased that Labour is in, but terribly depressed by the fact that the Trade Unions discourage men from working. For example, they will only allow bricklayers to lay 450 bricks a day, yet they must still work seven hours. This means that good bricklayers have to slack whether they want to or not, and are bored. And who benefits? No one.

Tuesday, 18th September

Travelled to London all yesterday, only having to stand from Berwick to Newcastle, where by dint of bribing the car attendant 2/- I got a seat. Tonight I dined with Colonel Mallaby, the secretary-elect of the N.T. On the whole a sympathetic man. Wondered if he has a strong personality: and decided that one would not perhaps take liberties with him. At least he is human. He gave me a good dinner at the Rag and a lot to drink. I probably talked too much. I liked him, and sensed that he liked me, but I may well be mistaken.

He gave me a few side-lines about the present Cabinet, for he attends all their meetings and takes their minutes. Attlee, he says, is undoubtedly not forceful, yet a man of unimpeachable integrity. At times he can become waspish, and asserts himself. Bevin is, he thinks, made in a big mould, is a true imperialist and may be considered the greatest Foreign Secretary since Palmerston. Most of the Cabinet are men of little calibre, and will soon be superseded by younger men. For instance, Pethick Lawrence sleeps throughout every Cabinet meeting. After Churchill of course Attlee is a flea.

Wednesday, 19th September

Harold dined with me at Brooks's. As Esher said the other day the fiction that Harold is still 'a young man' cannot be substantiated by his jaunty walk and the carnation he wears in his buttonhole. He must be 60, and is such an angelic man that I try not to think of his ever getting old, or dying. He told me in strict confidence this evening that the Government want to make him a peer, and Attlee has spoken to him about it. H. does not want to, and indeed will not be beholden to the Labour Government, yet he would warmly welcome a seat in Parliament. He is keen to remain in politics, and make speeches on the subjects he feels deeply and knows much about, without being subject to any party whip. He wants to be quite independent, and said he could only return to the House of Commons if elected to a University seat. Nigel has been invited to contest his old Leicester seat. Harold said Attlee was undoubtedly a nice man, honest as the day. He thinks highly of Bevin. All good people seem to. H. talked of the N. Trust and will join the Finance Committee, but feels that members of the committees should personally visit any doubtful property before making a pronouncement on its merits or demerits. He takes the view that if he serves he must be prepared to answer any question which might be put to him by a Royal Commission of Enquiry.

Thursday, 20th September

A long day. Trained to Swindon where Eardley met me. We drove to inspect thirty acres at Blunsdon St. Andrews which have been offered to the Trust. They consist of a deserted garden and the ruin of a house in the Gothic style, built of stone in about 1850, and burnt out in 1904. The ruin is romantic, being overgrown with ivy. It has trees pushing a way out of the dining-room windows. But no funds are offered, and we could not hold a garden and woodlands and leave them totally neglected for ever. Then we looked at another doubtful case in Woolstone village at the foot of the White Horse. The cottages offered were nothing out of the ordinary, just white stone with

235

thatched roofs. If the Trust doesn't take them and spend money on them, they will be condemned.

On the way to Clouds Hill in Dorset, E. told me that Wiltshire farmers found the German prisoners would not stop working. They are the best workers they have ever known, far better than the British. He repeated a story told him by someone who was present at Himmler's death. Himmler evidently bit a phial of poison which he was holding in his cheek. After his suicide he was lying on the floor, naked but for a khaki shirt. His face was green and twisted to one side, and he had an enormous erection which persisted for twelve hours after his death. The British troops were so angry with Himmler for having had a quick and apparently pleasant death that they kicked him in the balls.

Clouds Hill, T. E. Lawrence's cottage, is in the middle of Bovington Heath, which is a blasted waste of desolation, churned feet-deep in mud by a thousand army tanks. The cottage is embowered in rhododendrons. It is a pathetic little shoddy place. The visitors have stolen all they could lay their hands on, including the screw of the porthole window in Lawrence's bedroom, and the hasps of the other windows. The bunk gives an idea of his asceticism. Pat Knowles, his batman, is back from abroad. He and his wife, Mrs. Knowles, a pretty, gazelle-like woman, live in another cottage across the way where Lawrence fed with them. They conduct visitors over Clouds Hill, and dare not let them out of their sight for a minute. Knowles is a high-minded, cultivated proletarian, a youngish 45 with vestiges of gold hair. Bespectacled face now a little puffy, but must once have been handsome.

Saturday, 22nd September

Lord and Lady Bradford met and conducted me round Castle Bromwich Hall. It is a fine red-brick house of Elizabethan date with several late-seventeenth-century ceilings of the compartmented, baywreath type, Wren-ish, deeply undercut and in high relief. Much early and much William and Mary panelling. The painted ceiling over the staircase by Laguerre. The house is empty, having been vacated by the troops, and in consequence is in a filthy mess. Every window, and these were casemented and quarried, broken by several bombs dropped in the garden. All the heraldic glass has been destroyed in this way. Yet in other respects surprisingly little structural damage incurred. The most alarming threat to the building is the dry-rot which is rampant, particularly around the door behind the hall screen. The garden, now very neglected, is contained within a brick wall. It has descending

236

terraces, a contemporary maze and holly hedges in the formal style. I would say it is an important and complete garden of *circa* 1700.

Lord Bradford is a very courteous man, the epitome of good breeding. Lady B., whom I like, kept snubbing him. He accepted her rebukes without once answering back. She told him he ought to give the place to the Trust without any further thought. What was the good, she said, in letting it to unsatisfactory business firms who had no idea how to look after it. The family would never want to live in it again. This I think is incontrovertible. She pointed out that he had let the stable block to some depôt for £100 p.a., out of which he receives, after paying tax, £2. 10. 0. I suggested that perhaps Birmingham might have some use for this marvellous old house, still so tranquil, so well sited on its hill and yet now so close to the city.

On my way to Wickhamford I stopped at our property, Chadwich Manor, a little 1700 house with walls of red stretchers and purple headers, and a splendid oak staircase going right to the top attic. The tenants very friendly and welcoming, he in plumber's overall, smelling like a plumber. Hideous things in the house.

Monday, 24th September

I met Heywood Hill at Leamington Spa station and drove him to Charlecote. He spent two days going through the library books, searching for rare volumes, while Brian and Alice and I arranged the rooms. It must be beastly for them having me and hosts of London officials browsing through and meddling with their brother's possessions. They are so good about it.

Wednesday, 26th September

Heywood is convinced that Charlecote is eminently worthy, being a house full of interesting objects, and a collection of portraits displaying the family's ancient association with the place, a house set in a park of exceptional beauty. Miss Fairfax-Lucy amused him very much by describing the weird behaviour of her brother, Sir Montgomery, when he stayed with her for three months. He is so accustomed to solitude and the service of his black servants in Africa that he cannot reconcile himself to company and English war-time restrictions. He refused to let her address a word to him after 6 o'clock, and scolded her for saying 'Good night' because it implied that he might not have a good night. Brian told us that when at Eton he was the only boy not allowed home for long leave, his father, Sir Henry, either disapproving of the

237

unnecessary three-day holiday, or considering the train fare a waste of money. As children he, his brothers and sisters were practically starved. They used to walk into Stratford-on-Avon and flatten their faces against the window panes of the cake shops.

Heywood and I stayed at the King's Head, Wellesbourne, he for one night, I for two.

At 12 I arrived at Stoneleigh Abbey. Lord Leigh, whom I remember at Eton, is short, stocky, grey, with pale blue eyes and red veins on his cheeks. He looks less astute than he certainly is. He has definite and sound ideas about Stoneleigh, having already divided the house into three flats. He is going to show the state rooms to the public next year. These state rooms are comprised in the 1720 Francis Smith block, which is superb. All the rooms on the *piano nobile* are wainscoted in large oak fielded panels between robust pilasters with Corinthian capitals. The central saloon has a heavy ceiling, a little later in date, *circa* 1750 I would guess, just pre-Adam. Lord Leigh assured me several times that the plasterwork was by Cipriani, which I find hard to believe unless there was an earlier stuccoist of the same name as the well-known painter. The chairs, contemporary with the house, are upholstered either in velvet or petit-point. Many portraits of Leighs. The bedroom floor suite redecorated in 1850 for Queen Victoria in white and gold is very pretty. The French furniture and even the Chippendale chairs were likewise decorated in this manner. The house is built round a courtyard on Lacock Abbey lines, three sides of it being Jacobean over twelfth-century undercrofts. The Smith block is very rich and impressive, though built of porous and friable red sandstone.

Thursday, 27th September

Lunched alone with Kathleen (Kennet) who is more rugged than ever — her iron grey hair very closely cropped — and more lovable than ever.

After dinner with the Subercaseaux I talked with Paz and the Italian Ambassador for an hour about conditions in Italy, which he says are appalling. Firewood costs thousands of lire, and 99 per cent of the inhabitants freeze in the winter. He is a great admirer of the Pope who sits with a little fur over his knees and hands, because he will not have a fire while the people are without fuel. The Ambassador told the Pope during his last audience that the Australians were dissatisfied with not having a Cardinal. He spoke of the Russian Ambassador here, who will meet no one. Entering the Soviet Embassy is like being directed into the commonest, lowest schoolhouse in the East End.

Jamesey is in a gentle, complaisant mood which indicates that he is rather bored with me. He spends his days in Argyll House going through Lord Houghton's papers for his biography. He says Lord Houghton's commonplace book contains some revealing low-downs about his early contemporaries—a note that Byron always carried a contraceptive in his waistcoat pocket—that Bishop Heber was detected 'handling' a peer's son in the gallery of the House of Lords—that Lord Courtenay paid a butcher boy £250 for the privilege of kissing his arse—and that Lord John Russell once woke up in a hotel bedroom to feel the weight of a large woman on top of him, 'helping herself'.

Saturday, 29th September

I lunched at the Royal Empire Society with Major Ney, who wants me to sit on a committee for his imperial youth movement. He assures me he is very interested in Naworth Castle and talks gaily of raising £100,000 to endow the place, as though it were chicken feed.

Went to tea at Emerald's. Violet Trefusis was there—a large, clumsy, plain woman wearing a top-heavy hat, and sitting in such a way that one could see a naked expanse of thigh. Young Giles Romilly was also there. He is distant and distraught. He told me he had not yet recovered from being a prisoner of war; that being out of prison has no savour, no matter how relieved he knows he ought to feel at being free again. It is like wanting to smoke after a cold. The cigarette tastes of nothing. He is a communist, which I don't find endearing, but an interesting young man. Although he can't be more than 25 he has grey streaks in his black hair. He said he hated society women, the sort that were know-alls, were in the know, in the swim, had to be 'in with' everything, and were merely pretentious, pseudo-intellectuals. I asked him why then he mixed with them. He said he only did so to glean material for the novels he hoped to write. I said I too detested the sort of women he described, but all rich and grand women were not like that, nodding at Emerald, whom I never think of as a 'society woman', that hateful term.

When the guests left I stayed talking to Emerald about the world's great novels, about the discontent of the rich and the still greater discontent of the poor. 'It's less sad to be rich,' Emerald concluded. When Emerald gets talking about literature and music, about which she knows so much and which she loves so passionately, I realize that, for all her faults, she is a woman out of the common run. She is almost a phenomenon, and a rare and inspired talker. When she is with company her nonsense can be funnier than any nonsense I have ever enjoyed.

Esher was for once wrong when he criticized her yesterday. She shocked him by telling him how she took off her shoes to show her beautiful feet to a young man. 'Just fancy an old woman of eighty-two doing a thing like that,' he said. I said I thought it was enchanting of Emerald, for her feet are still beautiful, and her spontaneity is beautiful. Lady E. on this occasion asked if she might call me James, since everyone else seemed to do so. I said I was delighted with the concession, for James was well on the way to Jim, which my friends called me. Lord E. chuckled, for out of policy he steadfastly calls me Mr. L.-M. 'If we were on Christian name terms,' he said, 'it would be very awkward if I had to sack you.'

Sunday, 30th September

Malcolm [Bullock] dined at Brooks's. He told me he had just seen Sibyl Colefax, who asked him how he was. He replied that he was quite well, apart from his varicose veins. When she asked him why he had varicose veins, he said they were caused by his having to stand whenever he came to see me. Sibyl did not cotton on to the allusion, that her firm has not yet delivered my sofa, which it has been re-upholstering for months and months.

Monday, 1st October

This morning I went—oh never mind where. It is not interesting. Besides, my old typewriter has broken down, and I have cut the index finger of my right hand. Besides too, the war is over to all intents and purposes, so this diary ought to have an end. Its background was the war. Its only point was the war.

And the war is over now—to all intents and purposes—isn't it?

Index

The names and titles of entrants are given as they were in 1944 and 1945.

The names of properties in CAPITALS are those which today belong to the National Trust. Particulars and times of opening (which vary from year to year) may be obtained from the National Trust's *List of Properties* (circulated to members) and the *Historic Houses, Castles and Gardens* guide, which is issued annually.